Mathematical Methods in Operations Research

Mathematical Methods in Operations Research

RONALD L. GUE

Computer Sciences Center
Institute of Technology
Southern Methodist University

MICHAEL E. THOMAS

Department of Industrial and Systems Engineering
University of Florida

The Macmillan Company, New York

Collier-Macmillan Limited, London

Library of Congress catalog card number: 68–18474

THE MACMILLAN COMPANY, NEW YORK
COLLIER-MACMILLAN CANADA, LTD., TORONTO, ONTARIO

Printed in the United States of America

To
ROBERT H. ROY

PREFACE

In the quarter-century since the first applications of scientific principles to decision problems, a wide range of mathematical techniques, modeling procedures, and heuristic methods has been developed. The applications of this new methodology and the continued development of better methods have been greatly influenced by the availability of rapid-access, stored program computers. Most of these techniques are placed within the realm of operations research.

The enthusiasm with which this methodology has been received by decision-makers is demonstrated by the wide range of opportunities available for competently trained persons. The need for decision-makers trained in quantitative methods has led to the development of academic programs in many universities dealing with operations research. The development of this new discipline has in turn generated a need for texts and other teaching materials. This book will hopefully help fulfill the need.

The goal that we set in writing this book is to provide a reasonably rigorous and compact treatment of the major mathematical techniques available for solving decision problems. It is clear that we cannot include many important problem-areas such as inventory theory or replacement problems nor do we feel we could do justice to many of the heuristic, but extremely valuable methods. Hence the decision to focus primarily on the mathematical methods in operations research.

The book is designed for use in a two-semester senior or first-year graduate course. A firm grasp of calculus together with a knowledge of matrix algebra is all that is required for the chapters on optimization techniques. An additional background in probability and transform methods is prerequisite for the chapters on queueing theory and decisions and games, and the sections on signal flow graphs.

The three chapters following the Introduction deal with optimization of static systems. In Chapter 2 a development of the underlying theory of optimization of unconstrained differentiable functions is presented. This is followed by a derivation of conditions for optima of equality constrained functions.

Finally the Kuhn-Tucker conditions for problems with inequality constraints are developed. A firm grasp of this material is essential to understand the various solution procedures that are developed in succeeding chapters. The theory of linear programming is presented in Chapter 3 followed, in Chapter 4, by a discussion of some of the more useful algorithms for optimization of nonlinear problems.

Optimization of dynamic systems is the subject of Chapters 5 and 6. The two approaches—dynamic programming and the variational method—for handling dynamic systems are discussed and compared. Dynamic programming is presented in Chapter 5 and precedes the development of the concepts in the calculus of variations and the continuous and discrete maximum principles. The theory of queues is developed in Chapter 7. Concepts of statistical decision theory and game theory are developed in Chapter 8 and related to optimization problems discussed in the preceding chapters. Chapter 9 deals with various concepts in graphs and their applications to modeling and optimization. Appendixes on matrix algebra and z transforms are included for the reader who needs background in these important subjects. Indications are that these appendixes will become unnecessary as this material is becoming required or recommended in most undergraduate curricula.

The influences of many different people are apparent in both the material presented and the method of presentation. Much of the material has been influenced by our experiences at Johns Hopkins. Among those to whom we are most indebted are Professors Douglass Wilde and George Nemhauser. Many others have influenced our thinking through their published work. The National Science Foundation supported a short course on operations research for engineering professors in the summer of 1967. The comments of the participants together with those of our colleagues at the University of Florida and Southern Methodist University have been greatly appreciated. James R. Brya and David Pike contributed to the problems appearing in each chapter. Professor William Jewell devoted considerable time to reading two versions of the manuscript. His suggestions were most valuable. We are also deeply appreciative for the time and effort of Lisa Richburgh, Wanda Ezel, and Christina Lopez who shared the major portion of the typing.

Finally we wish to acknowledge the influence of Dean Robert Roy of Johns Hopkins University. Dean Roy has been a leading light in developing educational programs in operations research as well as an extremely persuasive force in modernizing engineering curricula. We both had the opportunity to grow under Dean Roy's guidance and to develop a philosophy of education that is greatly influenced by his example. We dedicate this book to him as a symbol of what we believe is outstanding in higher education.

R. L. G.
M. E. T.

CONTENTS

ix

Mathematical
Methods
in Operations
Research

CHAPTER 1

Introduction

1.1   History of Operations Research

The subject matter in this text is a far cry from the methodology used by Blackett's circus—one of the first operations research teams [2]. This team included three physiologists, two mathematical physicists, one astrophysicist, one Army officer, one surveyor, one general physicist, and two mathematicians. During the early 1940s there were no mathematical methods of operations research. The only methods available were those belonging to the discipline of each individual scientist.

Blackett's circus, like most of the early operations research teams, was a group of civilian scientists concerned with the study of military problems. The concern of the team was to provide scientific assistance in the coordination of British radar equipment at gun sites [2].

The earliest operations research studies are attributed to the British military during the early days of World War II [2]. Most of these studies consisted of mixed teams of civilian scientists tackling operational military problems. Another early study was concerned with the integration of a radar system for early warning into the existing British ground observer corps. Determination of the optimum size of a convoy and estimation of bomb casualties are additional examples of studies the British called operational research.

Operations research, sometimes abbreviated O.R., was formally begun in the United States in the early 1940s. Similar to its development in Great Britain, O.R. studies grew up around the problems developing from new radar equipment. The U.S. Navy had considerable success in developing strategies for mining operations and determining the best search patterns for submarines and surface vessels using O.R. groups.

Although many estimates of the value of the O.R. studies conducted during World War II were exaggerated [2], the value of the activity within the military was firmly established at the end of the war. Once the conflict of war had ended, interest in applying O.R. techniques began to grow.

Postwar interest in operations research in the United States was still centered in the military. A second industrial revolution provided the impetus to serious interest in operations research by American industry [5]. This revolution took the form of a new era in which machines replaced men as a source of control. This effect, together with the development of the digital computer and the growing complexity of the management process, provided a fertile environment for the rapid growth of operations research.

The initial success of operations research caused an interest in the development of educational programs. The Massachusetts Institute of Technology, Case Institute of Technology, and the Johns Hopkins University were early leaders in developing seminars, short courses, and conferences in operations research. These same institutions led the way, during the early 1950s, in offering degree programs in operations research.

Today, numerous universities throughout the country offer courses and degrees in operations research. These programs have developed primarily in engineering colleges. Departments of industrial engineering have housed most academic programs, but there is no agreement, at this time, on where such programs should logically be housed.

The reader wishing a more detailed discussion of the history of operations research should see reference [2].

1.2   Characteristics of O.R. Study

The problems to be solved and the resources available during the early years played a significant role in determining the nature and characteristics of an O.R. study. During these years, certain characteristics seemed to be critical in every study. Today they are considered the basic essentials of an O.R. project.

Systems Orientation

One of the most distinguishing features of an O.R. study is its concern with whole problems, or its systems orientation. This concern represents a realization that an activity by any part of an organization has some effect on every other part. Hence we see that the optimum operation of one part of a system may not be optimum for some other part. If some part of the system suffers a smaller level of attainment of its objectives when another part is optimized, the system is said to be suboptimized.

This text is not intended to discuss the subtleties of optimization and suboptimization. We do wish to identify them conceptually and point out their role in an O.R. study. Those wishing further discussion of these topics should see references [6, 7, and 8].

Mixed Teams

A second, frequently cited, characteristic of O.R. studies is that the analysis is usually conducted by mixed teams of scientists from diverse disciplines such as economics, psychology, mathematics, and sociology. This interdisciplinary character of the O.R. team was caused, during the early years, by the fact that no one was trained to do operations research. However, this characteristic, which was generated by necessity, soon became recognized as a valuable quality of an O.R. study.

Problem Solving

A third distinguishing feature of operations research is its method and approach to problem solving. The problems involved are complex decision problems where it must be determined which alternative a decision-maker should choose.

Before a decision can be made, a measure of effectiveness for each course of action, or alternative, must be determined. This measure indicates the effect of choosing each alternative. The discipline of operations research helps the decision-maker determine which course of action yields the best measure of effectiveness.

During the O.R. study, a model is usually developed that expresses the measure of effectiveness as a function of the alternatives and the uncontrollable variables in the problem. This is usually a mathematical model that has the following form:

$$E = f(\mathbf{C}, \mathbf{U}) \tag{1.1}$$

Equation (1.1) states that the measure of effectiveness, E, is a function of the controllable variables, or alternatives, $\mathbf{C}$, and the uncontrollable variables, $\mathbf{U}$. These uncontrollable variables may be deterministic but beyond the control of the decision-maker, or they may be random in nature.

1.3   Decision Models

We see that operations research is intimately associated with the decision process. *Webster's New International Dictionary* (2nd ed., unabridged) states that a decision is a "... settling or terminating ... by giving judgment ...; also, a determination or result arrived at after consideration." A decision process is a procedure, or the steps taken, in making a decision—generally we strive for a best decision. Operations research is, at least, concerned with some part of the decision process.

Our purpose in this section is to point out that all decision problems of concern in operations research may be defined in terms of a general decision problem. We intend to explicitly define the decision process and to establish a formal framework for the statement of decision problems. The major portion of this text is concerned with the mathematical methods used in the analysis of these problems.

In making the simplest decisions, we all exercise certain principles of decision making and use a framework for making our decisions. This framework is not rigorously defined in our mind but is an expression of an intuitive process that has been formed by years of experience. We shall use an example to develop some of the basic properties of the decision process.

Example: Suppose that a pharmacist has a demand for a certain drug at the rate of one unit per month ($r = 1$). The drug must be stocked every so often because he never wants to be in short supply. The drug wholesaler happens to be right around the corner from the drug store. When the pharmacist does order the drug, for practical purposes, it is delivered immediately. The decision the pharmacist must make is how much of the drug to order each time he sends an order to the wholesaler.

In helping the pharmacist make a decision, we must explicitly identify certain basic properties of the decision process. For example, we must determine what his *goals* or *objectives* are in this case. Every decision problem has one or more objectives. Suppose that after appropriate thought, the pharmacist decides he has two objectives:

Objective 1 (O_1): Minimize the average inventory carried per month.
Objective 2 (O_2): Minimize the number of orders placed per month.

In every decision problem, there must be two or more *alternatives*, or *courses of action*. In the case of the pharmacist, these take the form of the alternative order quantities available to him. These are 1, 2, 3, ... units.

With this information, we are now able to determine how well the decision-maker's objectives are satisfied for each alternative. As an example, Figure 1.1

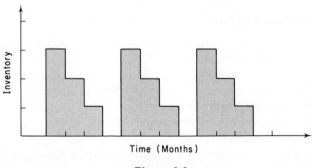

Time (Months)

Figure 1.1.

shows the inventory on hand if the druggist chooses to order four units of the drug each time an order is sent to the wholesaler. Note that since delivery is instantaneous, he waits until his customer comes into the drug store before he orders, even though he has no stock on the shelf.

We now must determine how well each of the pharmacist's objectives is satisfied for each course of action. Table 1.1 gives this information. To see

TABLE 1.1

Courses of Action	Level of Attainment for O_1 (units)	Level of Attainment for O_2 (orders/month)
1	0.00	1.00
2	0.50	0.50
3	1.00	0.30
4	1.50	0.25
5	2.00	0.20
$\vdots$	$\vdots$	$\vdots$

how these quantities were obtained, consider course of action 4. The average inventory carried, I_1, is found by weighting each quantity by the number of months this quantity was carried and then dividing by the total number of months in the inventory cycle.

$$I_1 = \frac{1(3) + 1(2) + 1(1) + 1(0)}{4} = 1.5 \text{ units}$$

For the same course of action we note that the number of units of the drug needed per month is $r = 1$. Noting that the drug must be reordered every 4 months in this case, we find as the average number of orders per month:

$$I_2 = \frac{r}{4} = \frac{1}{4} = 0.25 \frac{\text{order}}{\text{month}}$$

This is equivalent to one order every 4 months.

Note from Table 1.1 that the druggist cannot satisfy both objectives at the same time. O_1 and O_2 are *conflicting objectives*; one cannot be satisfied without a lower level of attainment of the other. We also point out that optimization of a single objective causing the lesser attainment of one or more conflicting objectives is called *suboptimization*. We shall call each element in Table 1.1 a *measure of efficiency* after Churchman, Ackoff, and Arnoff [9]. Each is a measure of the level of attainment of a particular objective for a given course of action.

We still do not have the problem in a form that will enable the pharmacist to make a decision. We must form a measure of effectiveness for each course of action. In forming this measure, there are at least two problems to be considered. The first relates to the units of the measures of efficiency. We cannot add drug units and orders per month. Some common measure must be developed. The second problem is related to how we combine the measures of efficiency once a common measure is obtained. Included in this problem is some needed determination of the relative importance of the two objectives.

A detailed discussion of these points here would confuse our purpose. Chapter 8 will have a more detailed discussion of these topics. For the purpose of our example we shall assume that each objective is equally important. Also suppose that we undertake a cost analysis for the pharmacist and find that the unit cost of storage, c_1, is $3 per unit per month. Suppose also that we find that the unit order cost, c_2, is $4 per order. By applying these unit costs, we obtain the efficiencies shown in Table 1.2, which have the common

TABLE 1.2

Courses of Action	Level of Attainment for O_1 ($/month)	Level of Attainment for O_2 ($/month)	Measure of Effectiveness ($/month)
1	0.00	4.00	4.00
2	1.50	2.00	3.50
3	3.00	1.20	4.20
4	4.50	1.00	5.50
5	6.00	0.80	6.80
⋮	⋮	⋮	⋮

unit $ per month. The measure of effectiveness was obtained by summing the efficiencies for the two objectives. While this summing operation is intuitively appealing it requires certain subtle assumptions [11]. The significance of these assumptions will be discussed in more detail in Chapter 8.

We note that by ordering two units of the drug each time, the pharmacist may minimize his measure of effectiveness, total cost per month. The minimum cost is $3.50 per month.

Now let us see if we can build a mathematical model that will, for practical purposes, give us the same information as Table 1.2. Let q be the quantity of the drug ordered each time. This is a controllable variable to be determined. By observing Table 1.1 we can easily verify that the average inventory carried per year may be expressed as a function of q:

$$I_1 = \frac{q-1}{2} \tag{1.2}$$

Recalling that r was the rate of demand in units per month we may express the number of orders placed per month as

$$I_2 = \frac{r}{q} \tag{1.3}$$

By recalling the unit carrying cost, c_1, and the unit ordering cost, c_2, defined earlier, we may now write a total cost equation:

$$C(q) = \frac{c_1(q - 1)}{2} + c_2\frac{r}{q} \tag{1.4}$$

This expression gives the measure of effectiveness as a mathematical function of the parameters, the controllable and the uncontrollable variables in the inventory system. Such a function is called an *objective function*. Note that for any value of q the equation gives the appropriate value of the measure of effectiveness found in Table 1.2.

At this point it may be useful to extend the example to a multiproduct inventory problem. Suppose our druggist has expanded his drug inventory system. Assume that he has a demand for each of five drugs at a rate r_i, $i = 1, \ldots, 5$. He wishes never to be short of each drug. Because the drug wholesaler is around the corner from the pharmacy, delivery is made immediately after the order is made. The pharmacist's objectives in determining how much of each drug to order remain the same: (1) minimize the average inventory of each drug carried and (2) minimize the number of orders for each drug per month. The unit carrying and ordering costs are c_{i1} and c_{i2}, respectively, $i = 1, \ldots, 5$. We must now find the optimal order quantities q_i for each drug, $i = 1, \ldots, 5$.

It is easy to see that for each drug we shall have an objective function of the form

$$C(q_i) = \frac{c_{i1}(q_i - 1)}{2} + \frac{c_{i2}r_i}{q_i} \qquad i = 1, \ldots, 5 \tag{1.5}$$

The total cost of the inventory system is now

$$C = \sum_{i=1}^{5} c(q_i) = \sum_{i=1}^{5}\left[\frac{c_{i1}(q_i - 1)}{2} + \frac{c_{i2}r_i}{q_i}\right] \tag{1.6}$$

We must find those values of $q_1, \ldots, q_5$ that minimize the value of the objective function.

TABLE 1.3

Item (i)	Unit Volume (a_i)
1	20
2	10
3	30
4	40
5	20

Suppose that, with the addition of other drug items, there is an additional complication. The pharmacy has a small storeroom, and after some reflection the druggist decides that he does not want his average inventory to exceed 600 cubic inches. After checking with the wholesaler he finds that each drug item has the unit volume shown in Table 1.3. This storage restriction may be stated mathematically as follows:

$$\frac{20(q_1 - 1)}{2} + \frac{10(q_2 - 1)}{2} + \frac{30(q_3 - 1)}{2} + \frac{40(q_4 - 1)}{2} + \frac{20(q_5 - 1)}{2} \le 600$$

$$(1.7)$$

In compact form, we may write

$$\sum_{i=1}^{5} \frac{a_i(q_i - 1)}{2} \le 600 \qquad (1.8)$$

The pharmacist also feels that to maintain good relations with the wholesaler he must make at least (on the average) two orders per month. That is,

$$\sum_{i=1}^{5} \frac{r_i}{q_i} \ge 2 \qquad (1.9)$$

Our decision problem now is to find values of $q_1, \ldots, q_5$ that satisfy constraints (1.8) and (1.9) and minimize (1.6).

1.4   Decision Problems in Operations Research

The example discussed above, although oversimplified, was used to point out that operations research is concerned with decision problems. In the course of the discussion, certain selected properties of the process of making a decision were identified. In an effort to tie together the concepts of a decision process, the decision problem should be related to frequently heard problem areas in operations research.

There is no single classification of decision problems subjected to analysis by operations research. A classification proposed by Ackoff [4] and Ackoff and Rivett [5] is useful in discussing the types of problems that operations research is concerned with. This classification is similar to the eight problem areas shown below:

1. Inventory	5. Sequencing
2. Allocation	6. Competition
3. Waiting lines	7. Replacement
4. Scheduling	8. Search

Inventory Problems

Inventory problems are concerned with the control and maintenance of quantities of physical goods. These goods may be many things. Cans on the retail grocer's shelf, water in a reservoir, and drugs in the pharmacy store-room are all examples of physical goods that generate inventory problems.

Decisions in inventory problems are related to time and quantity and are usually concerned with (1) when the inventory should be replenished and (2) how much should be added to inventory. The pertinent costs usually considered during the problem formulation include (1) carrying cost, (2) shortage cost, and (3) replenishment cost.

Carrying costs can include capital investments in inventory, storage costs, taxes, insurance, and others. Costs related to shortage costs include lost sales, overtime, and clerical costs. Replenishment costs may include ordering cost and setup costs for manufacturing operations.

More extensive discussion of inventory problems and their analysis can be found in any one of several texts; see, for example, Naddor [12] or Hadley and Whitin [13]. An advanced discussion may be found in Arrow, Karlin, and Scarf [16]. A thorough review of the analysis of inventory problems has been compiled by Hanssmann [15].

Allocation Problems

Allocation problems are concerned with the allocation of resources—which are usually limited—so that some measure of effectiveness is optimized. If there are enough resources to go around, the problem is greatly simplified.

These problems have been broadly classified into three areas: The first type of allocation problem occurs when there are a number of tasks to be performed and there are exactly enough resources to perform the tasks. Some of the tasks may be performed in different ways. The cost (or profit) obtained in accomplishing the tasks depends on the resource used. If each task requires one and only one resource the problem is called an *assignment problem*. If it takes more than one resource to accomplish the tasks and each resource may be used for more than one task, we have a *distribution problem*. A special type of distribution problem that has been subjected to considerable analysis is the transportation problem.

A second class of problems arises when the tasks require more resources than are available. Determining what "mix" of products to make in an oil refinery when production capacity is limited is an example of such a problem.

The third type of problem occurs when it is possible to control the quantity of resources used in accomplishing the tasks. This also includes cases where resources may be disposed of. Selection of sales territories and the allocation of salesmen to them is an example of such a problem.

A wide range of applications may be found in the reviews of Arnoff and Sengupta [17], Dreyfus [18], and Gass [19].

Waiting Line Problems

Waiting line problems are concerned with the design and planning of facilities to meet a randomly fluctuating demand for services. The service system itself is usually governed by some chance mechanism. If service facilities are not adequate to meet demand, this causes congestion to occur at the service facility and incurs certain costs. However, increased service capacity to reduce congestion usually causes increased idleness in the service system, thus incurring a cost of idle service facilities. Waiting line problems usually aim to design systems that balance the aggregate costs of idleness and congestion and minimize the total cost of the service system.

Analysis of waiting line problems has occurred in diverse areas of applications. For example, determination of admissions policies in a hospital has been formulated as a waiting line problem [19]. Determining the optimum number of toll booths at a tunnel is also a waiting line problem [22]. A review of applications may be found in Morse [20] and Saaty [21].

Scheduling Problems

Scheduling is the *timing* of arrivals (and departures) of units requiring service. These units may take the form of products in a manufacturing operation, planes arriving at an airport, or patients arriving in a doctor's office. Scheduling problems are concerned with minimizing costs associated with things such as total time to complete a project, idle service facilities, and waiting time for service.

The application of operations research methods to scheduling problems has been widespread. A good cross section of applications may be found in a book edited by Muth and Thompson [23].

Sequencing Problems

Sequencing refers to the *order* in which units requiring service are serviced. In terms of queueing theory this order is called the queue discipline. The terms sequencing and scheduling are often confused. Note that sequencing is concerned with ordering, whereas scheduling is concerned with timing.

A common example of a sequencing problem occurs in the job shop. In this situation, there is a requirement for processing J jobs or commodities on M machines or other facilities. We should point out that traditionally we think of the product being brought to the machine. In many applications, for example, the construction industry, the machines must be moved to the job.

Two problems which are closely related to sequencing problems are called the assembly line balancing problem and the traveling salesman problem. Usually an assembly line is made up of a sequence of work stations through which the product must pass in some preestablished order. Idle time of the work stations is a major concern in these problems. The ideal situation has the assembly line balanced so that all work stations take an equal amount of time and idle time is minimized. Line imbalance occurs when the work time for each station differs widely and idle time increases. Line balancing problems are usually concerned with minimizing idle time by suitably grouping work stations [9, 24].

The traveling salesman problem is one of the traditional problems in operations research. It is concerned with finding an optimal route for a salesman between a series of interconnected cities under the condition that each city is visited once and only once. The salesman's route is required to end at his home city.

Although this is the traditional formulation, equivalent problems exist in other contexts [9]. For example, consider an assembly line on which a number of different products are manufactured. Suppose that the setup cost for each product depends on the item that was produced before it. The problem is to find a sequence for production such that the total setup cost is minimized. This is also a traveling salesman problem.

Efficient analytic solutions to sequencing problems are not frequent. The optimization problems are very difficult to analyze. A review by Sisson [25] summarizes recent accomplishments in this area.

Competition Problems

Competition problems involve two or more individuals or organizations with conflicting objectives trying to optimize some measure of effectiveness. In these problems a decision made by one decision-maker can affect a decision made by one or more of the remaining decision-makers. Examples of competition problems range from two players struggling to win at chess to several large corporations struggling to maintain their share of the market.

An extension of the competition problem defined above occurs when one or more decision-makers are viewed as being in competition with nature.

Competition problems are usually difficult to analyze. For this reason, their problem formulation is usually reduced to another type of decision problem. A general discussion of competition problems in management science has been published by Shubik [26]. Fishburn [11] has made an extensive discussion of these problems in operations research.

Replacement Problems

Replacement problems are concerned with the replacement of items that deteriorate or fail. Light bulbs, cars, and television sets are obvious examples of this type of equipment in our own lives.

The first type of problem—items that deteriorate—is usually concerned with determining the optimum point in time for replacement and determining the best available equipment for replacement. Machinery, automobiles, linen, and uniforms are all examples of this type of equipment.

The second class of replacement problems is concerned with items that fail. The problem here is usually to determine whether or not all items should be replaced in a group and, if so, when. Light bulbs in a ball park are an example of this type of equipment. Obviously, in this case, it is extremely expensive to send a man up a tall tower each time a bulb burns out. This is a replacement problem in which all items would probably be replaced and the frequency of replacement would have to be determined.

These problems have been subjected to a considerable amount of study. Dean [27] has reviewed current applications as well as some of the mathematics required for the study of replacement.

Search Problems

Search problems are usually concerned with balancing the sum of two costs: (1) the costs associated with decision errors and (2) the cost of collecting and analyzing data that will reduce decision errors. The decision errors of concern are those related to the inaccuracy of information.

In the data-collection process there are generally two classes of errors that can be made. The first is sampling error. This type of error occurs when there is a "failure to detect what one is looking for due to inadequate coverage" [5]. The second class of error, observational error, occurs when there is a "failure to detect what one is looking for even though one has looked in the right place" [5].

There are many examples of search problems. Auditing, sea search of submarines, and trial borings before building construction are all examples. There are no current reviews of search problems. A brief early review may be found in Ackoff [4].

Applications of Operations Research

The classes of problems discussed above are not mutually exclusive. In fact, very few O.R. studies fall uniquely into one of the problem areas listed above.

The applications of operations research cover a wide gamut. A recent publication of the Operations Research Society contains a summary of the applications of operations research [28]. The reader wishing more detail on applications should consult this text as a reference.

1.5   Mathematical Methods in Operations Research

The years since the formation of Blackett's circus have seen the analysis of many decision problems by O.R. methodology. During the early years this methodology was nothing more than the methodology of the scientists involved in the project. It was inevitable that a set of tools and techniques that were most frequently used in the analysis would be identified. Likewise, it was to be expected that new techniques would be developed to solve those problems not amenable to analysis by existing techniques.

Today, well over twenty years after the formation of Blackett's circus, a collection of mathematical methods has evolved that is identified with operations research. Many of these techniques come from classical mathematics and other disciplines. Other methods have evolved to meet the needs of certain classes of decision problems that occur frequently in the O.R. study. Without question, the future will see the development of new techniques to meet the needs of new and different problems.

Because the methods of operations research are constantly growing, this text is entitled *Mathematical Methods in Operations Research*. The key word is *in*. Hopefully this will indicate to the operations researcher ten years from today that the authors see these methods as being a subset of the future mathematical methods of operations research.

In the discussion of Section 1.3, we saw that modeling the decision process and decision problem solving usually result in the expression of a measure of effectiveness as a mathematical function of controllable and uncontrollable variables—an objective function. In the process of constructing the objective function and finding the optimum values of the controllable variables in it, two broad classes of mathematical methods are required. These are the methods of optimization and stochastic modeling.

In a broad sense optimization methods are concerned with finding optimal values of the controllable variables in an objective function. On certain occasions these controllable variables may be subject to certain restrictions which may be expressed in mathematical form. Chapters 2, 3, 4, 5, 6, and 9 are primarily concerned with methods of optimization. Each is pointed at techniques available when the objective function and the restrictions on the controllable variables have various forms.

In many cases there is chance variation in some of the parameters of the objective function. These are uncontrollable variables. Generally, the use of stochastic modeling in operations research is pointed toward describing the behavior of uncontrollable variables. In many cases the system being studied and its chance behavior are so complex stochastic modeling is used to gain a better understanding of the system before attempting to construct an objective function. Chapter 7 is concerned with the chance properties of service systems.

Chapters 8 and 9 contain both methods of optimization and stochastic models. Their subject matter should not be classified as one or the other, exclusively.

In general, we draw a distinction between the decision problems discussed in Section 1.4 and the mathematical methods in operations research. In solving the decision problem, any one or possibly all of the mathematical methods may be used.

References Cited and Bibliography

[1] McCloskey, J. F., and F. N. Trefethen (eds.). *Operations Research for Management*, Vol. 1. Baltimore: Johns Hopkins Press, 1954.
[2] Trefethen, F. N. "A History of Operations Research." In reference [1].

[3] Johnson, E. A. "The Executive, the Organization and Operations Research." In reference [1].

[4] Ackoff, R. L. "The Development of Operations Research as a Science," *Operations Res.*, Vol. 4, No. 3 (June 1956).

[5] Ackoff, R. L., and P. Rivett. *A Manager's Guide to Operations Research.* New York: Wiley, 1963.

[6] Flagle, C. D., W. H. Huggins, and R. H. Roy. *Operations Research and Systems Engineering.* Baltimore: Johns Hopkins Press, 1960.

[7] Hitch, C. "Sub-Optimization in Operations Problems," *Operations Res.*, Vol. 1, No. 3 (May 1953).

[8] Miller, D. W., and M. K. Starr. *Executive Decisions and Operations Research.* Englewood Cliffs, N.J.: Prentice-Hall, 1964.

[9] Churchman, C. W., R. L. Ackoff, and E. L. Arnoff. *Introduction to Operations Research.* New York: Wiley, 1957.

[10] Ackoff, R. L. *Scientific Method.* New York: Wiley, 1962.

[11] Fishburn, P. C. *Decision and Value Theory.* New York: Wiley, 1964.

[12] Naddor, E. *Inventory Systems.* New York: Wiley, 1966.

[13] Hadley, G., and T. M. Whitin. *Analysis of Inventory Systems.* Englewood Cliffs, N.J.: Prentice-Hall, 1963.

[14] Ackoff, R. L. *Progress in Operations Research*, Vol. 1. New York: Wiley, 1961.

[15] Hanssmann, F. "A Survey of Inventory Theory from the Operations Research Viewpoint." Chapter 3 in reference [14].

[16] Arrow, K. J., S. Karlin, and H. Scarf. *Studies in the Mathematical Theory of Inventory and Production.* Stanford, Calif.: Stanford University Press, 1958.

[17] Arnoff, E. L., and S. S. Sengupta. "Mathematical Programming." Chapter 4 in reference [14].

[18] Dreyfus, S. "Dynamic Programming." Chapter 5 in reference [14].

[19] Young, J. P. "A Queueing Theory Approach to the Control of Hospital Inpatient Census." Doctoral Dissertation. Baltimore: Johns Hopkins University, 1962.

[20] Morse, P. M. *Queues, Inventories and Maintenance.* New York: Wiley, 1958.

[21] Saaty, T. L. *Elements of Queueing Theory.* New York: McGraw-Hill, 1961.

[22] Edie, L. C. "Traffic Delays at Toll Booths." *Operations Res.*, Vol. 2, No. 2 (May 1954).

[23] Muth, J. F., and G. L. Thompson (eds.). *Industrial Scheduling.* Englewood Cliffs, N.J.: Prentice-Hall, 1963.

[24] Salveson, M. E. "The Assembly Line Balancing Problem." *Ind. Eng.*, Vol. 6, No. 3 (May–June 1955).

[25] Sisson, R. L. "Sequencing Theory." Chapter 7 in reference [14].

[26] Shubik, M. "The Uses of Game Theory in Management Science." *Management Sci.*, Vol. 2, No. 1 (1955).

[27] Dean, B. V. "Replacement Theory." Chapter 8 in reference [14].

[28] Hertz, D. B., and R. T. Eddison. *Progress in Operations Research*, Vol. 2. New York: Wiley, 1964.

CHAPTER 2

Classical Optimization Techniques

2.1 Introduction

In this chapter we shall concern ourselves with developing the classical theory of optimization. These results are obtained through applications of the calculus to problems of locating maxima and minima of continuous functions and are useful mainly in theoretical analysis. However, a firm grasp of the ideas presented in following sections is essential for an understanding of the material in succeeding chapters. Classical optimization theory is usually the stepping-off point in developing solution techniques for nonlinear programming problems. Concepts very similar to those presented in this chapter will also prove useful in obtaining solution techniques for optimization of dynamic systems. Although classical optimization techniques are not suited for obtaining numerical solutions except for relatively simple problems, the theory forms a basis for attacking many types of applied problems.

2.2 Mathematical Tools[1]

In this section we present mathematical concepts that are pertinent to the material in the remaining sections. Most concepts are given as either definitions or unproved theorems, because they are usually contained in undergraduate calculus courses. Several texts on advanced calculus give a more rigorous discussion of these ideas. One excellent reference is Courant's *Differential and Integral Calculus* [1].

---

[1] This section is a review of concepts from elementary analysis. The reader may skip this material without loss of continuity.

Developments in classical optimization theory have been restricted to continuous and differentiable functions. A definition of these terms is appropriate.

A function of N variables $x_1, x_2, \ldots, x_N$ is *continuous* at the point $x_1^0, x_2^0, \ldots, x_N^0$ if for every $\epsilon > 0$ there corresponds $\delta_1, \ldots, \delta_N$ such that for $|h_i| < \delta_i$,

$$|f(x_1^0 + h_1, \ldots, x_N^0 + h_N) - f(x_1^0, \ldots, x_N^0)| \leq \epsilon \qquad (2.1)$$

where $\delta_i > 0$.

In Figure 2.1 we present a function of two variables that is not continuous along the line $x = 5$.

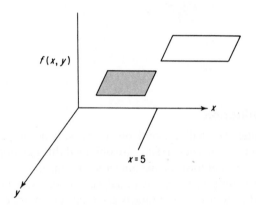

Figure 2.1.

A function $f(x_1, \ldots, x_N) = f(\cdot)^2$ is *differentiable* at a point $\mathbf{x}^0 = (x_1^0, \ldots, x_N^0)^3$ if the derivative of $f(\cdot)$ with respect to each of the independent variables, defined as

$$\lim_{h_i \to 0} \frac{f(x_1^0, \ldots, x_i^0 + h_i, \ldots, x_N^0) - f(x_1^0, \ldots, x_N^0)}{h_i} = \left.\frac{\partial f(x_1, \ldots, x_N)}{\partial x_i}\right|_{\mathbf{x} = \mathbf{x}^0} \qquad (2.2)$$

exists. Figure 2.2 shows a function, $f(x, y)$, which is continuous everywhere but has one point at which the derivative does not exist.

A function $f(\mathbf{x})$ takes on its *absolute minimum* at $\mathbf{x}^*$ if $f(\mathbf{x}) - f(\mathbf{x}^*) \geq 0$ for all $\mathbf{x}$ on which the function $f(\mathbf{x})$ is defined. The absolute minimum is often called the *global minimum*. The definition for a *global maximum* is obtained by reversing the sense of the inequality in the definition of the global minimum.

---

[2] This is a shorthand notation. The argument of the function should be easily determined from the discussion.

[3] The boldface quantities are N-dimensional vectors.

A function $f(\mathbf{x})$ has a *proper relative minimum* at $\mathbf{x}^*$ if there exists a $d > 0$ such that for every $\mathbf{h}$, except possibly $\mathbf{h} = \mathbf{0}$,

$$f(\mathbf{x}^* + \mathbf{h}) - f(\mathbf{x}^*) > 0 \qquad \text{for} \quad |h_i| \leq d \qquad i = 1, \ldots, N \qquad (2.3)$$

By reversing the sense of the inequality we obtain the corresponding definition of a proper relative maximum.

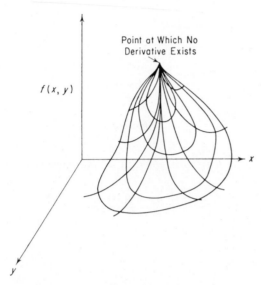

Point at Which No
Derivative Exists

$f(x, y)$

Figure 2.2.

A function $f(\mathbf{x})$ has an *improper relative minimum* at $\mathbf{x}^*$ if there exists a $d > 0$ such that for every $\mathbf{h}$

$$f(\mathbf{x}^* + \mathbf{h}) - f(\mathbf{x}^*) \geq 0 \qquad (2.4)$$

for $|h_i| \leq d$, $i = 1, \ldots, N$, and there exists at least one $\mathbf{h} \neq \mathbf{0}$ for which equality holds.

The definition of an improper relative maximum is obtained by reversing the inequality given above.

These definitions are illustrated in Figures 2.3 and 2.4, where contours of a function of two variables are shown. These contours are lines of constant $f(\cdot)$. Figure 2.3 shows a contour map of a function that contains two relative minima. Figure 2.4 gives a contour map of a function that has an improper relative minimum.

Mean Value Theorem: *If $f(x)$ is continuous in the closed interval $x^0 \leq x \leq x^0 + h$ and differentiable at every point in the open interval $x^0 < x < x^0 + h$,*

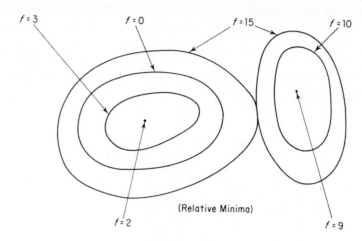

Figure 2.3.

then there exists at least one point x* in the open interval defined above where

$$\frac{f(x^0 + h) - f(x^0)}{h} = f'(x^*) \tag{2.5}$$

where

$$f'(x^*) = \frac{df(x)}{dx}\bigg|_{x=x^*}$$

Notice that x^* must lie in the open interval $x^0 < x^* < x^0 + h$. We may express any x in this interval as a function of a continuous parameter θ,

$$x = x^0 + \theta h$$

where $0 < \theta < 1$. Thus

$$x^* = x^0 + \theta h$$

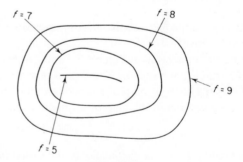

Figure 2.4.

The mean value theorem may be expressed in a more convenient form,

$$\frac{f(x^0 + h) - f(x^0)}{h} = f'(x^0 + \theta h) \qquad 0 < \theta < 1 \qquad (2.6)$$

We shall not prove the theorem stated above but will use it to derive necessary conditions for a proper maximum or proper minimum. We shall call each of the points that satisfy the definitions of a proper maximum, or minimum, *extreme points*. A proof of the mean value theorem may be found in references [1] and [2].

Before launching directly into deriving necessary and sufficient conditions for an extreme point, we must describe just what is meant by a necessary condition and a sufficient condition.

Necessary Condition

Let p and r be simple statements. When we say p is necessary for r, we mean that when r is true, then p is true and, conversely, if p is not true, then r is not true. For example, suppose r is the fact that an airplane is flying and p is the statement that the airplane got off the ground. Then we may say that p is necessary for r; that is, if the airplane is to fly, it is necessary that it leave the ground. Conversely, if the airplane does not leave the ground it is not flying.

Sufficient Condition

Again, suppose p and r are simple statements. If p is sufficient for r, then when p is true, r is true. For example, consider the election of the President of the United States. A sufficient condition for a candidate to be elected President is that he receive a majority of the electoral votes. However, this is not a necessary condition because one can be elected President without receiving a majority of the electoral votes cast.

Necessary and Sufficient Condition

If p and r are simple statements, then when we say p is necessary and sufficient for r, we mean that when p is true, r is true; and when r is true, then p is true. For an example of a necessary and sufficient condition we refer to the sport of football. A necessary and sufficient condition for a team to be the champions of the National Football League is for the team under consideration to win the championship game.

Theorem: *If the function $f(\cdot)$ is defined in an interval containing the point x^0, is continuously differentiable everywhere in the interval with the possible exception of x^0 itself, and if $f'(\cdot)$ vanishes at no more than a finite number of points, then $f(x)$ has a proper extreme point at x^0 if and only if the point x^0 separates the original interval into two subintervals in which $f'(x)$ has different signs. In particular, the function has a minimum if the derivative is negative to* *the left of x^0 and positive to the right. If the reverse situation occurs, $f(x)$ has a maximum.*

PROOF. The proof follows directly from the mean value theorem. The sufficiency part of the proof is given below and the remainder is left as an exercise.

Assume that to the left of x^0 there exists an interval

$$x_1 \leq x \leq x^0$$

such that

$$f'(x) \leq 0$$

and that to the right of x^0 a corresponding interval exists, $x^0 \leq x \leq x_2$, in which

$$f'(x) \geq 0$$

To show that x^0 is a local minimum we shall use the mean value theorem given above:

$$f(x^0 + h) - f(x^0) = hf'(x^0 + \theta h) \qquad 0 < \theta < 1$$

Suppose h is negative. The point $x^0 + h$ lies in the interval $x_1 \leq x \leq x^0$ and $f'(x^0) \leq 0$. By continuity, we know that if $f'(x^0) \leq 0$, then $f'(x^0 + \theta h) \leq 0$ for $0 < \theta < 1$. Therefore,

$$f(x^0 + h) - f(x^0) = hf'(x^0 + \theta h) \geq 0$$

Consider the case when h is positive so that the point $x + h$ lies in the interval $x^0 < x < x_2$, where $f'(x) \geq 0$. Thus $f(x^0 + h) - f(x^0) = hf'(x^0 + \theta h) \geq 0$, $0 < \theta < 1$.

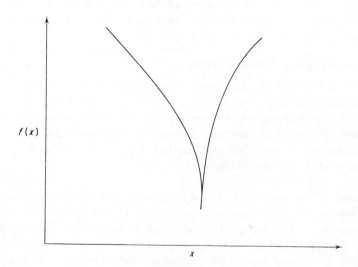

Figure 2.5.

This theorem is useful in situations where the derivative is not defined. However, the theorem is applicable only for functions of a single variable. Figures 2.5 and 2.6 show examples of functions which do not possess a derivative at the extreme point.

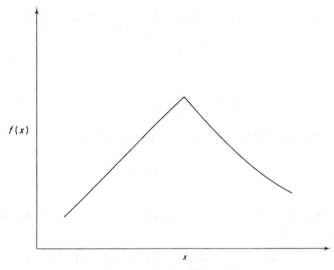

Figure 2.6.

We now proceed to a discussion of Taylor's theorem—a very important result in analysis. Much of the future work in this chapter is based on this theorem and consequently we shall delve more deeply into Taylor's result.

The essential result of the theorem is that we may approximate a given function $f(\mathbf{x})$ by a polynomial of order n, if the first $n + 1$ partial derivatives of the function are continuous. To be more explicit, suppose we wish to infer the value of $f(\cdot)$ at $\mathbf{x}^* + h$ from information of $f(\cdot)$ evaluated at $\mathbf{x}^*$. Taylor's theorem [3] has the following form:

Theorem: *The function $f(\mathbf{x}^* + \mathbf{h})$ may be expanded as follows:*

$$f(\mathbf{x}^* + \mathbf{h}) = f(\mathbf{x}^*) + G_n(\mathbf{x}^*) + R_n(\mathbf{x}^* + \mathbf{h}, \mathbf{x}^*) \qquad (2.7)$$

where $R_n(\mathbf{x}^* + \mathbf{h}, \mathbf{x}^*)$ is the remainder term of Lagrange's form [1] defined below and $G_n(\mathbf{x}^*)$ is an nth-order polynomial in $\mathbf{h}$.

To describe $G_n(\cdot)$ it is necessary to introduce additional notation. Let

$$d^m f(\mathbf{x}^*) = \sum_{i=1}^{N} \sum_{j=1}^{N} \cdots \sum_{k=1}^{N} h_i h_j \cdots h_k \frac{\partial^m f(\mathbf{x}^*)}{\partial x_i \, \partial x_j \cdots \partial x_k} \qquad (2.8)$$

where there are m sums and an h_i associated with each summation. For example, when $n = 3$ and $m = 2$, the term $d^m f(\mathbf{x})$ has the form

$$d^2 f(x_1, x_2, x_3) = \sum_{i=1}^{3} \sum_{j=1}^{3} h_i h_j \frac{\partial^2 f(x_1, x_2, x_3)}{\partial x_i \, \partial x_j}$$

$$= h_1^2 \frac{\partial^2 f(x_1, x_2, x_3)}{\partial x_1^2} + 2 h_1 h_2 \frac{\partial^2 f(x_1, x_2, x_3)}{\partial x_1 \, \partial x_2}$$

$$+ 2 h_1 h_3 \frac{\partial^2 f(x_1, x_2, x_3)}{\partial x_1 \, \partial x_3} + h_2^2 \frac{\partial^2 f(x_1, x_2, x_3)}{\partial x_2^2}$$

$$+ 2 h_2 h_3 \frac{\partial^2 f(x_1, x_2, x_3)}{\partial x_2 \, \partial x_3} + h_3^2 \frac{\partial^2 f(x_1, x_2, x_3)}{\partial x_3^2}$$

$G_n(x)$ may be expressed as a sum of the terms defined above:

$$G_n(x) = \sum_{i=1}^{N} \frac{1}{i!} d^i f(\mathbf{x}) \tag{2.9}$$

The remainder term R_n can also be expressed in terms of the notation defined above. Thus

$$R_n(\mathbf{x} + \mathbf{h}, \, \mathbf{x}) = \frac{1}{(n+1)!} d^{n+1} f(\mathbf{x} + \theta \mathbf{h}) \qquad 0 < \theta < 1 \tag{2.10}$$

Example: Suppose we wish to express the function shown below by a third-order $(n = 3)^4$ Taylor's series approximation about the point $(x_1 = 2, x_2 = 1, x_3 = -1)$

$$f(x_1, x_2, x_3) = x_2 e^{x_1} + x_2^3 x_3$$

In this problem $G_n(x)$ would be given by

$$G_3(2, 1, -1) = d^1 f(2, 1, -1) + \frac{d^2 f(2, 1, -1)}{2!} + \frac{d^3 f(2, 1, -1)}{3!}$$

$$d^1 f(2, 1, -1) = \sum_{i=1}^{3} h_i \frac{\partial f(x_1, x_2, x_3)}{\partial x_i} \Bigg|_{x_1 = 2, x_2 = 1, x_3 = -1}$$

$$= h_1 \frac{\partial f(x_1, x_2, x_3)}{\partial x_1} \Bigg|_{2, 1, -1}$$

$$+ h_2 \frac{\partial f(x_1, x_2, x_3)}{\partial x_2} \Bigg|_{2, 1, -1} + h_3 \frac{\partial f(x_1, x_2, x_3)}{\partial x_3} \Bigg|_{2, 1, -1}$$

$$= h_1 e^2 + h_2 (e^2 - 3) + h_3$$

---

[4] Note that the order of the approximation, n, does not have to equal the number of variables, N.

$$d^2f(2, 1, -1) = \sum_{i=1}^{3} \sum_{j=1}^{3} h_i h_j \frac{\partial^2 f(x_1, x_2, x_3)}{\partial x_i \, \partial x_j}\bigg|_{2,1,-1}$$

$$= h_1^2 e^2 - 6h_2^2 + 2h_1 h_2 e^2 - 6h_2 h_3$$

$$d^3f(2, 1, -1) = \sum_{i=1}^{3} \sum_{j=1}^{3} \sum_{k=1}^{3} h_i h_j h_k \frac{\partial^3 f(x_1, x_2, x_3)}{\partial x_i \, \partial x_j \, \partial x_k}\bigg|_{2,1,-1}$$

$$= h_1^3 e^2 + 3h_1^2 h_2 e^2 - 6h_2^3 + 18h_2^2 h_3$$

Therefore,

$$G_3(2, 1, -1) = \sum_{i=1}^{3} \frac{1}{i!} d^i f(2, 1, -1) = h_1 e^2 + h_2(e^2 - 3) + h_3$$

$$+ \frac{1}{2!} (e^2 h_1^2 - 6h_2^2 + 2e^2 h_1 h_2 + 6h_2 h_3)$$

$$+ \frac{1}{3!} (h_1^3 e^2 + 3e^2 h_1^2 h_2 - 6h_2^3 + 18h_2^2 h_3)$$

Suppose we wish to approximate $f(x_1, x_2, x_3)$ at the point $x_1 = 1$, $x_2 = x_3 = 0$. Using the third-order approximation developed above, we may perform the calculation. The vector $\mathbf{h}$ for this particular $\mathbf{x}$ is

$$\mathbf{h} = \mathbf{x} - \mathbf{x}^* = \begin{pmatrix} 1 \\ 0 \\ 0 \end{pmatrix} - \begin{pmatrix} 2 \\ 1 \\ -1 \end{pmatrix} = \begin{pmatrix} -1 \\ -1 \\ +1 \end{pmatrix}$$

Thus

$$G_3(2, 1, -1) = -e^2 - e^2 + 3 + 1$$
$$+ \tfrac{1}{2}(e^2 - 6 + 2e^2 + 6)$$
$$+ \tfrac{1}{6}(-e^2 - 3e^2 - 6 + 18)$$
$$= -2e^2 + 4 + \tfrac{3}{2}e^2 - \tfrac{2}{3}e^2 + 2$$
$$= -\tfrac{7}{6}e^2 + 6$$

$$f(\mathbf{x}) = f(\mathbf{x}^* + \mathbf{h}) = f(2, 1, -1) + G_3(2, 1, -1) = (e^2 - 1) - \tfrac{7}{6}e^2 + 6$$

It should be pointed out that the value of θ in the remainder term is chosen to make

$$f(\mathbf{x}^* + \mathbf{h}) = f(\mathbf{x}^*) + G_n(\mathbf{x}^*) + R_n(\mathbf{x}^* + \mathbf{h}, \mathbf{x}^*)$$

Taylor's theorem guarantees that a θ exists to accomplish this.

The final theorem that we shall discuss is the implicit function theorem. This theorem applies to a set of M equations in N variables. In particular, consider the following equations:

$$h_i(\mathbf{x}) = 0 \qquad i = 1, \ldots, M < N \tag{2.11}$$

where

$$\mathbf{x} = (x_1, \ldots, x_N)$$

and $h_i(\mathbf{x})$ are differentiable.

We would like to know if we can use these M equations to eliminate M of the N variables at the point $\mathbf{x}^0$. In particular, we want to know if there exist M functions, $\psi(\cdot)$, such that

$$x_i^0 = \psi_i(x_{M+1}^0, \ldots, x_N^0) \qquad i = 1, \ldots, M \qquad (2.12)$$

The implicit function theorem gives a condition that, if satisfied, guarantees the existence and uniqueness of the functions $\psi_i(\cdot)$ and moreover ensures that these functions, $\psi_i(\cdot)$, are continuous and differentiable in some neighborhood of $\mathbf{x}^0$. This result will be useful in optimization of a function of N variables when certain constraints are imposed on the variables.

Implicit Function Theorem: *A necessary and sufficient condition for the functions $\psi_i(\cdot)$ to exist is that the rank of the following matrix evaluated at $\mathbf{x}^0$ be M:*

$$P_{\mathbf{x}^0}(h_1, \ldots, h_M) = \begin{bmatrix} \dfrac{\partial h_1}{\partial x_1} & \cdots & \dfrac{\partial h_1}{\partial x_N} \\ \vdots & & \vdots \\ \dfrac{\partial h_M}{\partial x_1} & \cdots & \dfrac{\partial h_M}{\partial x_N} \end{bmatrix} \qquad (2.13)$$

Each of the partial derivatives is evaluated at the point $\mathbf{x}^0$.

The condition given above guarantees that there exist M functions $\psi_i(\cdot)$, $i = 1, \ldots, M$, which allow us to express M of the variables in terms of the remaining $N - M$ variables. However, the result does not tell us which M variables may be eliminated. In many cases it is necessary to determine which M of the variables may be eliminated. The theorem gives an additional condition to aid in selecting the variables that may be eliminated.

Define the *Jacobian* as

$$J_{\mathbf{x}}(h_1, \ldots, h_M) = \begin{bmatrix} \dfrac{\partial h_1}{\partial x_1} & \cdots & \dfrac{\partial h_1}{\partial x_M} \\ \vdots & & \vdots \\ \dfrac{\partial h_M}{\partial x_1} & \cdots & \dfrac{\partial h_M}{\partial x_M} \end{bmatrix} \qquad (2.14)$$

There are $\binom{N}{M} = N!/(N - M)!$ Jacobians which may be formed from the matrix P defined above. These various Jacobians are formed by selecting M of the following column vectors:

$$\begin{bmatrix} \dfrac{\partial h_1}{\partial x_j} \\ \vdots \\ \dfrac{\partial h_M}{\partial x_j} \end{bmatrix} \qquad j = 1, \ldots, N$$

If a Jacobian associated with a given set of variables, say $x_p, \ldots, x_{p+M}$, is not zero, then there exists a set of functions $\psi_i(\cdot)$, $i = p, \ldots, p + M$ which allow us to eliminate $x_p, \ldots, x_{p+M}$; that is,

$$\begin{aligned} x_p^0 &= \psi_p(x_1^0, \ldots, x_{p-1}^0, x_{p+M+1}^0, \ldots, x_N^0) \\ \vdots \quad &\vdots \\ x_{p+M}^0 &= \psi_{p+M}(x_1^0, \ldots, x_{p-1}^0, x_{p+M+1}^0, \ldots, x_N^0) \end{aligned} \tag{2.15}$$

These functions are unique, continuous, and differentiable in some neighborhood of $\mathbf{x}^0$. The proof of the implicit function theorem may be found in reference [1].

2.3   Unconstrained Problems

This section contains a derivation of necessary and sufficient conditions for maxima and minima of functions where no constraints are imposed. In the initial development, we shall restrict ourselves to functions of just one variable, because a good intuitive grasp is more easily obtained when the function can be easily visualized. After grasping the concepts of optimization for a one-dimensional problem, we shall move on to multivariable problems.

There are two approaches we could take in finding the maximum, or minimum, of a function. It is instructive to discuss the characteristics of each, since both approaches are useful in solving nonlinear programming problems. The first approach is more intuitively appealing and involves making observations of the function to determine if a given point is a relative maximum (or minimum). A physical analog is a mountain climber trying to locate the peak of a mountain. He has picked a foggy day to climb and consequently he can observe only the terrain in the immediate neighborhood of his current location. He has assumed that there are no crevasses or cliffs (continuity) and that the mountain has only one peak (unimodality). Which path should he choose to get to the top? The solution is quite simple: He always takes the path that is going up. He chooses this path by observing which way is up in the neighborhood of his current location; that is, he makes observations of the function. Our friend knows he has reached the top when he reaches a location where all paths from that point descend. Methods that are based on observing the function and moving in what appears to be a promising direction are called *direct methods* [4].

The second approach is the one that is introduced in elementary calculus courses. This method involves constructing conditions which, if satisfied, assure us that a given point is indeed a local or relative maximum. These conditions are derived analytically from the function under consideration, but since we use some derived property of the function instead of the function itself, this approach is called an *indirect method*. The remainder of this chapter is devoted to developing indirect methods for optimization.

Functions of One Variable

Consider a function $f(x)$ that is continuous and has a continuous first derivative in some interval $a \le x \le b$. Recall from the mean value theorem of differential calculus [equation (2.6)],

$$f(x^0 + h) - f(x^0) = hf'(x^0 + \theta h) \qquad 0 < \theta < 1$$

For a relative maximum the quantity shown above must be nonpositive. The factor h can be either positive or negative. Consider the case when h is negative. We have

$$f(x^0 + h) - f(x^0) = hf'(x^0 + \theta h) \le 0$$

Dividing through by h we obtain

$$\frac{f(x^0 + h) - f(x^0)}{h} = f'(x^0 + \theta h) \ge 0 \qquad h < 0$$

Taking the limit as $h \to 0$ yields

$$\frac{d^- f(x^0)}{dx} \ge 0$$

where $[d^- f(x^0)]/dx$ means the left-hand derivative. We approached $h = 0$ from $h < 0$. Now suppose $h > 0$. The quantity

$$f(x^0 + h) - f(x^0) = hf'(x^0 + \theta h)$$

must still be negative for $f(x)$ to be a maximum at x_0. Therefore,

$$\frac{f(x^0 + h) - f(x^0)}{h} \le 0 \qquad h > 0$$

Taking the limit as $h \to 0$, $h > 0$, we obtain

$$\frac{d^+ f(x)}{dx} \le 0$$

Since we have assumed continuity of the derivative we obtain

$$\left. \frac{d^+ f(x)}{dx} \right|_{x=x^0} = \left. \frac{d^- f(x)}{dx} \right|_{x=x^0} = \left. \frac{df(x)}{dx} \right|_{x=x^0} = 0$$

which is the necessary condition for a maximum of a function possessing a continuous first derivative. Notice that the same condition is also necessary for a minimum of $f(x)$ at x^0. In fact, the derivative may vanish at points that are neither maxima nor minima. This condition is just necessary—not

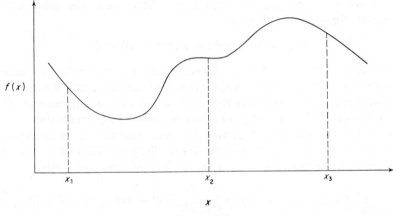

Figure 2.7.

sufficient. The vanishing of the derivative at x^0 indicates that $f(x)$ evaluated at x^0 is either a maximum, minimum, or an inflection point. Every point where $f'(x)$ vanishes is called a *critical point* or *stationary point* of $f(x)$. Figure 2.7 gives an example of a function that has a minimum at x_1, an inflection point at x_2, and a maximum at x_3. A plot of the derivative of the

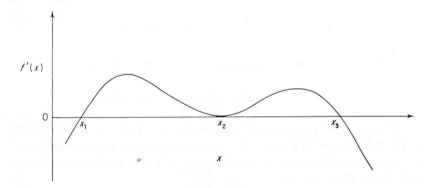

Figure 2.8.

function given in Figure 2.7 is shown in Figure 2.8. Notice the derivative passes through zero at points x_1, x_2, and x_3.

To derive the necessary condition for a minimum, we shall take a different approach. Assume that at x^0, $f'(x)$ is continuous and greater than zero.

Assume further that $f(x^0)$ is a relative minimum. From the definition of a relative minimum we have

$$f(x^0 + h) - f(x^0) = hf'(x^0 + \theta h) \geq 0 \qquad 0 < \theta < 1$$

Since $f'(x^0) > 0$ by assumption, there exists an h, $|h| > 0$, such that $f'(x^0 + \theta h) > 0$. The previous statement follows from the definition of continuity. Suppose $h < 0$. Then

$$f(x^0 + h) - f(x^0) = hf'(x^0 + \theta h) < 0$$

because h is negative and $f'(x^0 + \theta h)$ is positive. This contradicts the definition of a relative minimum. Thus $f(x)$ cannot be a minimum at x^0 if $f'(x^0) > 0$. A similar argument establishes that $f(x)$ cannot have a minimum at x^0 if $f'(x^0)$ is negative. The proof given above is a proof by contradiction.

Now that the necessary condition has been established, let us derive a sufficient condition for a relative maximum. Suppose $f(x)$ and its first two derivatives are continuous at x^0. Applying Taylor's theorem yields

$$f(x^0 + h) - f(x^0) = hf'(x^0) + \frac{h^2}{2!} f''(x^0 + \theta h) \qquad 0 < \theta < 1$$

Suppose $f(x)$ has a relative maximum at x^0. Then from the argument given above, we know that $f'(x)$ evaluated at x^0 must vanish. Thus we may write

$$f(x^0 + h) - f(x^0) = \frac{h^2}{2!} f''(x^0 + \theta h) \qquad 0 < \theta < 1$$

For $f(x^0)$ to be a maximum, the quantity given above must be negative. Thus

$$f(x^0 + h) - f(x^0) = \frac{h^2}{2!} f''(x^0 + \theta h) < 0 \qquad 0 < \theta < 1$$

Suppose $f''(x^0) > 0$. Then, by continuity, $f''(x^0 + \theta h) > 0$ and

$$f(x^0 + h) - f(x^0) = \frac{h^2}{2!} f''(x^0 + \theta h) > 0$$

and x^0 cannot be a maximum. Conversely, if $f''(x^0) < 0$ at $f'(x^0) = 0$, $f(x^0)$ is a maximum. If $f''(x^0) = 0$, we must investigate higher-order terms. Let us emphasize what was proved above. If $f'(x^0) = 0$, a sufficient condition for $f(x)$ to be maximum at x^0 is

$$f''(x^0) < 0 \tag{2.16}$$

If the first and second derivatives vanish at x^0, we must investigate higher-order terms in the Taylor's series expansion of $f(x)$. Assume that the first $n - 1$ derivatives of $f(x)$ evaluated at x^0 vanish. The following theorem will prove useful in determining sufficient conditions in such a situation.

Theorem: *If $f(x)$ and its first n derivatives are continuous, then $f(x)$ is an extreme point at x^0 if and only if n is even, where n is the order of the first nonvanishing derivative at x^0. The function $f(x)$ has a maximum or minimum at x^0 according to whether $f^n(x^0) < 0$ or > 0, respectively.*

PROOF. Assume

$$f'(x^0) = \cdots = f^{(n-1)}(x^0) = 0$$

and further

$$f^{(n)}(x^0) \neq 0$$

where n is even. Then from Taylor's theorem we have

$$f(x^0 + h) - f(x^0) = \frac{h^n}{n!} f^{(n)}(x^0 + \theta h) \qquad 0 < \theta < 1$$

Because we assumed that $f^{(n)}(x)$ is continuous, $f^{(n)}(x^0 + \theta h)$ will have the same sign as $f^{(n)}(x^0)$. Therefore, $f(x_0 + h) - f(x_0)$ will have the same sign as $f^{(n)}(x^0)$ and will be positive when $f^{(n)}(x^0)$ is positive and negative when $f^{(n)}(x^0)$ is negative. Thus x^0 will be an extreme point and will be a maximum or minimum depending on the sign of $f^{(n)}(x^0)$.

To prove the "only if" clause in the theorem, assume that the order of the first nonvanishing derivative is odd. Assume further that $f^{(n)}(x^0) > 0$. Using Taylor's theorem we may write

$$f(x^0 + h) - f(x^0) = \frac{h^n}{n!} f^{(n)}(x^0 + \theta h) \qquad 0 < \theta < 1$$

For x^0 to be an extreme point, the quantity shown above must be either nonpositive or nonnegative, depending on the character of the extreme point. However, when n is odd, the factor h^n becomes positive or negative with h. Since the sign of $f^{(n)}(x^0 + \theta h)$ does not change as h goes from positive to negative, the term

$$\frac{h^n}{n!} f^{(n)}(x^0 + \theta h)$$

changes sign as h^n changes sign. Thus

$$f(x^0 + h) - f(x^0)$$

has one sign for positive h and a different sign for negative h. This contradicts the definition of an extreme point, and consequently $f(x^0)$ cannot be a maximum or minimum at x^0, and the theorem is proved.

Example: Suppose $f(x) = (x - 5)^{10}$. Then

$$\frac{df(x)}{dx} = 10(x - 5)^9$$

vanishes when $x = 5$ as do all the first nine derivatives. The first nonvanishing derivative is the tenth; that is,

$$\frac{d^{10}f(x)}{dx^{10}}\bigg|_{x=5} = 10! > 0$$

Thus $f(x) = (x - 5)^{10}$ has a minimum at $x^0 = 5$, because the first nonvanishing derivative is even and positive. Consider another function

$$f(x) = (x - 5)^5$$

Notice that the necessary condition $[f'(x) = 0]$ is satisfied again at $x = 5$. However, the first nonvanishing derivative is the fifth, and therefore $f(x)$ does not have an extreme point at $x = 5$, because

$$f(5 + h) - f(5) = \frac{h^5}{5!}\,5! = h^5$$

changes sign as h goes from positive to negative. A graph of each function is given in Figures 2.9 and 2.10, respectively.

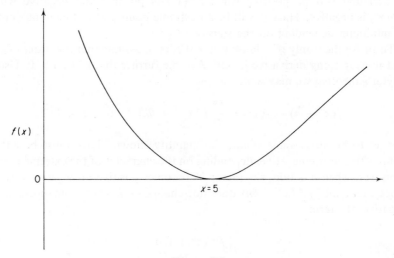

Figure 2.9.

Functions of N Variables

In the following material, we shall extend the proofs for a one-dimensional function given in the previous section to functions of a finite, but arbitrary, number of variables. The proofs will be accomplished through use of Taylor's theorem, which was discussed earlier in the chapter.

Theorem: *A necessary condition for a continuous function $f(\mathbf{x})$ with continuous first and second partial derivatives to have an extreme point at $\mathbf{x}^0$ is that each first partial derivative of $f(\mathbf{x})$, evaluated at $\mathbf{x}^0$, vanish.*

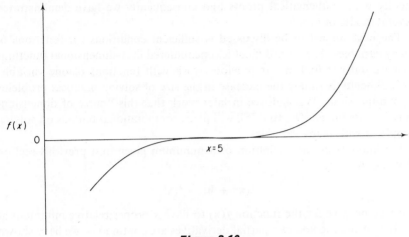

Figure 2.10.

PROOF. The proof is obtained by contradiction. Suppose one of the partial derivatives, say the pth, does not vanish. Then by Taylor's theorem,

$$f(x^0 + h) - f(x^0) = \sum_{i=1}^{N} h_i \left.\frac{\partial f(x)}{\partial x_i}\right|_{x=x^0} + R_1(x^0 + \theta h, x^0)$$

$$= h_p \left.\frac{\partial f(x)}{\partial x_p}\right|_{x=x^0} + R_1(x^0 + \theta h, x^0)$$

$R_1(x^0 + \theta h, x^0)$ is of order h_i^2, so for small h the terms of order h will dominate the higher-order terms and therefore

$$f(x^0 + h) - f(x^0)$$

will have the same sign as terms of order h. Suppose

$$\left.\frac{\partial f(x)}{\partial x_p}\right|_{x=x^0} > 0$$

Then the difference $f(x^0 + h) - f(x)$ will have the same sign as h_p; that is, when $h_p > 0$ the difference is positive, and when $h_p < 0$ the difference is negative. Consequently, x^0 cannot be an extreme point. The argument when

$$\left.\frac{\partial f(x)}{\partial x_p}\right|_{x=x^0} < 0$$

is similar to the one given above. Thus we may conclude that when any of the partial derivatives are not identically zero at x^0, the point x^0 is not an extreme point.

A proof similar to the one given in the section on functions of one variable can be obtained, as the mean value theorem can be extended to functions of many variables. However, we wish to aid the reader in developing a facility with mathematical proofs and consequently we have demonstrated several modes of proof.

The next subject to be discussed is sufficient conditions for functions of many variables. There are difficulties encountered in N-dimensional functions that we did not find in our previous work with functions of one variable. This difficulty is simply the increase in the size of solving practical problems in N-dimensions. We shall see in later work that this "curse of dimensionality," as Bellman refers to it [5], will place computational bounds on solving problems with many variables.

We know from our definition of a minimum given in a previous section that the quantity

$$f(\mathbf{x}^0 + \mathbf{h}) - f(\mathbf{x}^0)$$

must be positive for the function $f(\mathbf{x})$ to have a proper relative minimum at $\mathbf{x}^0$. If $f(\cdot)$ and the first two partial derivatives are continuous, we have shown that a necessary condition for a relative minimum at $\mathbf{x}^0$ is that

$$\frac{\partial f(\mathbf{x})}{\partial x_i}\bigg|_{\mathbf{x}=\mathbf{x}^0} = 0 \qquad i = 1, \ldots, N \tag{2.17}$$

We shall use this fact, together with Taylor's theorem, to derive sufficient conditions for a minimum $f(\mathbf{x})$ at $\mathbf{x}^0$.

Theorem: *A sufficient condition for $f(\mathbf{x})$ to have a relative minimum at $\mathbf{x}^0$, that is, where*

$$\frac{\partial f(\mathbf{x})}{\partial x_i}\bigg|_{\mathbf{x}=\mathbf{x}^0} = 0 \qquad i = 1, \ldots, N$$

is that the matrix of second partial derivatives of $f(\mathbf{x})$, called the Hessian, be positive definite.

PROOF.   From previous work we know

$$f(\mathbf{x}^0 + \mathbf{h}) - f(\mathbf{x}^0) = \sum_{i=1}^{N} h_i \frac{\partial f(\mathbf{x})}{\partial x_i}\bigg|_{\mathbf{x}=\mathbf{x}^0} + \frac{1}{2!} \sum_{i=1}^{N} \sum_{j=1}^{N} h_i h_j \frac{\partial^2 f(\mathbf{x})}{\partial x_i \, \partial x_j}\bigg|_{\mathbf{x}=\mathbf{x}^0+\theta\mathbf{h}}$$

$$0 < \theta < 1$$

Evoking the necessary conditions stated in the theorem, we have

$$f(\mathbf{x}^0 + \mathbf{h}) - f(\mathbf{x}^0) = \frac{1}{2!} \sum_{i=1}^{N} \sum_{j=1}^{N} h_i h_j \frac{\partial^2 f(x)}{\partial x_i \, \partial x_j}\bigg|_{\mathbf{x}=\mathbf{x}^0+\theta\mathbf{h}} \qquad 0 < \theta < 1$$

Thus

$$f(\mathbf{x}^0 + \mathbf{h}) - f(\mathbf{x}^0)$$

will have the same sign as

$$\sum_{i=1}^{N} \sum_{j=1}^{N} h_i h_j \frac{\partial^2 f(\mathbf{x})}{\partial x_i \, \partial x_j}\bigg|_{\mathbf{x}^0 = \mathbf{x}^0 + \theta \mathbf{h}}$$

However, since $\partial^2 f(\mathbf{x})/\partial x_i \, \partial x_j$ is continuous in the neighborhood of $\mathbf{x}^0$,

$$\frac{\partial^2 f(\mathbf{x})}{\partial x_i \, \partial x_j}\bigg|_{\mathbf{x}=\mathbf{x}^0}$$

will have the same sign as

$$\frac{\partial^2 f(\mathbf{x})}{\partial x_i \, \partial x_j}\bigg|_{\mathbf{x}=\mathbf{x}^0 + \theta \mathbf{h}}$$

for all small $\mathbf{h}$, $0 < |h_i| < \delta$. Thus if

$$\sum_{i=1}^{N} \sum_{j=1}^{N} h_i h_j \frac{\partial^2 f(\mathbf{x})}{\partial x_i \, \partial x_j}\bigg|_{\mathbf{x}=\mathbf{x}^0}$$

is positive, $f(\mathbf{x}^0 + \mathbf{h}) - f(\mathbf{x}^0)$ will also be positive and $f(\mathbf{x})$ will be a minimum at $\mathbf{x}^0$. However, the term

$$\sum_{i=1}^{N} \sum_{j=1}^{N} h_i h_j \frac{\partial^2 f(\mathbf{x})}{\partial x_i \, \partial x_j}\bigg|_{\mathbf{x}=\mathbf{x}^0}$$

is a quadratic form and we may write it as $\mathbf{h}^T \mathbf{H} \mathbf{h}$, where $\mathbf{h}^T = (h_1, \ldots, h_N')$ and

$$\mathbf{H} = \frac{\partial^2 f(\mathbf{x})}{\partial x_i \, \partial x_j}\bigg|_{\mathbf{x}=\mathbf{x}^0} \tag{2.18}$$

a matrix whose elements are the second partial derivatives of $f(\mathbf{x})$ evaluated at the point $\mathbf{x}^0$. This matrix, $\mathbf{H}$, is called the Hessian of the function $f(\mathbf{x})$. We know from our study of matrix algebra that a necessary and sufficient condition for this quadratic form to be positive is that the Hessian be a positive definite matrix [4]. Thus we have proved the theorem.

Example: Find the minimum of

$$f(\mathbf{x}) = x_1^2 + x_2^2 + x_3^2 - 4x - 8x_2 - 12x_3 + 56$$

$$\frac{\partial f(\mathbf{x})}{\partial x_1} = 2x_1 - 4 = 0$$

$$\frac{\partial f(\mathbf{x})}{\partial x_2} = 2x_2 - 8 = 0$$

$$\frac{\partial f(\mathbf{x})}{\partial x_3} = 2x_3 - 12 = 0$$

Solving the equations for a point (x_1, x_2, x_3) we obtain $x_1 = 2$, $x_2 = 4$, $x_3 = 6$, which is the only point that satisfies the necessary conditions.

We must determine whether this point is a minimum. The Hessian, evaluated at (2, 4, 6), is

$$\begin{bmatrix} 2 & 0 & 0 \\ 0 & 2 & 0 \\ 0 & 0 & 2 \end{bmatrix}$$

which is positive definite. Therefore, the point (2, 4, 6) yields a minimum of $f(\mathbf{x})$.

Corollary: *If the Hessian of a function $f(\mathbf{x})$ is indefinite when evaluated at the point, $\mathbf{x}^*$, where the necessary conditions are satisfied, then the point $\mathbf{x}^*$ is not an extreme point.*

The proof is left as an exercise for the reader.

Semidefinite Case

We now proceed to the problem of determining sufficient conditions for the case when the Hessian of a given function is semidefinite. When we considered functions of one variable, the problem of determining sufficient conditions for functions where the second-order terms vanished was resolved quite easily. One simply investigated the higher-order terms in the Taylor series expansion. The same procedure is followed in functions of N variables. However, the algebra becomes very difficult, and in practice one seldom investigates stationary points for sufficiency.

There have been several attempts to develop sufficient conditions for extreme points of functions of many variables. Examples of some of these attempts and their failures are contained in reference [3]. One attempt was made by Lagrange as an extension of one-dimensional arguments. He argued that if the second-order terms are semidefinite, the third-order terms must vanish and fourth-order terms would yield the required information. If the fourth-order terms are semidefinite, one must then investigate higher-order terms. However, Peano developed a counterexample to this argument. Peano's counterexample is given below.

Example: Consider

$$f(x, y) = (y^2 - x)^2 = y^4 - 2y^2 x + x^2$$

Notice that any point where $x = y^2$ is a minimum of $f(x, y)$. Let us apply Lagrange's argument. The necessary conditions are

$$\frac{\partial f(x, y)}{\partial x} = 2(x - y^2) = 0$$

$$\frac{\partial f(x, y)}{\partial y} = 4y^3 - 4yx = 0$$

The necessary conditions are satisfied along the curve $y^2 = x$. The second-order terms are

$$\frac{\partial^2 f(x, y)}{\partial x^2} = 2$$

$$\frac{\partial^2 f(x, y)}{\partial x \, \partial y} = -4y$$

$$\frac{\partial^2 f(x, y)}{\partial y^2} = 12y^2 - 4x = 8y^2$$

The Hessian is given by

$$\begin{bmatrix} 2 & -4y \\ -4y & 8y^2 \end{bmatrix}$$

which is positive semidefinite for any y. Lagrange argued that the third partial derivatives must all vanish since the Hessian is semidefinite. Let us investigate one of the third-order terms, in particular:

$$\frac{\partial^3 f(x, y)}{\partial x \, \partial y^2}$$

which is equal to -4. Since this term does not vanish, Lagrange would argue that $x = y^2$ is not a minimum. However, we can see that $f(x, y)$ cannot be negative, is zero only when $y^2 = x$, and is positive for any other values of x and y. We should note that the solution obtained is an improper minimum.

When Lagrange's argument was shown to be erroneous, Serret modified the argument. Serret concluded that one should investigate higher-order terms only for those values of h_i for which the quadratic form $\mathbf{h}^T \mathbf{H} \mathbf{h}$ is zero. However, Peano's second counterexample proved this conclusion false.

For example, when

$$f(x, y) = (y^2 - x)(y^2 - 2x)$$

$$= y^4 - 3y^2 x + 2x^2$$

$$\frac{\partial f(x, y)}{\partial x} = -3y^2 + 4x = 0$$

$$\frac{\partial f(x, y)}{\partial y} = 4y^3 - 6yx = 0$$

The point $(x = 0, y = 0)$ satisfies the necessary conditions shown above. The Hessian, evaluated at $(x = 0, y = 0)$, is

$$\mathbf{H} = \begin{bmatrix} 4 & 0 \\ 0 & 0 \end{bmatrix}$$

which is positive semidefinite. Let us expand $f(x, y)$ in a Taylor's series about $(x = 0, y = 0)$. We obtain

$$f(x + h, y + k) = \frac{1}{2!} h^2 \frac{\partial^2 f(x, y)}{\partial x^2}\bigg|_{0,0} + hk \frac{\partial^2 f(x, y)}{\partial x \, \partial y}\bigg|_{0,0}$$

$$+ \frac{1}{2!} k^2 \frac{\partial^2 f(x, y)}{\partial y^2}\bigg|_{0,0} + R_2(x + h, y + k; x, y)$$

The second-order term, $2h^2$, is positive for all h and k except $h = 0$. Following Serret's argument we look at the third-order terms—but only for the value of h where the second-order term vanishes, namely, $h = 0$.

The third-order terms are given by

$$\frac{1}{3!} (-18hk^2)$$

which vanishes when $h = 0$. Investigating the fourth-order terms we obtain

$$f(x + h, y + k) - f(x, y)|_{0,0} = h^2 - 3hk^2 + k^4 + R_4(x + h, y + k; x, y)$$

Applying Serret's argument we see that when $h = 0$ (that is, when the second-order terms vanish), the form is positive definite and consequently the point $(0, 0)$ is a minimum. However, notice that for $x < y^2 < 2x$ the function is negative and for $y^2 < x$ or $y^2 > 2x$ the function is positive, and consequently the point $(0, 0)$ is a saddle point, since it decreases for all y in the range $x < y^2 < 2x$ and increases in the range $y^2 < x$ and $y^2 > 2x$. Peano's counterexample proves Serret's argument erroneous.

The question of sufficient conditions was finally resolved by Scheffer. His arguments, which are presented below, involve breaking the problem up into several one-dimensional optimization problems. Recall we wrote Taylor's series as

$$f(\mathbf{x}^0 + \mathbf{h}) = f(\mathbf{x}^0) + G_n(\mathbf{x}^0) + R_n(\mathbf{x}^0 + \theta\mathbf{h}, \mathbf{x}^0)$$

Suppose $\mathbf{x}^0$ is a stationary point. We choose one element of the vector $\mathbf{h}$, say h_p, to be constant, and allow all other elements of $\mathbf{h}$ to vary so that $|h_i| \leq h_p$. The minimum of $G_n(\mathbf{x}_0)$ with respect to these h_i is determined over the $(n - 1)$-dimensional space. This minimum is called $G_n(\mathbf{x}^0)^p$. This procedure is repeated for each h_i, $i = 1, \ldots, N$. If $\min_p G_n(\mathbf{x}^0)^p$ is positive, then $\mathbf{x}^0$ is a minimum, because $f(\mathbf{x}^0 + \mathbf{h}) - f(\mathbf{x}^0) > 0$. If some $G_n(\mathbf{x}^0)^p$ are positive and others are negative, then $\mathbf{x}^0$ is not an extreme point. If $\min_p G_n(\mathbf{x}^0)^p$ is zero, then n is increased by 1 and the entire process repeated.

The material presented above was not intended to be inclusive. Rather we hope to give the reader some indication of the difficulties involved in determining sufficient conditions for an extreme point. For a fuller discussion of this material, the interested reader should see reference [3].

Recall that we mentioned earlier that one seldom investigates a stationary point for sufficiency in actual applications of the theory because of the complications involved. Normally all solutions to the necessary conditions are generated and the objective function is evaluated for each solution. The best of these is then called the optimal solution. However, conclusions based on such a procedure should be drawn with the utmost caution, because such results may be erroneous.

2.4   Constrained Problems

The final topic of this chapter is the question of optimization of functions when side conditions are placed on the variables. Conceptually the problem is no more difficult than the unconstrained problem, but computational difficulties are substantially increased by the addition of constraints on the variables. The theory that is developed below does not, in many cases, lend itself to the efficient attainment of solutions from a computational point of view. However, many of the more efficient computational solution procedures are based on this theory.

The need for this development is pointed out by the variety of systems encumbered by constraints. The amount of stock carried in an inventory system is limited by the size of the storage facility. The flow rate of fluid in a series pipe system is limited by the capacity of the smallest link of pipe. Upon reflection one is aware of other systems where constraints must be considered.

Consider the problem of maximizing a differentiable function of two variables, $f(x, y)$, subject to the differentiable equality constraint $g(x, y) = 0$. There are two ways of approaching the problem. The first way involves solving the constraint for one of the variables, say y, and substituting the result into $f(x, y)$. Thus given $g(x, y) = 0$, obtain $y = g^{-1}(x)$, and upon substituting this for y, the problem reduces to one of

$$\max_{x} f[x, g^{-1}(x)]$$

There is one difficulty associated with this approach. The implicit function theorem guarantees, under certain conditions, the existence of the inverse function, $g^{-1}(\cdot)$, but it gives no aid in obtaining the inverse. Suppose the constraint is of the form

$$g(x, y) = e^{xy^2} + x \cos y = 0$$

Although the existence of the inverse is guaranteed for most points in the (x, y) space, we would have difficulty in obtaining the analytical form of the inverse function.

The difficulty discussed above can be circumvented by the Lagrange multiplier technique, which involves adding one variable to the problem for each constraint. This technique is the basis for the remainder of the chapter. The development will be made initially for a function of two variables to allow us to draw upon some intuitive concepts of geometry. Extensions to an arbitrary number of variables follows the two-dimensional proof.

Consider the problem mentioned above of maximizing $f(x, y)$ subject to the constraint $g(x, y) = 0$. Suppose we could obtain an analytic expression for $y = g^{-1}(x)$. If such a function exists, it is differentiable and possesses a continuous first derivative. We can therefore transform the problem into a one-variable problem, as is shown below:

$$\max_x f[x, g^{-1}(x)]$$

A necessary condition for $f(\cdot)$ to have a maximum at some point (x^0, y^0) is that the derivative of $f(\cdot)$ with respect to x vanish at (x^0, y^0). The total differential of $f(x, y)$ may be written

$$df(x, y) = \frac{\partial f}{\partial x} \, dx + \frac{\partial f}{\partial y} \, dy \tag{2.19}$$

and the total derivative

$$\frac{df(x, y)}{dx} = \frac{\partial f(x, y)}{\partial x} + \frac{\partial f(x, y)}{\partial y} \frac{dy}{dx} \tag{2.20}$$

If we substitute the definition of y in the above expression and evaluate the derivatives at x^0, we obtain

$$\frac{df(x, y)}{dx}\bigg|_{x=x^0} = \frac{\partial f(x, y)}{\partial x}\bigg|_{x=x^0} + \frac{\partial f(x, y)}{\partial y} \frac{dg^{-1}(x)}{dx}\bigg|_{x=x^0}$$

which must vanish if x^0 is a stationary point.

To obtain an expression for $dg^{-1}(x)/dx$ we write the total derivative of $g(\cdot)$:

$$\frac{dg(x, y)}{dx} = \frac{\partial g(x, y)}{\partial x} + \frac{\partial g(x, y)}{\partial y} \frac{dg^{-1}(x)}{dx} = 0 \tag{2.21}$$

This expression may be rearranged to yield

$$\frac{dg^{-1}(x)}{dx} = -\frac{\partial g(x, y)}{\partial x}\bigg/\frac{\partial g(x, y)}{\partial y}$$

Substituting this definition into the necessary condition we obtain

$$\frac{\partial f}{\partial x}\bigg|_{x=x^0} - \frac{\partial f}{\partial y}\left(\frac{\partial g}{\partial x}\bigg/\frac{\partial g}{\partial y}\bigg|_{x=x^0}\right) = 0$$

Define λ as

$$\lambda = -\frac{\partial f(x, y)}{\partial y}\bigg/\frac{\partial g(x, y)}{\partial y}\bigg|_{x=x^0} \tag{2.22}$$

We may now rewrite the necessary condition as

$$\frac{\partial f(x, y)}{\partial x}\bigg|_{\substack{x=x^0 \\ y=y^0}} + \lambda \frac{\partial g(x, y)}{\partial x}\bigg|_{\substack{x=x^0 \\ y=y^0}} = 0$$

From the definition of λ we have

$$\frac{\partial f(x, y)}{\partial y}\bigg|_{\substack{x=x^0 \\ y=y^0}} + \lambda \frac{\partial g(x, y)}{\partial y}\bigg|_{\substack{x=x^0 \\ y=y^0}} = 0$$

and of course the constraint $g(x, y) = 0$. The symbol λ is called the Lagrange multiplier. Notice that the necessary conditions, which are represented by the last three equations shown above, do not require us to invert $g(x, y) = 0$. The requirement is that the inverse exists and the implicit function theorem gives us conditions under which the inverse function can be theoretically obtained. In the derivation above we assumed that $\partial g(x, y)/\partial y$ did not vanish at a stationary point. This assumption was necessary to define the Lagrange multiplier λ. We arbitrarily chose to define λ in terms of partial derivatives with respect to y. However, equivalent results would have been obtained if we had defined λ in terms of partial derivatives with respect to x. The derivation requires only that at least one of the partial derivatives of $g(x, y)$ not vanish at a stationary point.

There is a compact method of generating the necessary conditions shown above and involves constructing the *Lagrange function*, which is formed by multiplying the constraint by a Lagrange multiplier and adding this product to the objective function,

$$F(x, y, \lambda) = f(x, y) + \lambda g(x, y) \tag{2.23}$$

When the Lagrange function, $F(\cdot)$, is partially differentiated with respect to each of its arguments and the results are equated to zero, the necessary conditions derived above are obtained. For example,

$$\frac{\partial F(x, y, \lambda)}{\partial x} = 0 = \frac{\partial f(x, y)}{\partial x} + \lambda \frac{\partial g(x, y)}{\partial x}$$

$$\frac{\partial F(x, y, \lambda)}{\partial y} = 0 = \frac{\partial f(x, y)}{\partial y} + \lambda \frac{\partial g(x, y)}{\partial y}$$

$$\frac{\partial F(x, y, \lambda)}{\partial \lambda} = 0 = g(x, y)$$

Example: min $x^2 + y^2$ subject to $g(x, y) = x - y - 5 = 0$. Form the Lagrange function

$$F(x, y, \lambda) = x^2 + y^2 + \lambda(x - y - 5)$$

$$\frac{\partial F(x, y, \lambda)}{\partial x} = 2x + \lambda = 0$$

$$\frac{\partial F(x, y, \lambda)}{\partial y} = 2y - \lambda = 0$$

$$\frac{\partial F(x, y, \lambda)}{\partial \lambda} = x - y - 5 = 0$$

Solving these equations, we find $x = 2.5$, $y = -2.5$, and $\lambda = -5$.

The derivation given above can be extended to include functions of several variables as well as additional constraints. Consider a function of N variables, $f(\mathbf{x})$, subject to M equality constraints of the form

$$g_i(\mathbf{x}) = 0 \qquad i = 1, \ldots, M < N$$

Suppose we wish to locate all relative maxima of $f(\mathbf{x})$ subject to these M constraints. At a relative maximum, $\mathbf{x}^0$, we require that the differential of $f(\cdot)$ vanish,

$$df = \sum_{i=1}^{N} \frac{\partial f(\mathbf{x})}{\partial x_i} \bigg|_{\mathbf{x}=\mathbf{x}^0} dx_i = 0 \qquad (2.24)$$

The reasoning behind this statement is similar to arguments given before.

If first-order terms of the Taylor series do not vanish, we could improve the value of $f(\cdot)$ through a proper choice of the dx_i in the neighborhood of $\mathbf{x}^0$. However, we cannot require each partial derivative to vanish. In many cases a relative maximum will occur at the boundary of one or more of the constraints where the partial derivatives of the objective function do not necessarily vanish. The total differential of each of the constraint functions is

$$dg_i = \sum_{j=1}^{N} \frac{\partial g_i(\mathbf{x})}{\partial x_j} dx_j = 0 \qquad i = 1, \ldots, M \qquad (2.25)$$

Multiply each of these equations by an associated Lagrange multiplier λ_i and add this to df. The result is

$$df + \sum_{i=1}^{M} \lambda_i \, dg_i = \sum_{j=1}^{N} \left[\frac{\partial f(\mathbf{x})}{\partial x_j} + \sum_{i=1}^{M} \lambda_i \frac{\partial g_i(\mathbf{x})}{\partial x_j} \right] dx_j = 0$$

Suppose we choose to eliminate the first M variables, $x_1, \ldots, x_M$. These M variables will then become dependent variables and the remaining $N - M$ variables will be independent variables. Since each of the differentials $dx_{M+1}, \ldots, dx_N$ corresponds to an independent variable and may be chosen to be nonzero, the coefficient of each differential must vanish,

$$\frac{\partial f(\mathbf{x})}{\partial x_j} + \sum_{i=1}^{M} \lambda_i \frac{\partial g_i(\mathbf{x})}{\partial x_j} = 0 \qquad j = M+1, \ldots, N$$

Thus we are left with

$$\sum_{j=1}^{M} \left[\frac{\partial f(\mathbf{x})}{\partial x_j} + \sum_{i=1}^{M} \lambda_i \frac{\partial g_i(\mathbf{x})}{\partial x_j} \right] dx_j = 0$$

The differentials $dx_j, j = 1, \ldots, M$, are dependent and are uniquely determined by the values of the independent differentials. Therefore, to guarantee that

$$df + \sum_{i=1}^{M} \lambda_i \, dg_i$$

vanishes, we must require that the coefficients of $dx_j, j = 1, \ldots, M$, be zero,

$$\frac{\partial f(\mathbf{x})}{\partial x_j}\Big|_{\mathbf{x}=\mathbf{x}^0} + \sum_{i=1}^{M} \lambda_i \frac{\partial g_i(\mathbf{x})}{\partial x_j}\Big|_{\mathbf{x}=\mathbf{x}^0} = 0 \qquad j = 1, \ldots, M$$

or

$$\sum_{i=1}^{M} \lambda_i \frac{\partial g_i(\mathbf{x})}{\partial x_j} = -\frac{\partial f(\mathbf{x})}{\partial x_j} \text{ at } \mathbf{x} = \mathbf{x}^0, j = 1, \ldots, M$$

Rewriting this in matrix form we have

$$\hat{J}_{x_1, \ldots, x_M}[g_1(\mathbf{x}), \ldots, g_M(\mathbf{x})]\boldsymbol{\lambda} = -\Delta f(\mathbf{x})$$

where $\hat{J}(\cdot)$ is the matrix of the Jacobian of the $g_i(\mathbf{x})$, $\boldsymbol{\lambda}$ is a column vector of Lagrange multipliers, and Δf is the vector of partial derivatives of $f(\mathbf{x})$. If we assume $\Delta f(\mathbf{x})$ is not null, we have M nonhomogeneous equations which are linear in $\boldsymbol{\lambda}$. In general, a solution to these equations exists if and only if the coefficient matrix of $\boldsymbol{\lambda}$ is not singular, which is the identical condition required by the implicit function theorem to allow the elimination of $x_1, \ldots, x_M$. Notice that we could have let any $N - M$ variables be the independent variables if the Jacobian formed by the remaining variables is nonsingular.

As we pointed out before, the necessary conditions can be generated from the Lagrange function. Define the Lagrange function $F(\mathbf{x}, \boldsymbol{\lambda})$ as

$$F(\mathbf{x}, \boldsymbol{\lambda}) = f(\mathbf{x}) + \sum_{i=1}^{M} \lambda_i g_i(\mathbf{x}) \qquad (2.26)$$

Theorem: *A necessary condition for $f(\mathbf{x})$ to have a relative maximum at $\mathbf{x}^0$ is that the partial derivatives of the Lagrange function with respect to each of its arguments vanish.*

PROOF. If we take the partial derivatives of $F(\mathbf{x}, \boldsymbol{\lambda})$ with respect to each of its arguments and equate the result to zero, we obtain

$$\frac{\partial F(\mathbf{x}, \boldsymbol{\lambda})}{\partial x_j} = \frac{\partial f(\mathbf{x})}{\partial x_j} + \sum_{i=1}^{M} \lambda_i \frac{\partial g_i(\mathbf{x})}{\partial x_j} = 0 \qquad j = 1, \ldots, N \qquad (2.27)$$

$$\frac{\partial F(\mathbf{x}, \boldsymbol{\lambda})}{\partial \lambda_i} = g_i(\mathbf{x}) = 0 \qquad\qquad i = 1, \ldots, M \qquad (2.28)$$

which are identical to the set of equations derived above. These equations are also necessary conditions for a relative minimum of $f(\mathbf{x})$.

Now we wish to develop sufficient conditions for a relative maximum of $f(\mathbf{x})$ subject to the constraints $g_i(\mathbf{x})$. Notice that a solution, $\mathbf{x}^0$, must be feasible to be a candidate for a relative maximum; that is, it must satisfy $g_i(\mathbf{x}^0) = 0$, $i = 1, \ldots, M$. If a solution is feasible, the Lagrange function $F(\mathbf{x}, \boldsymbol{\lambda})$ is given by

$$F(\mathbf{x}, \boldsymbol{\lambda}) = f(\mathbf{x}) + \sum_{i=1}^{M} \lambda_i g_i(\mathbf{x}) = f(\mathbf{x})$$

A point $\mathbf{x}^0$ is a relative maximum if

$$f(\mathbf{x}^0 + \mathbf{h}) - f(\mathbf{x}^0) < 0$$

However, the elements of $\mathbf{h}$ are not all independent, since the constraints evaluated at $\mathbf{x}^0 + \mathbf{h}$ must be satisfied,

$$g_i(\mathbf{x}^0 + \mathbf{h}) = 0 \qquad i = 1, \ldots, M$$

Therefore,

$$F(\mathbf{x}^0 + \mathbf{h}, \boldsymbol{\lambda}) - F(\mathbf{x}^0, \boldsymbol{\lambda}) = f(\mathbf{x}^0 + \mathbf{h}) - f(\mathbf{x}^0)$$

Expanding $F(\cdot)$ in a Taylor series in $\mathbf{x}$ about $\mathbf{x}^0$ we obtain

$$F(\mathbf{x}^0 + \mathbf{h}, \boldsymbol{\lambda}) - F(\mathbf{x}^0, \boldsymbol{\lambda}) =$$

$$\sum_{j=1}^{N} \frac{\partial F(\mathbf{x}, \boldsymbol{\lambda})}{\partial x_j}\bigg|_{\mathbf{x}=\mathbf{x}^0} h_j + \frac{1}{2!} \sum_{i=1}^{N} \sum_{j=1}^{N} h_i h_j \frac{\partial^2 F(\mathbf{x}, \boldsymbol{\lambda})}{\partial x_i \, \partial x_j}\bigg|_{\mathbf{x}=\mathbf{x}^0} + R_2(\mathbf{x}^0 + \mathbf{h}, \boldsymbol{\lambda}; \mathbf{x}^0, \boldsymbol{\lambda})$$

The necessary conditions derived above require that each derivative of $F(\mathbf{x}, \boldsymbol{\lambda})$ vanish. The equation shown reduces to

$$F(\mathbf{x}^0 + \mathbf{h}, \boldsymbol{\lambda}) - F(\mathbf{x}^0, \boldsymbol{\lambda}) =$$

$$\frac{1}{2} \sum_{i=1}^{N} \sum_{j=1}^{N} h_i h_j \frac{\partial^2 F(\mathbf{x}, \boldsymbol{\lambda})}{\partial x_i \, \partial x_j}\bigg|_{\mathbf{x}=\mathbf{x}^0} + R_2(\mathbf{x}^0 + \mathbf{h}, \boldsymbol{\lambda}; \mathbf{x}^0, \boldsymbol{\lambda})$$

Theorem: *A sufficient condition for $f(\mathbf{x})$ to have a proper relative maximum at $\mathbf{x}^0$ is that the quadratic form*

$$Q = \sum_{i=1}^{N} \sum_{j=1}^{N} h_i h_j \frac{\partial F(\mathbf{x}, \boldsymbol{\lambda})}{\partial x_i \, \partial x_j}\bigg|_{\mathbf{x}=\mathbf{x}^0}$$

be negative definite for all values of $\mathbf{h}$ for which the constraints are satisfied.

PROOF. Suppose that the quadratic form of the theorem is not negative definite. Then $F(\mathbf{x}^0 + \mathbf{h}) - F(\mathbf{x}^0)$ will not be negative for all admissible $\mathbf{h}$ and $\mathbf{x}^0$ is not a relative maximum. However, notice that the quadratic form is required to be negative definite only for the **h** satisfying the constraints, because any point where the constraints are not satisfied does not meet the requirements of the necessary conditions; that is,

$$g_i(\mathbf{x}^0) = 0 \qquad i = 1, \ldots, M$$

Hancock [3] shows that a necessary condition for the quadratic form Q to be negative definite for all admissible **h** is that each root of the polynomial, u_i, defined by the determinant shown below be negative:

$$\begin{vmatrix} (F_{11} - u) & \cdots & F_{1N} & g_{11} & \cdots & g_{M1} \\ \vdots & & \vdots & \vdots & & \vdots \\ F_{N1} & \cdots & (F_{NN} - u) & g_{1N} & \cdots & g_{MN} \\ g_{11} & \cdots & g_{1N} & 0 & \cdots & 0 \\ \vdots & & \vdots & \vdots & & \vdots \\ g_{M1} & \cdots & g_{MN} & 0 & \cdots & 0 \end{vmatrix} = 0$$

where

$$F_{ij} = \frac{\partial^2 F(\mathbf{x}, \boldsymbol{\lambda})}{\partial x_i \, \partial x_j}\bigg|_{\mathbf{x} = \mathbf{x}^0}$$

$$g_{ij} = \frac{\partial g_i(\mathbf{x})}{\partial x_j}\bigg|_{\mathbf{x} = \mathbf{x}^0}$$

The determinant given above yields a $(N - M)$-order polynomial in u. If each root of this equation is negative, the point $\mathbf{x}^0$ is a relative maximum. If we are investigating $f(\mathbf{x})$ for a minimum, then the roots u_i must all be positive. When some of the roots of the polynomial are positive while others are negative, the point $\mathbf{x}^0$ is not an extreme point. The remaining possibility, which is similar to the semidefinite case discussed earlier for unconstrained problems, remained unresolved.

Example: In the problem of page 39, determine whether $x = 2.5$, $y = -2.5$ is a minimum.

$$F_{11} = 2 \qquad F_{22} = 2 \qquad F_{12} = F_{21} = 0$$
$$g_{12} = -1 \qquad g_{11} = 1$$

Thus the roots of the equation shown below must be determined.

$$\begin{vmatrix} 2 - u & 0 & 1 \\ 0 & 2 - u & -1 \\ 1 & -1 & 0 \end{vmatrix} = 0$$

which yields $u = 2 > 0$. Thus $x = 2.5$, $y = -2.5$ yields a minimum.

The derivations presented above have been restricted to the case where at least one of the Mth-order Jacobians, constructed from M of the variables and the M constraints, did not vanish. When this condition is not satisfied, the results given above do not represent necessary conditions for an extreme point. Consider the classic example given by Courant [1]:

$$\min f(x, y) = x^2 + y^2$$

subject to

$$g(x, y) = (x - 1)^3 - y^2 = 0$$

The constraint is pictured in Figure 2.11. When we form the Lagrange function and differentiate it with respect to its arguments, we obtain

$$\frac{\partial F(x, y, \lambda)}{\partial x} = 0 = 2x + 3\lambda(x - 1)^2$$

$$\frac{\partial F(x, y, \lambda)}{\partial y} = 0 = 2y - 2\lambda y$$

$$\frac{\partial F(x, y, \lambda)}{\partial \lambda} = 0 = (x - 1)^3 - y^2$$

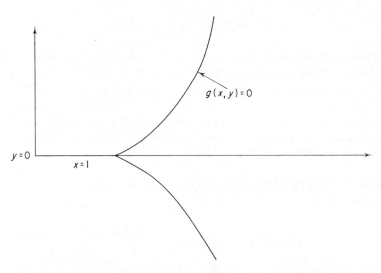

Figure 2.11.

One can see from Figure 2.11 that the minimum occurs at $(x = 1, y = 0)$ and this point satisfies the last two equations. However the $\partial F(x, y)/\partial x$ evaluated at $(1, 0)$ equals 2. The point is a minimum but does not satisfy the necessary conditions. If we evaluate $\partial g/\partial x$ and $\partial g/\partial y$ at $(1, 0)$, we find that both vanish, and consequently the conditions upon which the derivation of the necessary conditions was based are not satisfied. These conditions,

$$\frac{\partial F(\mathbf{x}, \boldsymbol{\lambda})}{\partial x_j} = 0 \qquad j = 1, \ldots, N$$

$$\frac{\partial F(\mathbf{x}, \boldsymbol{\lambda})}{\partial \lambda_i} = 0 \qquad i = 1, \ldots, M$$

are necessary only when at least one of the Jacobians formed by the M constraints and M of the variables does not vanish.

There is a simple way of circumventing the difficulty discussed above. We are interested in generating all points that may be extreme points. The Lagrange multiplier technique generates that subset of points for which one of the Jacobians does not vanish. The other possibilities for extreme points are points where the Jacobian vanishes. It can be shown [11] that these points can be generated by solving the set of equations

$$\begin{bmatrix} \text{matrix associated with} \\ J_{x_1, \ldots, x_M}(g_1, \ldots, g_M) \end{bmatrix} \begin{bmatrix} \lambda_1 \\ \vdots \\ \lambda_M \end{bmatrix} = \begin{bmatrix} 0 \\ \vdots \\ 0 \end{bmatrix}$$

where the vector $\boldsymbol{\lambda}$ is required to be nonnull. A necessary condition for a solution of these equations to exist is that the Jacobian vanish. All points $\mathbf{x}^*$ for which the Lagrange multiplier technique fails are thus generated. These equations form a set of necessary conditions for an extreme point when the Lagrange multiplier technique fails.

The two mutually exclusive sets of conditions can be generated by a simple modification of the Lagrange multiplier technique. Construct $F(\mathbf{x}, \boldsymbol{\lambda})$ as

$$F(\mathbf{x}, \boldsymbol{\lambda}) = \lambda_0 f(\mathbf{x}) + \sum_{i=1}^{M} \lambda_i g_i(\mathbf{x}) \qquad (2.29)$$

where λ_0 is a constant whose value is either 0 or 1. When $\lambda_0 = 1$, the necessary conditions for the case where the Jacobian does not vanish are generated, and, when $\lambda_0 = 0$, the necessary conditions are generated for the Jacobian to vanish. Therefore the equations

$$\frac{\partial F(\mathbf{x}, \boldsymbol{\lambda})}{\partial x_j} = 0 \qquad j = 1, \ldots, N$$

$$\frac{\partial F(\mathbf{x}, \boldsymbol{\lambda})}{\partial \lambda_i} = 0 \qquad i = 1, \ldots, M$$

are first evaluated when $\lambda_0 = 0$ and then when $\lambda_0 = 1$. These two cases generate all feasible extreme points.

Example: Consider the problem given by Courant [1]:

$$\min f(x, y) = x^2 + y^2$$

subject to

$$g(x, y) = 0 = (x - 1)^3 - y^2$$

Form the Lagrange function

$$F(x, y, \lambda_0, \lambda_1) = \lambda_0(x^2 + y^2) + \lambda_1[(x - 1)^3 - y^2]$$

$$\frac{\partial F(x, y, \lambda_0, \lambda_1)}{\partial x} = \lambda_0 x + 3\lambda_1(x - 1)^2 = 0$$

$$\frac{\partial F(x, y, \lambda_0, \lambda_1)}{\partial y} = 2\lambda_0 y - 2\lambda_1 y = 0$$

$$\frac{\partial F(x, y, \lambda_0, \lambda_1)}{\partial \lambda_1} = (x - 1)^3 - y^2 = 0$$

Set $\lambda_0 = 1$ and we have the same equations that failed to generate the point $(1, 0)$ in the previous example. Now set $\lambda_0 = 0$ and we obtain

$$3\lambda_1(x - 1)^2 = 0$$
$$2\lambda_1 y = 0$$
$$(x - 1)^2 - y^2 = 0$$

which have the nontrivial solution $x = 1$, $y = 0$. This point is the desired minimum.

Inequality Constraints

This section is concerned with developing the necessary and sufficient conditions for inequality constrained optimization problems. These conditions are called the *Kuhn-Tucker* [7] *conditions*, after the men who developed them.

Suppose we wish to maximize the function $f(\mathbf{x})$, which is constrained by the set of inequality constraints

$$g_i(\mathbf{x}) \le b_i \qquad i = 1, \ldots, M$$

The constraint inequalities can be transformed into equalities by increasing the number of variables in the problem. If we add a nonnegative slack variable u_i^2 to each inequality we obtain[5]

$$g_i(\mathbf{x}) + u_i^2 = b_i \qquad i = 1, \ldots, M \qquad (2.30)$$

Subtracting b_i yields

$$\bar{g}_i(\mathbf{x}, u_i) = g_i(\mathbf{x}) + u_i^2 - b_i = 0 \qquad i = 1, \ldots, M \qquad (2.31)$$

---

[5] u_i is squared to insure it is nonnegative. Had we not squared it we would require $u_i \ge 0$.

The problem is now in the form for application of the theory given in the preceding section: max $\mathbf{f}(\mathbf{x})$ subject to

$$\bar{g}_i(\mathbf{x}, u_i) = 0 \qquad i = 1, \ldots, M$$

The solution is obtained by generating all stationary points of the Lagrange function, which is given by

$$F(\mathbf{x}, \boldsymbol{\lambda}, \mathbf{u}) = f(\mathbf{x}) + \sum_{i=1}^{M} \lambda_i \bar{g}_i(\mathbf{x}, u_i) \tag{2.32}$$

The stationary points are obtained by solving the equations

$$\frac{\partial F(\mathbf{x}, \boldsymbol{\lambda}, \mathbf{u})}{\partial x_j} = 0 = \frac{\partial f(\mathbf{x})}{\partial x_j} + \sum_{i=1}^{M} \lambda_i \frac{\partial g_i(\mathbf{x})}{\partial x_j} \qquad j = 1, \ldots, N$$

$$\frac{\partial F(\mathbf{x}, \boldsymbol{\lambda}, \mathbf{u})}{\partial \lambda_i} = 0 = \bar{g}_i(\mathbf{x}, u_i) = g_i(\mathbf{x}) + u_i^2 - b_i \qquad i = 1, \ldots, M$$

$$\frac{\partial F(\mathbf{x}, \boldsymbol{\lambda}, \mathbf{u})}{\partial u_i} = 0 = 2\lambda_i u_i \qquad i = 1, \ldots, M$$

Multiply the last equation shown above by $u_i/2$ to yield

$$\lambda_i u_i^2 = 0 \tag{2.33}$$

and solve $\bar{g}_i(\mathbf{x}, u_i)$ for

$$u_i^2 = b_i - g_i(\mathbf{x})$$

Combining these two equations yields

$$\lambda_i[b_i - g_i(\mathbf{x})] = 0 \qquad i = 1, \ldots, M \tag{2.34}$$

This equation together with

$$\frac{\partial F(\mathbf{x}, \boldsymbol{\lambda}, \mathbf{u})}{\partial x_j} = 0 \qquad j = 1, \ldots, N$$

and the constraints $g_i(\mathbf{x}) \leq b_i$ represent a subset of necessary conditions for a maximum of $f(\mathbf{x})$. The final requirement is

$$\lambda_i \leq 0 \qquad i = 1, \ldots, M \tag{2.35}$$

The proof of this last condition is given below.

Suppose that the conditions derived above are satisfied at the point $(\mathbf{x}^0, \boldsymbol{\lambda}^0, \mathbf{u}^0)$ and furthermore suppose that this point is a relative maximum. Let $z^0 = f(\mathbf{x}^0)$ and define

$$g_i(\mathbf{x}^0, u_i^0) = b_i \qquad i = 1, \ldots, M$$

Theorem:

$$\frac{\partial z^0}{\partial b_i} = -\lambda_i^0 \tag{2.36}$$

This theorem gives us a quantitative measure of the change in the optimal value of the objective function with respect to changes in the constraints. Consequently, the λ_i^0 have been called sensitivity coefficients as well as dual variables, adjoint functions, and shadow prices [8].

PROOF. From the chain rule of differential calculus we have

$$\frac{\partial z^0}{\partial b_i} = \sum_{j=1}^{N} \frac{\partial f(\mathbf{x})}{\partial x_j} \frac{\partial x_j}{\partial b_i}\bigg|_{\mathbf{x}=\mathbf{x}^0} \tag{2.37}$$

$$\frac{\partial g_k(\mathbf{x}, u_k)}{\partial b_i}\bigg|_{\substack{\mathbf{x}=\mathbf{x}_0 \\ u_k=u_k^0}} = \sum_{j=1}^{N} \frac{\partial g_k(\mathbf{x}, u_k)}{\partial x_j}\bigg|_{\substack{\mathbf{x}=\mathbf{x}^0 \\ u_k=u_k^0}} \frac{\partial x_j}{\partial b_i} = \delta_{ik} \tag{2.38}$$

where

$$\delta_{ik} = \begin{cases} 1 & i = k \\ 0 & i \neq k \end{cases}$$

Multiplying δ_{ik} by λ_k^0 and summing over all values of k yields

$$\sum_{k=1}^{M} \lambda_k^0 \delta_{ik} = \sum_{k=1}^{M} \lambda_k^0 \sum_{j=1}^{N} \frac{\partial g_k(\mathbf{x}, u_k)}{\partial x_j}\bigg|_{\substack{\mathbf{x}=\mathbf{x}^0 \\ u_k=u_k^0}} \frac{\partial x_j}{\partial b_i} \tag{2.39}$$

The expression given above equals λ_i^0, since $\delta_{ik} = 0$ unless $k = i$. Therefore,

$$\lambda_i^0 = \sum_{k=1}^{M} \lambda_k^0 \sum_{j=1}^{N} \frac{\partial g_k(\mathbf{x}, u_k)}{\partial x_j}\bigg|_{\substack{\mathbf{x}=\mathbf{x}^0 \\ u_k=u_k^0}} \frac{\partial x_j}{\partial b_i}$$

Add this result to $\partial z^0/\partial b_i$ to obtain

$$\frac{\partial z^0}{\partial b_i} + \lambda_i^0 = \sum_{j=1}^{N} \left[\frac{\partial f(\mathbf{x})}{\partial x_j} + \sum_{k=1}^{M} \lambda_k^0 \frac{\partial g_k(\mathbf{x}, u_k)}{\partial x_j}\right]_{\substack{\mathbf{x}=\mathbf{x}^0 \\ u_k=u_k^0}} \frac{\partial x_j}{\partial b_i} \tag{2.40}$$

However, the right side vanishes, because the term in brackets must equal zero to satisfy the necessary conditions. Thus

$$\frac{\partial z^0}{\partial b_i} = -\lambda_i^0$$

From the derivation of the necessary conditions given previously in this section, we know that either $\lambda_i^0 = 0$, or $u_i^0 = 0$, or both vanish at the optimal condition. Let us investigate the case when $u_i^0 \neq 0$. This implies that the constraint is satisfied as a strict inequality at $\mathbf{x}^0$ and consequently if we relaxed the constraint (make b_i larger) the extreme point will not be affected. Therefore, the change in the optimal value of the objective function with changes in b_i will be zero,

$$\frac{\partial z^0}{\partial b_i} = -\lambda_i^0 = 0$$

Now suppose that $\lambda_i^0 \neq 0$. This implies that the slack variable u_i^0 vanishes. Thus

$$g_i(\mathbf{x}^0) = b_i$$

Suppose $\lambda_i^0 > 0$. Then

$$\frac{\partial z^0}{\partial b_i} < 0$$

This means that as b_i is increased, the objective function decreases. However, as b_i increases, more of the space becomes feasible and the optimal value of the objective function clearly cannot decrease. Thus at an optimal solution $\lambda_i \leq 0$.

Let us reiterate what has been developed. Given the problem to maximize $f(\mathbf{x})$ subject to the M inequality constraints

$$g_i(\mathbf{x}) \leq b_i \qquad i = 1, \ldots, M$$

the necessary conditions for a relative maximum at $\mathbf{x}^0$ are [6]

$$(1) \quad \frac{\partial F(\mathbf{x}^0, \boldsymbol{\lambda}^0, \mathbf{u}^0)}{\partial x_i} = 0 \qquad i = 1, \ldots, N$$

$$(2) \quad \lambda_i(g_i(\mathbf{x}^0) - b_i) = 0 \qquad i = 1, \ldots, M$$

$$(3) \quad \lambda_i^0 \leq 0 \qquad\qquad\quad i = 1, \ldots, M$$

$$(4) \quad g_i(\mathbf{x}^0) \leq b_i \qquad\qquad i = 1, \ldots, M$$

One can show by a similar argument that if a relative minimum of $f(\mathbf{x})$ is desired, the sense of the inequality on condition 3 is reversed,

$$\lambda_i^0 \geq 0 \qquad i = 1, \ldots, M$$

As an example consider the following problem.

$$\min f(\mathbf{x}) = \mathbf{cx} + \tfrac{1}{2}\mathbf{x}^T\mathbf{Gx}$$

subject to

$$\mathbf{Ax} \leq \mathbf{b} \qquad \mathbf{x} \geq 0$$

---

[6] Conditions 2 and 4 arise from setting the partial derivative of $F(\cdot)$ with respect to u_i and λ_i to zero respectively.

where

$$c = (2, 4) \quad G = \begin{bmatrix} 2 & 3 \\ 3 & 6 \end{bmatrix} \quad A = \begin{bmatrix} -1 & 4 \\ 6 & 2 \\ 1 & -1 \end{bmatrix} \quad b = \begin{bmatrix} 4 \\ 1 \\ 3 \end{bmatrix} \quad x = \begin{bmatrix} x_1 \\ x_2 \end{bmatrix}$$

Forming the Lagrange function we have

$$
\begin{aligned}
F(\mathbf{x}, \boldsymbol{\lambda}, \mathbf{u}) = \; & 2x_1 + 4x_2 + x_1^2 + 3x_2^2 + 3x_1 x_2 \\
& + \lambda_1(-x_1 + 4x_2 + u_1^2 - 4) + \lambda_2(6x_1 + 2x_2 - u_2^2 - 1) \\
& + \lambda_3(x_1 - x_2 + u_3^2 - 3) + \lambda_4(-x_1 + u_4^2) + \lambda_5(-x_2 + u_5^2)
\end{aligned}
$$

The necessary conditions are

(1) $\dfrac{\partial F(\cdot)}{\partial x_1} = 2 + 2x_1 + 3x_2 - \lambda_1 + 6\lambda_2 + \lambda_3 - \lambda_4 = 0$

$\dfrac{\partial F(\cdot)}{\partial x_2} = 4 + 3x_1 + 6x_2 + 4\lambda_1 + 2\lambda_2 - \lambda_3 - \lambda_5 = 0$

(2) $\lambda_1(-x_1 + 4x_2 - 4) = 0 \qquad \lambda_4 x_1 = 0$

$\lambda_2(6x_1 + 2x_2 - 1) = 0 \qquad \lambda_5 x_2 = 0$

$\lambda_3(x_1 - x_2 - 3) = 0$

(3) $\mathbf{x} \geq \mathbf{0}$

$A\mathbf{x} \leq \mathbf{b}$

(4) $\lambda_1, \lambda_2, \lambda_3, \lambda_4, \lambda_5 \geq 0$

The reader can verify that the following values yield a solution.

$$x_1 = x_2 = \lambda_1 = \lambda_2 = \lambda_3 = 0 \qquad \lambda_4 = 2 \qquad \lambda_5 = 4$$

We shall demonstrate in the following pages that this is the only solution as $F(\mathbf{x}, \boldsymbol{\lambda}, \mathbf{u})$ is a convex function.

Next we shall show that if $f(\mathbf{x})$ is strictly concave and $g_i(\mathbf{x})$, $i = 1, \ldots, M$, are convex, the conditions given above are sufficient as well as necessary for an absolute maximum. Suppose that $f(\mathbf{x})$ and $g_i(\mathbf{x})$ satisfy the condition specified above. Then

$$F(\mathbf{x}, \boldsymbol{\lambda}, \mathbf{u}) = f(\mathbf{x}) + \sum_{i=1}^{M} \lambda_i [g_i(\mathbf{x}) + u_i^2 - b_i]$$

If $\lambda_i \leq 0$, then $\lambda_i g_i(\mathbf{x})$ is concave if $g_i(\mathbf{x})$ is convex. Therefore,

$$f(\mathbf{x}) + \sum_{i=1}^{M} \lambda_i g_i(\mathbf{x})$$

is strictly concave. Since $\lambda_i u_i = 0$ and $\lambda_i b_i$ is a constant, if

$$f(\mathbf{x}) + \sum_{i=1}^{M} \lambda_i g_i(\mathbf{x})$$

is concave, $F(\mathbf{x}, \lambda, \mathbf{u})$ is concave. We have shown above that a necessary condition for $f(\mathbf{x})$ to be a maximum at $\mathbf{x}^0$ is that $F(\mathbf{x}, \lambda, \mathbf{u})$ have a stationary point at $\mathbf{x}^0$. However, if $F(\mathbf{x}, \lambda, \mathbf{u})$ is strictly concave, its derivatives vanish at one point only. Consequently, this point must be the relative maximum. Therefore, the conditions 1, 2, 3, and 4 are sufficient as well as necessary for an absolute maximum of $f(\mathbf{x})$ at $\mathbf{x}^0$.

We should point out the restriction on the development given. The necessary conditions derived above were based on the derivation given in the section on equality constraints. One of the requirements for these conditions was that at least one of the Jacobians composed of the M constraints and M of the $N + M$ variables x_i, $i = 1, \ldots, N$, u_j, $j = 1, \ldots, M$, be nonzero. This requirement is implied in the development given above.

There are several special cases of the Kuhn-Tucker conditions. Suppose P of the constraints are of the form $x_i \geq 0$, $i = 1, \ldots, P$. We can convert these constraints to the form used above,

$$-x_i \leq 0 \qquad i = 1, \ldots, P$$

where $b_i = 0$, $i = 1, \ldots, P$ and $g_i(\mathbf{x}) = -x_i$. The Lagrange multiplier associated with each of these constraints must be nonpositive. The Kuhn-Tucker conditions are

$$\left. \frac{\partial f(\mathbf{x})}{\partial x_j} + \sum_{i=1}^{M} \lambda_i \frac{\partial g_i(\mathbf{x})}{\partial x_j} \right|_{\substack{\mathbf{x}=\mathbf{x}^0 \\ \lambda=\lambda^0}} = 0 \qquad j = 1, \ldots, N$$

$$\begin{aligned}
\lambda_i^0 x_i^0 &= 0 & i &= 1, \ldots, P \\
\lambda_i^0 [g_i(\mathbf{x}^0) - b_i] &= 0 & i &= P + 1, \ldots, M \\
\lambda_i^0 &\leq 0 & i &= 1, \ldots, M \\
x_i &\geq 0 & i &= 1, \ldots, P \\
g_i(\mathbf{x}^0) &\leq b_i & i &= P + 1, \ldots, M
\end{aligned}$$

Alternative Derivation of the Kuhn-Tucker Conditions

There are several alternative derivations of the Kuhn-Tucker conditions. Wilde [9], Bernholtz [10], and Hadley [11] all have given different derivations. Bernholtz's derivation is outlined below.

Suppose that $f(\mathbf{x})$ is differentiable and that the functions $g_i(\mathbf{x})$, $i = 1, \ldots, M$ are continuously differentiable. If $f(\mathbf{x})$ has a relative maximum at $\mathbf{x}^0$ subject to $g_i(\mathbf{x}) = 0$, there will exist constants $\lambda_1^0, \ldots, \lambda_M^0$ such that

$$\left. \frac{\partial f(\mathbf{x})}{\partial x_j} + \sum_{i=1}^{M} \lambda_i^0 \frac{g_i(\mathbf{x})}{x_j} \right|_{\mathbf{x}=\mathbf{x}^0} = 0 \qquad j = 1, \ldots, N$$

$$g_i(\mathbf{x}) = 0 \qquad i = 1, \ldots, M$$

when evaluated at $\mathbf{x}^0$ provided that one of the two mutually exclusive sets of conditions hold:

A. (1) $M \geq N$.
    (2) At $\mathbf{x}^0$, at least one of the Jacobians of order N does not vanish. Or

B. (1) There exists an integer h, $0 < h < N$ such that at $\mathbf{x}^0$ all Jacobians of order greater than h vanish, but at least one Jacobian of order h does not vanish.

(2) Corresponding to any vector differential $d\mathbf{x} = (dx_1, \ldots, dx_N) \neq 0$ for which $dg_i(\mathbf{x}) = 0$, there exists a differential arc $\mathbf{x} = \mathbf{a}(t)$ defined for $-1 \leq t \leq 1$ which lies in the intersection of the surfaces $g_i(\mathbf{x}) = 0$ and which is such that $\mathbf{x}^0 = \mathbf{a}(0)$ and $d\mathbf{x} = \mathbf{a}'(0) \, dt$.

The proof is as follows. Suppose condition A holds. Then the columns of the Jacobian are linearly independent and form a basis for some N-dimensional linear vector space. Thus we can introduce M constants λ_i^0 to satisfy the linear nonhomogeneous equations

$$\sum_{i=1}^{M} \lambda_i^0 \frac{\partial g_i(\mathbf{x})}{\partial x_j}\bigg|_{\mathbf{x}=\mathbf{x}^0} = -\frac{\partial f(\mathbf{x})}{\partial x_j}\bigg|_{\mathbf{x}=\mathbf{x}^0}$$

A similar argument can be obtained if condition B is satisfied. Bernholtz next derives a result similar to the relationship given previously for the sensitivity coefficient,

$$\frac{\partial f(\mathbf{x}^0)}{\partial b_i} = -\lambda_i^0 \qquad i = 1, \ldots, M$$

Let $z = \mathbf{x}^0 + \theta(\mathbf{y} - \mathbf{x}^0)$, where $\mathbf{x}^0$ is a relative maximum of $f(\mathbf{x})$ subject to $g_i(\mathbf{x}) = 0$, $i = 1, \ldots, M$, and $\mathbf{y}$ is chosen so that

$$\sum_{i=1}^{N} \frac{\partial g_j(\mathbf{x}^0)}{\partial x_i} (y_i - x_i^0) \neq 0$$

for some $j \in I$, where $I = \{1, \ldots, N\}$ if condition A holds and $I = \{1, \ldots, h\}$ if B holds and

$$\sum_{i=1}^{N} \frac{\partial g_k(\mathbf{x}^0)}{\partial x_i} (y_i - x_i^0) = 0$$

for all k in I except $k = j$.

Then by Taylor's theorem

$$f(\mathbf{z}) + \sum_{i \in I} \lambda_i^0 g_i(\mathbf{z}) = f(\mathbf{x}^0) + \sum_{i \in I} \lambda_i^0 g_i(\mathbf{x}^0)$$

$$+ \theta \sum_{i=1}^{N} \frac{\partial f(\mathbf{x})}{\partial x_i}\bigg|_{\mathbf{x}=\mathbf{x}^0} (y_i - x_i^0)$$

$$+ \theta \sum_{i=1}^{N} \lambda_j^0 \frac{\partial g_j(\mathbf{x})}{\partial x_i}\bigg|_{\mathbf{x}=\mathbf{x}^0} (y_i - x_i^0) + \theta \delta(\theta)$$

$$= f(\mathbf{x}^0) + \theta \delta(\theta) \tag{2.41}$$

where $\delta(\theta) \to 0$ as $\theta \to 0$. Using Taylor's theorem again we obtain

$$g_j(\mathbf{z}) = \theta \sum_{i=1}^{N} \frac{\partial g_j(\mathbf{x})}{\partial x_i}\bigg|_{\mathbf{x}=\mathbf{x}^0} (y_i - x_i^0) + \delta_j(\theta)\theta = (A + \delta_j)\theta \qquad (2.42)$$

where $\delta \to 0$ as $\theta \to 0$ and A is a constant. Therefore,

$$\frac{f(\mathbf{z}) - f(\mathbf{x}^0)}{g_j(\mathbf{z})} + \lambda_j^0 = -\frac{\lambda_j^0 - \left[\sum\limits_{i \in I} \lambda_j g_i(\mathbf{z}) - \theta\delta(\theta)\right]}{g_j(\mathbf{z})}$$

$$= -\lambda_j - \left[(A + \delta_j)\theta\lambda_j + \sum_{\substack{i \in I \\ i \neq j}} \lambda_i \delta_i \theta - \theta\delta(\theta)\right]\Big/(A + \delta_j)\theta$$

$$= -\left[\sum_{\substack{i \in I \\ i = j}} \lambda_i^0 \delta_i \theta - \theta\delta(\theta)\right]\Big/(A + \delta_j)\theta$$

$$= 0 \qquad (2.43)$$

On taking the limit as $\theta \to 0$ the right side equals 0 and the result is

$$\lim_{\theta \to 0} \frac{f(\mathbf{z}) - f(\mathbf{x}^0)}{g_j(\mathbf{z})} = -\lambda_j^0$$

When $g_i(\mathbf{x}) \leq 0$, the necessary conditions

$$\frac{\partial f(\mathbf{x})}{\partial x_j} + \sum_{i=1}^{M} \lambda_i^0 \frac{\partial g(\mathbf{x})}{\partial x_j}\bigg|_{\mathbf{x}=\mathbf{x}_0} = 0 \qquad j = 1, \ldots, N$$

are still satisfied if either condition A or B holds. This proof is similar to the previous one and is left as an exercise.

To show that $\lambda_{j_i}^0 \leq 0$ we use the definition of λ_j^0,

$$\lim_{\theta \to 0} \frac{f(\mathbf{z}) - f(\mathbf{x}^0)}{g_j(\mathbf{z})} = -\lambda_j^0$$

Choose θ small enough so that $g_j(\mathbf{z}) < 0$ and $f(\mathbf{z}) < f(\mathbf{x}^0)$ by definition of relative maximum. Hence

$$\frac{f(\mathbf{z}) - f(\mathbf{x}^0)}{g_j(\mathbf{z})} \geq 0$$

and thus $\lambda_j^0 < 0$ for all λ_j^0 not identically equal to zero.

Problems

1. Expand the following function in a Taylor series about the point $x = 1$, $y = 1$.

$$f(x_1, y) = xe^y + x^2y^2 + x^{-2}y^3$$

2. Expand the following in a Taylor series about $(0, 0, 0)$.

$$f(x, y, z) = x^2 + 6y^2 + xz + 3x^2y + 4y^2z + z^2 + 2zy^2$$

3. Find and classify all stationary points for the following.

   (a) $f(x) = \mathbf{a}^T\mathbf{x} + \mathbf{b}$,

$$\mathbf{a} = \begin{pmatrix} a_1 \\ a_2 \\ \vdots \\ a_N \end{pmatrix} \qquad \mathbf{x} = \begin{pmatrix} x_1 \\ x_2 \\ \vdots \\ x_N \end{pmatrix}$$

   (b) $f(x_1, x_2) = 30x_1^2 + 15x_2^2 - 62.5x_1 - 20x_2$.
   (c) $f(x_1, x_2, x_3) = 10x_1^2 + 5x_2^2 + 15x_1x_2 - 5x_1x_3 + 3x_2x_3 - x_3^2$.

4. Show that $x = 0$, $y = 1$ is a critical point for

$$f(x, y) = x^2 + 6xy^2 - 12xy + 6x + 12x^2y - 12x^2 + 9y^4$$
$$- 36y^3 + 54y^2 - 36y + 9 + 12x^6y^2 - 24x^6y + 12x^6$$

   and classify the critical point. Can you say that $(0, 1)$ is a maximum or a minimum? Can you say that $(0, 1)$ is not a maximum or a minimum?

5. Prove that a positive definite quadratic form has a unique stationary point and that this point yields a minimum.

6. Let $f(x, y) = ax^2 + by^2 + cxy$. Suppose

$$\frac{\partial f}{\partial x}\bigg|_{x^0, y^0} = \frac{\partial f}{\partial y}\bigg|_{x^0, y^0} = 0$$

   Under what conditions can we say that the necessary conditions are sufficient for a minimum?

7. Find all extreme points of $F(x) = x^3 - 3x^2 + 3x + 9$ with $-\infty < x < \infty$. Also, sketch $F(x)$.

8. Find all extreme points of $f(x)$ where $f(x) = x^3 + x^2 + x - 1$, where $-\infty < x < \infty$. Sketch $f(x)$.

9. Classify the extreme points of the following quadratic forms.

   (a) $F = 4x_1^2 + 2x_1x_2 + x_2^2$.
   (b) $F = -4x_1^2 - 2x_1x_2 - x_2^2$.
   (c) $F = 4x_1^2 + 4x_1x_2 + x_2^2$.
   (d) $F = 4x_1^2 + 5x_1x_2 + x_2^2$.
   (e) $F = x_1^2 + 3x_2^2 + 3x_3^2 + 2x_1x_2 + 4x_2x_3 + 2x_1x_3$.

10. Find the minimum of

$$f(x, y) = x^2 + xy + y^2 - 4x - 5y \qquad -\infty < x, y < \infty$$

11. Minimize

$$f(x, y, z) = x^2 + y^2 + z^2 + xy + xz + yz + 4x - 4y + 8z$$
$$-\infty < y, x, z < \infty$$

12. Find the minimum of

$$f(x, y) = x^2y^2 - 4x^2y + 4x^2 + 2xy^2 + y^2 - 8xy + 8x - 4y + 4$$
$$-\infty < x, y < \infty$$

13. Find all extreme points of

$$f(x) = +\sqrt{1 - \cos^2 x} \qquad -\infty < x < \infty$$

14. Assume that we want to construct a tin can with walls of negligible thickness. We must keep the total surface area within the constraint $A = 2\pi r^2 + 2\pi rl = A_0$. Find the values of l and r that maximize the volume

    (a) By the method of direct substitution.
    (b) By the Lagrange multiplier method.
    (c) Compare the results.

15. Find the rectangle of greatest area that can be inscribed in the circle $x^2 + y^2 = 25$.

16. Solve Problem 15 but add the constraint that the ratio of the length of rectangle to the height must be $\leq \frac{1}{4}$.

17. What point on the curve $4y = x^2$ is nearest the point $(0, 4)$?

18. Prove that a global maximum must be a local maximum.

19. Show that if $f''(x) > 0$ for $x_i \leq x \leq x_f$ and $f'(x^0) = 0$, $x_i < x^0 < x_f$, then $f(x)$ is convex for $x_i \leq x \leq x_f$.

20. Prove that if the Hessian of a function $f(\mathbf{x})$ is indefinite when evaluated at $\mathbf{x}^*$, where the necessary conditions are satisfied, then $\mathbf{x}^*$ is not an extreme point.

21. Prove that a function $f(\mathbf{x})$ is convex in $a_i \leq x_i \leq b_i$, $i = 1, \ldots, N$ if and only if the Hessian is positive semidefinite for all $x_i \in [a_i, b_i]$, $i = 1, \ldots, N$.

22. Minimize $f(x, y) = x^2 + y^2$ subject to $(x - 1)^2 + xy - y = 0$.

23. Minimize $f(x, y) = (x - 1)^2 + y^2$ subject to $y^2 = 4x$.

24. Find all critical points of $x^2 + y^2 + 3xy + 6x + 19y$ subject to $3y + x = 5$.

25. Maximize $f(x, y, z) = xyz$ subject to $x^2 + y^2 + z^2 = 27$, $x, y, z \geq 0$.

26. Find a critical point of $f(x, y) = y^2x^{5/2} + yx^2 + y^{7/2}x^3$. Does the point $(0, 0)$ satisfy the definition of a minimum? If we restrict x and y to nonnegative values, does $(0, 0)$ satisfy the definition of a minimum?

27. Find the critical points and classify them:

    (a) $f(x) = (1 - x)^5$.
    (b) $f(x, y, z) = x^2 + 2y^2 + \frac{3}{2}z^2 + 4xy + 2xz + 2yz$.
    (c) $f(x, y) = (x - 2)^2 + 3y^2$
    subject to $x + 2y = 10$.

28. Given the continuous function, $f(x)$, for $x_1 \leq x_0 \leq x_2$ shown here, what are the necessary and sufficient conditions for a maximum at point x_0, where the function is not differentiable at x_0? Justify your answer.

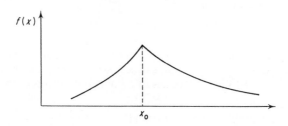

29. We have derived an expression for λ_i^0 at the optimal solution; for example,

$$\lambda_i^0 = -\frac{\partial f(x^0)}{\partial b_i}$$

There is an alternative expression of λ_i^0 in terms of matrices associated with the Jacobian. Given: maximize $f(x_1, x_2, x_3, x_4)$ subject to $g_i(x_1, x_2, x_3, x_4) \leq 0$, $i = 1, 2, 3$, and that the rank of the Jacobian associated with x_1, x_2, x_3, y_1, y_2, and y_3 is 3, derive these alternative expressions.

30. (a) Maximize

$$f(\mathbf{x}) = \prod_{n=1}^{N} x_n$$

subject to

$$\sum_{n=1}^{N} x_n = 10 \quad x_n \geq 0 \quad n = 1, \ldots, N$$

(b) Give an estimate of how $f(\mathbf{x}^0)$ changes if the constraint is changed to read

$$\sum_{n=1}^{N} x_n = 9.9$$

(c) Use the result of part (a) to show that

$$\prod_{n=1}^{8} x_n^{1/8} \leq \sum_{n=1}^{8} \frac{x_n}{8}$$

31. Let $f(x, y) = ax^2 + bxy + cy^2$. Suppose that at (x_0, y_0)

(a) $\dfrac{\partial f}{\partial x} = \dfrac{\partial f}{\partial y} = 0.$

(b) The quadratic form is negative semidefinite.

Prove that $f(x_0, y_0)$ is a maximum.

32. Find the solution that minimizes $f(x, y) = x^2 + 6xy - 4x - 2y$ subject to $x^2 + 2y \leq 1$, $y - x \leq 0.5$.

33. Determine necessary conditions for

$$\min \sum_{i=1}^{N} \sum_{j=1}^{N} c_{ij} x_i x_j$$

subject to

$$\sum_{j=1}^{N} a_{ij} x_j \leq b_i \qquad i = 1, \ldots, M$$

$$x_j \geq 0 \qquad j = 1, \ldots, N$$

34. Suppose the right side of the constraints in Problem 32 are changed so that the constraints now read:

$$x^2 + 2y \leq 1.1 \qquad y - x \leq 0.4$$

Without resolving the problem, estimate the new value of the objective function for the constraints given above.

35. Show under what conditions $-\partial f/\partial b_i = \lambda_i$ can be thought of as a one-sided derivative.

36. For the problem max $f(x_j)$, subject to $g_i(x_j) = b_i$, $i = 1, \ldots, M$, we have shown that at an optimal solution x^*, where $f^* = f(x^*)$ and $g_i(x^*) = b_i^*$,

(1)
$$\frac{\partial f^*}{\partial b_i^*} = \lambda_i + \sum_{j=1}^{N} \left[\frac{\partial f}{\partial x_j} + \sum_{k=1}^{M} \lambda_k \frac{\partial g_j}{\partial x_j} \right] \frac{dx_j}{db_i}$$

from which it follows that

(2)
$$\frac{\partial f^*}{\partial b_i^*} = -\lambda_i$$

for the problem max $f(x)$

$$g_i(x) \leq 0 \qquad i = 1, \ldots, M$$
$$x \geq 0$$

Show that (1) also holds and then use the Kuhn-Tucker conditions to prove that statement (2) once again follows from statement (1).

37. Find the length of line of maximum length from the origin to some point in the first quadrant such that the following constraints are met:

$$x + 2y \leq 3 \qquad 2x + y \leq 3$$

38. Given the subset of necessary conditions

$$\frac{\partial f}{\partial x_j} + \sum_{i=1}^{M} \lambda_i \frac{\partial y_i}{\partial x_j} = 0 \qquad j = 1, \ldots, N$$

(a) Show when we can solve for λ uniquely in terms of x.
(b) Show when we can solve for x in terms of λ.

39. Given a convex programming problem, for example, $\min f(\mathbf{x})$ subject to $\mathbf{x} \geq 0$

$$g_i(\mathbf{x}) \leq 0 \qquad i = 1, \ldots, M$$

where $\mathbf{x} = (x_1, \ldots, x_N)$ and the optimal solution to $\min f(\mathbf{x})$ occurs at $\mathbf{x}^*$, and at $\mathbf{x}^*$

$$g_i(\mathbf{x}^*) > 0 \qquad i = 1, 2, 3$$

Prove that the optimal solution to the convex programming problem lies on the boundary of at least one of the three constraints

$$g_i(\mathbf{x}) = 0 \qquad i = 1, 2, 3$$

40. We have derived sufficient conditions for an optimal solution to the problem

$$\min f(\mathbf{x}) \qquad \mathbf{x} = (x_1, \ldots, x_N)$$

subject to

$$g_i(\mathbf{x}) \leq b_i \qquad i = 1, \ldots, M < N$$

when $f(\mathbf{x})$ and $g_i(\mathbf{x})$, $i = 1, \ldots, M$, are convex and at least one is strictly convex.

(a) Derive sufficient conditions when the above restrictions are relaxed.
(b) Derive sufficient conditions when, in addition to the above constraints,

$$g_i(\mathbf{x}) \leq b_i \qquad i = 1, \ldots, M$$

we introduce some new constraints

$$g_i(\mathbf{x}) = b_i \qquad i = M + 1, \ldots, P < N$$

41. In many O.R. applications we are required to develop an empirical relationship to approximate the system under consideration. In many instances the model is built by determining the parameters of a hypothesized function that will give the best fit to the data which has been—or is to be—gathered. "Best fit" is usually defined to be the set of parameters that minimizes the sum of squares of the prediction from the actual data. For example, define

$$\mathbf{y} = \begin{pmatrix} y_1 \\ \vdots \\ y_N \end{pmatrix}$$

as the vector of observations of $f(\mathbf{x})$, the hypothesized function, where

$$\mathbf{x} = \begin{pmatrix} x_1 \\ \vdots \\ x_N \end{pmatrix}$$

is a vector of parameters to be estimated. The objective is to determine the vector $\mathbf{x}$ to minimize

$$\sum_{i=1}^{N} [y_i - f(\mathbf{x})]^2$$

(a) Construct the necessary conditions for **x** to be an optimal set of parameters in the sense defined above.

(b) In the case when $f(\mathbf{x})$ is linear in the parameters, give a solution for **x** in terms of **y**.

42. In many cases we are not as completely free in our choice of parameters as was the case in Problem 41. Many times the parameters must satisfy certain relationships. For example, consider $\mathbf{Bx} = \mathbf{g}$, where

$$\mathbf{B} = (b_{ij}) \qquad i = 1, \ldots, M; \quad j = 1, \ldots, P$$

$$\mathbf{g} = \begin{bmatrix} g_1 \\ \vdots \\ g_P \end{bmatrix}$$

Derive the necessary conditions for an optimal solution when $f(\mathbf{x})$ is linear in **x**, and **y** is again specified data.

43. Consider a simple two-commodity lot-size inventory system where q_1 is the amount of commodity 1 ordered each time an order is placed and q_2 is the amount of commodity 2. Assume that the rate of demand for each during the period is r. Let c_1 be the cost of carrying one unit of commodity 1 for a unit time period and d_1 the equivalent cost for commodity 2. Define c_3 and d_3 to be unit replenishment cost. One can then construct the cost function

$$C(q_1, q_2) = \frac{c_1 q_1}{2} + \frac{d_1 q_2}{2} + \frac{c_3 r}{q_1} + \frac{d_3 r}{q_2}$$

(a) Find the optimal lot size for commodities 1 and 2 that minimizes the total cost.

(b) Suppose one finds that his storage capacity is limited so that the amount in inventory may not exceed 100 cubic yards. The volume of one unit of commodity 1 is 0.5 yard^3 per unit and one unit of commodity 2 occupies 1 yard^3. If $c_1 = d_1 = 10$, $c_3 = 100$, and $d_3 = 200$, find the optimal lot size for each commodity.

(c) Express the ratio of lot size of commodity 1 to that of commodity 2 when $c_1 = d_1$ for any c_3 and d_3.

44. Derive necessary conditions for $f(\mathbf{x})$ to have a maximum when **x** is defined only on discrete values. For example when **x** is defined on the set of non-negative integers.

45. Extend the arguments used in Problem 44 to the case when the function has several variables as its argument and each is defined on the set of non-negative integers.

46. Consider

$$\max f(\mathbf{x})$$
$$x_i = 0, 1, 2, 3, 4, \ldots \qquad i = 1, \ldots, N$$

Discuss sufficiency conditions for this problem.

References Cited and Bibliography

[1] Courant, R. *Differential and Integral Calculus*, Vol. II. New York: Wiley-Interscience, 1936.

[2] Granville, W. A., P. F. Smith, and W. R. Longley. *Elements of Differential and Integral Calculus*. Boston: Ginn, 1941.

[3] Hancock, H. *Theory of Maxima and Minima*. New York: Dover, 1950.

[4] Wilde, D. J. *Optimum Seeking Methods*. Englewood Cliffs, N.J.: Prentice-Hall, 1963.

[5] Bellman, R. E., and S. A. Dreyfus. *Applied Dynamic Programming*. Princeton, N.J.: Princeton University Press, 1962.

[6] Hadley, G. *Linear Algebra*. Reading, Mass.: Addison-Wesley, 1961.

[7] Kuhn, H. W., and A. W. Tucker. "Nonlinear Programming," *Proceedings of the Second Berkeley Symposium on Mathematical Statistics and Probability* (J. Neyman, ed.). Berkeley: University of California Press, 1951, pp. 402–411.

[8] Wilde, D. J., and C. Beightler. *Foundations of Optimization*. Englewood Cliffs, N.J.: Prentice-Hall, 1967.

[9] Wilde, D. J. "Differential Calculus in Nonlinear Programming," *Operations Res.*, Vol. 10, No. 6 (1962).

[10] Bernholtz, B. "A New Derivation of the Kuhn-Tucker Conditions," *Operations Res.*, Vol. 12, No. 2 (1964).

[11] Hadley, G. *Non-Linear and Dynamic Programming*. Reading, Mass.: Addison-Wesley, 1964.

CHAPTER 3

Linear Programming

3.1 Introduction

Among the decision models discussed in Chapter 1, those leading to a linear objective function whose variables are subject to linear constraints seem to have the simplest mathematical form. In science and engineering the properties of linearity have frequently led to analysis that might not be possible under more complex forms of mathematical formulation. We should also point out that the linear model is frequently a less accurate indicator of system behavior than nonlinear formulations.

The extensive use of the linear programming model as a tool of operations research has been for a combination of reasons. It has served as a reasonably good predictor of real-life behavior. More importantly, the great mathematical advances made in developing methods of solving the linear programming problem (and associated problems) have made it one of the most frequently used mathematical methods of operations research.

This chapter contains a rigorous discussion of the mathematical methods used in the solution of linear programming problems. The solution method is called the *simplex technique.* Emphasis is placed on the conceptual approach rather than on the answers obtained.

3.2 *N*-Dimensional Geometry[1]

A familiarity with *N*-dimensional geometry is an important part of the required background for this chapter. For those with limited exposure to the

---

[1] The reader familiar with the concepts of linear algebra and *N*-dimensional geometry may skip Sections 3.2 and 3.3 without loss of continuity.

subject, this section will summarize the concepts to be used in the remainder of the chapter.

Vectors and Euclidean Space

Vectors are matrices with single rows or single columns. We use both row vectors,

$$\mathbf{a} = (a_1, \ldots, a_N)$$

and column vectors,

$$\mathbf{b} = \begin{bmatrix} b_1 \\ \vdots \\ b_N \end{bmatrix}$$

Vectors may be viewed as points in N-dimensional space. However, there is no distinction between row and column vectors in N-dimensional space.

A *unit vector*, denoted by $\mathbf{e}_i$, is a vector with 1 as its ith component and zeros elsewhere. For example,

$$\mathbf{e}_1 = (1, 0, 0, \ldots, 0) \qquad \mathbf{e}_2 = (0, 1, 0, \ldots, 0)$$

A *null vector*, or a zero vector, written $\mathbf{0}$, is a vector in which all components are zero.

A *sum vector* is a vector, written $\mathbf{1}$, having 1 for each component. To see why this is called the sum vector, consider the following product:

$$(1, 1, \ldots, 1) \begin{bmatrix} a_1 \\ a_2 \\ \vdots \\ a_N \end{bmatrix} = \sum_{i=1}^{N} a_i$$

We shall frequently need the concept of a vector inequality. Given two N-component vectors, $\mathbf{a}$ and $\mathbf{b}$, $\mathbf{a} > \mathbf{b}$ means $a_i > b_i$, $i = 1, \ldots, N$. Also $\mathbf{a} \geq \mathbf{b}$ means $a_i \geq b_i$, $i = 1, \ldots, N$.

A *scalar product* for two N-component vectors $\mathbf{a}$ and $\mathbf{b}$ is defined as

$$\sum_{i=1}^{N} a_i b_i \tag{3.1}$$

This definition holds whether or not $\mathbf{a}$ and $\mathbf{b}$ are row or column vectors. The vector notation for equation (3.1) is always adjusted to fit this definition. For example, if $\mathbf{a}$ is a row vector and $\mathbf{b}$ is a column vector, then their scalar product is denoted by $\mathbf{ab}$.

An N-dimensional *Euclidean space*, E^N, is defined as the collection of all vectors, $\mathbf{a} = (a_1, \ldots, a_N)$. For these vectors, addition and multiplication by a scalar are defined by the rules for matrix operations.[2] Associated with any two vectors, **a** and **b**, in the collection is a nonnegative number, called the distance between the two vectors, which is given by

$$|\mathbf{a} - \mathbf{b}| = [(\mathbf{a} - \mathbf{b})^T(\mathbf{a} - \mathbf{b})]^{1/2}$$
$$= \left[\sum_{i=1}^{N} (a_i - b_i)^2\right]^{1/2}$$

where **a** and **b** are *N*-component column vectors.

Linear Dependence

A vector **a** from E^N is said to be a *linear combination* of the vectors $\mathbf{a}_1, \mathbf{a}_2, \ldots, \mathbf{a}_k$ from E^N if **a** can be written

$$\mathbf{a} = \lambda_1\mathbf{a}_1 + \lambda_2\mathbf{a}_2 + \cdots + \lambda_k\mathbf{a}_k$$

for some set of scalars λ_i.

A set of vectors from E^N is said to be *linearly dependent* if there exist scalars λ_i, not all zero, such that

$$\lambda_1\mathbf{a}_1 + \lambda_2\mathbf{a}_2 + \cdots + \lambda_M\mathbf{a}_M = \mathbf{0}$$

If the only set of λ_i for which this equality holds is $\lambda_1 = \lambda_2 = \cdots = \lambda_M = 0$, then the vectors are said to be *linearly independent*.

A vector **a** is said to be linearly dependent on a set of vectors $\mathbf{a}_1, \ldots, \mathbf{a}_M$ if **a** can be written as a linear combination of $\mathbf{a}_1, \ldots, \mathbf{a}_M$. Note that no set of linearly independent vectors can contain the null vector.

The following properties of vectors may be derived. The reader who is interested in the proofs should see a text on linear algebra such as Hadley [1]:

1. If a set of vectors $\mathbf{a}_1, \ldots, \mathbf{a}_M$ from E^N contains two or more vectors, then the set is linearly dependent if and only if some one of the vectors is a linear combination of the others.
2. If a set of vectors is linearly independent, then any subset of these vectors is also linearly independent.
3. If any given set of vectors is linearly dependent, any larger set of vectors containing the given set is also linearly dependent.

Bases

The use of the word basis is a familiar one in solving linear programming problems. The concept will be important in the work to follow. A *basis* for E^N is a set of *N* linearly independent vectors. Any vector in E^N can be expressed as a linear combination of the basis vectors.

---

[2] See Appendix A.

Rank

Recall that the columns of some $M \times N$ matrix $\mathbf{A}$ can be considered to be vectors in E^N. With this thought we make the following definition.

The *rank* (column rank) of an $M \times N$ matrix $\mathbf{A}$, written $r(\mathbf{A})$, is the maximum number of linearly independent columns in $\mathbf{A}$.

The definition above is given for column rank. An equivalent definition of row rank is obtained by exchanging the word column for the word row. However, it can be shown [1] that row rank equals column rank.

Theorem: *The rank of an $M \times N$ matrix $\mathbf{A}$ is k if and only if every minor of $\mathbf{A}$ having order $k + 1$ vanishes, while there is at least one minor of order k which does not vanish.*

The proof of the theorem may be found in Hadley [1]. With its statement we now have a way of determining the rank of a matrix. The rank is the order of the largest nonvanishing minor of $\mathbf{A}$.

Convex Sets

The notion of a convex set will prove important in developing a conceptual use of the geometry of linear programming. Space will not allow a detailed discussion of convex sets. However, we shall summarize certain concepts important to the development of the chapter. Those wishing a more detailed discussion should see a text on linear algebra such as Hadley [1].

A *set* consists of a finite or an infinite number of elements.

A *convex combination* of the points $\mathbf{x}_1, \mathbf{x}_2, \ldots, \mathbf{x}_N$ is a point

$$\mathbf{x} = \alpha_1 \mathbf{x}_1 + \alpha_2 \mathbf{x}_2 + \cdots + \alpha_N \mathbf{x}_N$$

where the scalar $\alpha_i \geq 0$ and $\sum_{i=1}^{N} \alpha_i = 1$. A subset C of E^N is *convex* if and only if for all pairs $\mathbf{x}_1$ and $\mathbf{x}_2$ in C any convex combination $\mathbf{x} = \alpha_1 \mathbf{x}_1 + \alpha_2 \mathbf{x}_2$ is also in C. Before citing examples of convex sets it will be helpful to state two theorems.

Theorem: *Any point on the line segment joining two points in E^N can be expressed as a convex combination of the two points.*

Theorem: *Any point that can be expressed as a convex combination of two points in E^N lies on the line segment joining the two points.*

The significance of these two theorems is found in the fact that geometrically a convex set is one that contains all line segments joining any two points in the set. This provides an easy intuitive check on whether or not a set is convex. For example, consider Figure 3.1(a). The set of points contained in the circle is convex, because there is no line segment that falls outside the set that can be drawn between two points in the set. On the other hand, the set shown in Figure 3.1(b) is not convex, because the line falls outside the set. The proof of both theorems stated above may be found in Gass [2].

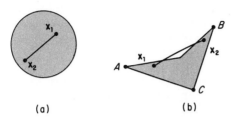

(a)   (b)

Figure 3.1.

A point **x** is an *extreme point* of a convex set if and only if there does not exist other points $x_1, x_2, x_1 \neq x_2$ in the set such that

$$\mathbf{x} = \alpha\mathbf{x}_1 + (1 - \alpha)\mathbf{x}_2$$

where $0 < \alpha < 1$.

Given a set A, not convex, the smallest convex set that contains A is called the *convex hull* of A. This definition could be stated more rigorously as follows: The convex hull of a set A is the *intersection* of all convex sets which contain A. Figure 3.2 shows a set that is not convex (a) and its convex hull (b).

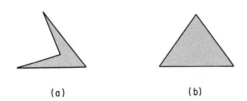

(a)   (b)

Figure 3.2.

Theorem: *The convex hull of a finite number of points* $x_1, \ldots, x_M$ *is the set of all convex combinations of* $x_1, \ldots, x_M$.

The proof of this theorem, which follows from the two theorems stated above, is given in Hadley [1]. If the set S consists of a finite number of points, the convex hull of S is a *convex polyhedron*. A *simplex* is an *n*-dimensional convex polyhedron having exactly $n + 1$ vertices. In two dimensions, a simplex is a triangle. We shall also be interested in the intersection of convex sets in E^N.

Theorem: *The intersection of n convex sets is a convex set.*

The proof of this theorem is left to the reader as an exercise.
Consider the equation $z = \mathbf{cx}$ or

$$z = \sum_{j=1}^{N} c_j x_j$$

If $N = 2$ we have a straight line. If $N = 3$ we have a plane. For some arbitrary N the equation defines a hyperplane. The hyperplane $z = \mathbf{cx}$ divides E^N into three mutually exclusive and exhaustive sets:

1. The points $\mathbf{x}$ for which $\mathbf{cx} < z$.
2. The points $\mathbf{x}$ for which $\mathbf{cx} = z$.
3. The points $\mathbf{x}$ for which $\mathbf{cx} > z$.

(1) and (3) are called *open half-spaces*. The set of points $\mathbf{x}$ for which $\mathbf{cx} \leq z$ and $\mathbf{cx} \geq z$ are called *closed half-spaces*. It is easy to show that open and closed half-spaces are convex sets. Later this will lead us to the conclusion that the set of points satisfying the constraints for a linear programming problem is a convex set.

3.3 Solution of Linear Equations

The solution of simultaneous linear equations is directly related to the solution of the linear programming problem. For this reason, it may be helpful to review certain basic properties of linear equations.

Consider a set of simultaneous equations with the form

$$
\begin{aligned}
a_{11}x_1 + a_{12}x_2 + \cdots + a_{1N}x_N &= b_1 \\
\vdots \qquad\qquad \vdots \qquad\ \vdots \\
a_{M1}x_1 + a_{M2}x_2 + \cdots + a_{MN}x_N &= b_M
\end{aligned}
\tag{3.2}
$$

We can write these equations in matrix form as $\mathbf{Ax} = \mathbf{b}$, where $\mathbf{A} = [a_{ij}]$, $\mathbf{x} = [x_1, \ldots, x_N]$ [3] and $\mathbf{b} = [b_1, \ldots, b_M]$.

If the matrix $\mathbf{A}$ is square, $M = N$, and nonsingular, there is a unique solution, $\mathbf{x} = \mathbf{A}^{-1}\mathbf{b}$. All that is needed to find this solution is $\mathbf{A}^{-1}$. Considerable insight into the nature of solutions to equations (3.2) may be gained by examining the rank of the matrix $\mathbf{A}$, $r(\mathbf{A})$, and the rank of the augmented matrix $(\mathbf{A}, \mathbf{b})$: $r(\mathbf{A}, \mathbf{b})$. Note that $r(\mathbf{A}, \mathbf{b}) \geq r(\mathbf{A})$, since every minor in $\mathbf{A}$ also appears in $(\mathbf{A}, \mathbf{b})$.

---

[3] We shall use brackets to denote column vectors and parentheses to denote row vectors.

Consider the case where $r(\mathbf{A}, \mathbf{b}) > r(\mathbf{A})$. Recalling the definition of rank, this means that $\mathbf{b}$ is linearly independent of vectors $\mathbf{P}_j$ in $\mathbf{A}$, where $\mathbf{A} = (\mathbf{P}_1, \mathbf{P}_2, \ldots, \mathbf{P}_N)$. This is equivalent to saying that there are no x_j such that

$$\sum_{j=1}^{N} x_j \mathbf{P}_j = \mathbf{b}$$

or there is no $\mathbf{x}$ such that

$$\mathbf{A}\mathbf{x} = \mathbf{b}$$

Therefore, there is no solution to the set of equations. Such equations are said to be *inconsistent*.

Consider the case where $r(\mathbf{A}, \mathbf{b}) = r(\mathbf{A}) = k$. In this case it is easy to show that there is at least one solution to the equations. This argument is left to the reader as an exercise.

We shall now study the equations when $r(\mathbf{A}, \mathbf{b}) = r(\mathbf{A}) = k < M$. It is possible to show [1] that this means there are k independent equations. In other words, all but k equations may be ignored in solving equations (3.2). Any solution to these will satisfy the remaining $M - k$ equations. These equations are said to be *redundant*.

If $r(\mathbf{A}, \mathbf{b}) = r(\mathbf{A}) = M = N$ there is a unique solution as discussed above.

If $r(\mathbf{A}, \mathbf{b}) = r(\mathbf{A}) = k < N$ it can be argued that there are an infinite number of solutions to equations (3.2). This case is of particular interest because the general formulation of the linear programming problem will have this property.

Basic Solutions

Consider a set of M equations, $\mathbf{A}\mathbf{x} = \mathbf{b}$, in N unknowns, $N > M$, where $r(\mathbf{A}) = r(\mathbf{A}, \mathbf{b}) = M$. Choose M linearly independent $\mathbf{P}_j$ from $\mathbf{A}$ and obtain an equation of the form

$$\sum_{j=1}^{M} x_j \mathbf{P}_j = \mathbf{b}$$

where there are some number $d \leq M$ nonzero x_j. The x_j satisfying this equation form a solution called a *basic solution*. If $d = M$, we have a nondegenerate basic solution; in the case $d < M$ we have a degenerate basic solution.

Note that the maximum number of basic solutions for M equations in $N > M$ unknowns is $\binom{N}{M} = N!/M!(N - M)!$ This is significant in that it will indicate that the simplex technique will yield a solution to the linear programming problem in a finite number of steps.

3.4   Mathematical Formulation of the Linear Programming Problem

The general formulation of the linear programming problem may be stated as follows: We wish to find the values of R decision variables such that we maximize or minimize

$$z = \sum_{j=1}^{R} c_j x_j \tag{3.3}$$

subject to the constraints

$$\sum_{j=1}^{R} a_{ij} x_j \left(\begin{matrix} \leq \\ \geq \\ = \end{matrix}\right) b_i \qquad i = 1, \ldots, M \tag{3.4}$$

$$x_j \geq 0 \qquad j = 1, \ldots, R$$

The algebraic formulation above may be restated in vector form

$$\max z = \sum_{j=1}^{R} c_j x_j \tag{3.5}$$

subject to

$$\sum_{j=1}^{R} x_j \mathbf{P}_j \left(\begin{matrix} \leq \\ \geq \\ = \end{matrix}\right) \mathbf{b} \qquad x_j \geq 0 \qquad j = 1, \ldots, R \tag{3.6}$$

where

$$\mathbf{b} = \begin{bmatrix} b_1 \\ \vdots \\ b_N \end{bmatrix} \qquad \mathbf{P}_j = \begin{bmatrix} a_{1j} \\ \vdots \\ a_{Mj} \end{bmatrix}$$

$\mathbf{b}$ is called the *requirements vector*. $\mathbf{P}_j$ is called an *activity vector*. It is possible to generalize this formulation further in matrix form:

$$\max z = \mathbf{c}\mathbf{x} \tag{3.7}$$

subject to

$$\mathbf{A}\mathbf{x} \left(\begin{matrix} \leq \\ \geq \\ = \end{matrix}\right) \mathbf{b} \qquad \mathbf{x} \geq 0 \tag{3.8}$$

where

$$\mathbf{x} = \begin{bmatrix} x_1 \\ \vdots \\ x_R \end{bmatrix} \qquad \mathbf{c} = (c_1, \ldots, c_R) \qquad \mathbf{A} = (\mathbf{P}_1, \ldots, \mathbf{P}_N)$$

$\mathbf{c}$ is called the *price vector*.

We shall call the linear programming problem defined above the problem I formulation.

Slack and Surplus Variables

The problem defined above contained inequalities. In developing solution procedures we shall find it much easier to work with equality constraints. This section is concerned with converting these inequalities to equalities through the use of slack and surplus variables. We shall call the resulting new problem the problem II formulation.

Consider a set of constraints of the form

$$\sum_{j=1}^{R} a_{ij}x_j \le b_i \qquad i = 1, \ldots, P \tag{3.9}$$

We shall define a new variable to add to the left side of inequation (3.9) such that

$$\sum_{j=1}^{R} a_{ij}x_j + x_{R+i} = b_i \qquad i = 1, \ldots, P \tag{3.10}$$

where $x_{R+i} \ge 0$. These new variables are called *slack variables*. The name is derived from the fact that each x_{R+i} represents the difference between the maximum available resource, b_i, and the amount actually used. We shall also add $c_{R+i} = 0$, $i = 1, \ldots, P$ to the price vector. This is done, since it is of no value to have the slack variables have a nonzero value.

Suppose that among the constraints of inequation (3.4) we have constraints of the form

$$\sum_{j=1}^{R} a_{ij}x_j \ge b_i \qquad i = P + 1, \ldots, S \tag{3.11}$$

We shall define a set of new variables to be subtracted from the left side such that

$$\sum_{j=1}^{R} a_{ij}x_j - x_{R+i} = b_i \qquad i = P + 1, \ldots, S \tag{3.12}$$

where $x_{R+i} \ge 0$. These variables are called *surplus variables*. Each x_{P+i}, $i = P + 1, \ldots, S$ represents the amount by which the minimum requirement, b_i, is exceeded. Once again we shall add to the price vector $c_{R+i} = 0$, $i = (P + 1), \ldots, S$.

We may also have, as members of inequation (3.4), constraints of the form

$$\sum_{j=1}^{R} a_{ij}x_j = b_i \qquad i = S + 1, \ldots, M \tag{3.13}$$

However, there is no need to define new variables, because the constraint is already in equality form.

With these definitions we are able to state the problem II formulation of the linear programming problem:

$$\max z = \sum_{j=1}^{N} c_j x_j \tag{3.14}$$

subject to

$$\sum_{j=1}^{N} a_{ij} x_j = b_i \qquad i = 1, \ldots, M \tag{3.15}$$

$$x_j \geq 0 \qquad j = 1, \ldots, N$$

Note that $c_j = 0$ for $j = R + 1, \ldots, N$.

3.5   Geometry of Linear Programming

Linear programming problems involving two variables can be solved graphically. In practice, problems with such a small number of variables rarely occur. However, graphical solution does provide some insight into the mechanics of the simplex technique. On occasion this insight may be generalized to many-variable problems.

The solution process may best be described through the use of an example. Consider the following problem: $\max z = 11x_1 + 4x_2$ subject to

$$7x_1 + 6x_2 \leq 84$$
$$2x_1 + x_2 \leq 16$$
$$x_1, x_2 \geq 0$$

We must find the points in a two-dimensional *solutions space* that satisfy the constraints. These points are described in the $x_1 x_2$ plane by sets of numbers (x_1, x_2). It is immediately apparent that the nonnegativity constraints, $x_1 \geq 0$, $x_2 \geq 0$ restrict our concern to the nonnegative quadrant. Any solution that is feasible must lie in the nonnegative quadrant.

Next we turn to the inequality constraints. Suppose for a moment that the equalities hold. The resulting linear equations are graphed in Figure 3.3. Now consider the points lying below the lines. For example, the point (2, 6) when substituted into the first constraint yields $7(2) + 6(6) = 50 < 84$ and hence satisfies the constraint. When substituting into the second constraint, we find $2(2) + 1(6) = 10 < 16$ and the second constraint is also satisfied. In fact, we could verify that any point in the shaded area satisfies the constraints. We note that this area is a convex set of points in the $x_1 x_2$ plane.

To solve the linear programming problem we must find the point, or points, in the shaded area that maximize the objective function. We shall develop an intuitively based method for accomplishing this graphically. For any fixed value of z, $z = 11x_1 + 4x_2$ is a straight line. Any point on the line will yield the same value of z. Consider the case $z = 20$. The line $20 = 11x_1 + 4x_2$ is plotted in Figure 3.3. Any point in the shaded area lying on the line represents a feasible solution with $z = 20$. Note that as z becomes larger we generate a series of parallel lines. Ultimately we would like to make z as large as possible while still having at least one point in the shaded area lying on the

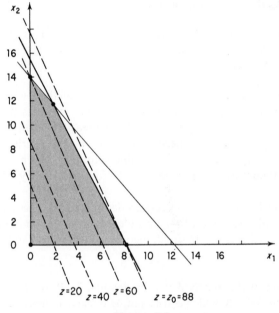

Figure 3.3.

line. The maximum value of the objective function is $z = z_0 = 88$ and occurs at the extreme point $(8, 0)$. We shall see later that optimal solutions to the linear programming problem occur at the extreme points of the convex set of feasible solutions and in searching for these solutions we need only consider these extreme points.

We should point out that graphical solutions are virtually impossible in more than three dimensions. Their discussion here is primarily conceptual and not intended to provide a tool for solution.

3.6   Theory of the Simplex Method

We now turn to a development of the theory of the simplex method. The approach of this section will be to state, discuss, and in some cases prove a sequence of theorems that will lead us to develop a computational scheme for solving linear programming problems. Emphasis will be placed on the mathematical methods required for the algorithm rather than the ultimate computational scheme. The arguments contained in this section will be based primarily on algebra. References to geometry will be used only for intuitive purposes.

For the moment we shall assume the constraints of the linear programming problem given by equations (3.14) and (3.15) are consistent $[r(\mathbf{A}) = r(\mathbf{A, b})]$ and are not redundant $[r(\mathbf{A}) = M]$. Later we shall see that the simplex method checks these assumptions for us.

Theorem: *Given a set of M simultaneous linear equations in N unknowns, $N \geq M$, $\mathbf{Ax} = \mathbf{b}$ with $r(\mathbf{A}) = M$, if there is a feasible solution $\mathbf{x} > 0$, there is a basic feasible solution.*

We have indicated previously that the simplex method will only be concerned with basic feasible solutions. This theorem indicates that there is no case where the linear programming may have a feasible solution and no basic feasible solution. Hence we need not worry about overlooking feasible solutions if we only examine basic feasible solutions. The proof of this and the following theorems in this section may be found in Hadley [3] unless stated otherwise.

At this point in the discussion certain definitions are necessary before we may proceed with the theory. In the problem II formulation of equation (3.8) we have generated a set of M simultaneous equations in N unknowns:

$$\mathbf{Ax} = \mathbf{b} \tag{3.16}$$

The jth column of the matrix $\mathbf{A}$ will be denoted by $\mathbf{P}_j$ for $j = 1, \ldots, N$. We shall define a matrix, $\mathbf{B}$, which consists of M linearly independent columns of $\mathbf{A}$ and hence forms a basis in E^M. $\mathbf{B}$ will be called the *basis matrix*.

Any column of $\mathbf{A}$ can be written as a linear combination of the columns of $\mathbf{B}$:

$$\mathbf{P}_j = y_{1j}\mathbf{P}_1 + y_{2j}\mathbf{P}_2 + \cdots + y_{Mj}\mathbf{P}_M$$

$$= \sum_{i=1}^{M} y_{ij}\mathbf{P}_i \tag{3.17}$$

where $\mathbf{B} = (\mathbf{P}_1, \ldots, \mathbf{P}_M)$.[4] We could write equation (3.17) as a matrix equation,

$$\mathbf{P}_j = \mathbf{B}\mathbf{Y}_j \tag{3.18}$$

where

$$\mathbf{Y}_j = \begin{bmatrix} y_{1j} \\ \vdots \\ y_{Mj} \end{bmatrix}$$

---

[4] We shall assume $\mathbf{B}$ consists of the first M columns of $\mathbf{A}$. This may be done without loss of generality.

We may also solve (3.18) to find

$$\mathbf{Y}_j = \mathbf{B}^{-1}\mathbf{P}_j \tag{3.19}$$

Any basis matrix $\mathbf{B}$ determines a basic solution to $\mathbf{Ax} = \mathbf{b}$. This basic solution is defined by an M-components vector $\mathbf{x}_B$, where

$$\mathbf{Bx}_B = \mathbf{b}$$
$$\mathbf{x}_B = \mathbf{B}^{-1}\mathbf{b} \tag{3.20}$$

The variables, $\mathbf{x}_B$, in the basic solution are called the *basic variables.*

Corresponding to the basic variables in $\mathbf{x}_B$, there is an M-component row vector

$$\mathbf{c}_B = (c_{B1}, \ldots, c_{BM}) \tag{3.21}$$

For any basic feasible solution we have the objective function

$$z = \mathbf{c}_B\mathbf{x}_B$$

We shall also define a new variable that will be useful in the discussion to follow:

$$z_j = y_{1j}c_{B1} + \cdots + y_{Mj}c_{BM}$$
$$= \sum_{i=1}^{M} y_{ij}c_{Bi} = \mathbf{c}_B\mathbf{Y}_j \tag{3.22}$$

Improving a Basic Feasible Solution

Once we obtain a basic feasible solution to the linear programming problem we shall find it necessary to generate new basic feasible solutions. This section is concerned with the development of criteria to choose vectors for removal from, and entry into, the basis.

Suppose we have a basic feasible solution to the linear programming problem of the form

$$\sum_{i=1}^{M} x_{Bi}\mathbf{P}_i = \mathbf{b} \tag{3.23}$$

If we are attempting to maximize the objective function, we would like to be able to find a new basic feasible solution with a larger value of the objective function. We shall attempt to change the basis vectors in the matrix $\mathbf{B}$ only one at a time.

Recall that any one of the vectors not in the basis may be expressed as a linear combination of the basis vectors:

$$\mathbf{P}_j = \sum_{i=1}^{M} y_{ij}\mathbf{P}_i \qquad j = M + 1, \ldots, N \tag{3.24}$$

We should note that, unless defined otherwise, $\mathbf{P}_j$ will usually refer to a vector not in the basis and $\mathbf{P}_i$ will refer to a vector in the basis.

Consider some vector $\mathbf{P}_r$ for which $y_{rj} \neq 0$. Using equation (3.24) we can write

$$\mathbf{P}_j = y_{rj}\mathbf{P}_r + \sum_{\substack{i=1 \\ i \neq r}}^{M} y_{ij}\mathbf{P}_i$$

We may now solve this equation for $\mathbf{P}_r$:

$$\mathbf{P}_r = \frac{1}{y_{rj}}\mathbf{P}_j - \sum_{\substack{i=1 \\ i \neq r}}^{M} \frac{y_{ij}}{y_{rj}}\mathbf{P}_i \tag{3.25}$$

We shall choose some $\mathbf{P}_j$, where at least one $y_{rj} \neq 0$, to insert into the basis and remove $\mathbf{P}_r$ from the basis. It can be easily shown [3] that the vectors $\mathbf{P}_i, i = 1, \ldots, M, i \neq r, \mathbf{P}_j$ are linearly independent and form a basis for E^M. If we substitute equation (3.25) into the basic solution given by equation (3.23), we find

$$\sum_{\substack{i=1 \\ i \neq r}}^{M} x_{Bi}\mathbf{P}_i + \frac{x_{Br}}{y_{rj}}\mathbf{P}_j - x_{Br}\sum_{\substack{i=1 \\ i \neq r}}^{M} \frac{y_{ij}}{y_{rj}}\mathbf{P}_i = \mathbf{b} \tag{3.26}$$

With algebra this reduces to

$$\sum_{\substack{i=1 \\ i \neq r}}^{M} \left(x_{Bi} - x_{Br}\frac{y_{ij}}{y_{rj}}\right)\mathbf{P}_i + \frac{x_{Br}}{y_{rj}}\mathbf{P}_j = \mathbf{b} \tag{3.27}$$

which has the form of a new basic solution. Note that to have feasibility, we must require

$$x_{Bi} - x_{Br}\frac{y_{ij}}{y_{rj}} \geq 0 \qquad i \neq r$$

$$\frac{x_{Br}}{y_{rj}} \geq 0 \tag{3.28}$$

If we assume $x_{Br} \neq 0$, this requires that $y_{rj} > 0$.[5] In the case where all $y_{ij} \leq 0, i \neq r$, the new solution will be feasible. However, if not all $y_{ij} \leq 0$, then we must be careful in choosing a vector $\mathbf{P}_r$ to be removed from the basis. Otherwise, the feasibility requirement of the new basic solution may be violated.

When $y_{ij} > 0$, equation (3.28) reduces to

$$\frac{x_{Bi}}{y_{ij}} - \frac{x_{Br}}{y_{rj}} \geq 0$$

---

[5] The basic solution where $x_B = 0$ is said to be degenerate. The implications of this assumption will be covered later.

Feasibility may be maintained in the new solution if we determine column r of $\mathbf{B}$ to be removed as follows:

$$\frac{x_{Br}}{y_{rj}} = \min_i \left\{ \frac{x_{Bi}}{y_{ij}}, \; y_{ij} > 0 \right\}$$

In this way we assure that feasibility is maintained. We shall define

$$\theta = \frac{x_{Br}}{y_{rj}}$$

We define the new basis matrix as $\hat{\mathbf{B}}$ and the new basic feasible solution as

$$\hat{\mathbf{x}}_B = \hat{\mathbf{B}}^{-1}\mathbf{b}$$

We have shown that these new basic variables have the following form:

$$\hat{x}_{Bi} = x_{Bi} - x_{Br}\frac{y_{ij}}{y_{rj}} \qquad i \neq r$$

$$\hat{x}_{Br} = \frac{x_{Br}}{y_{rj}}$$

Note that θ may not be unique. In this case the new basic solution is degenerate. When $\theta = 0$, this means that $x_{Br} = 0$ or we start with a degenerate solution. In this case

$$\hat{x}_{Bi} = x_{Bi} \qquad i \neq r$$
$$\hat{x}_{Br} = 0$$

Thus the new basic solution is also degenerate.

Note, however, that the new basic solution is not always degenerate if the original one was. If $y_{ij} < 0$ for every $x_{Bi} = 0$, none of the degenerate variables will enter into the computations.

Once we determine a new basic feasible solution we still must discover whether or not the objective is improved. The following theorem will give us a measure to determine whether or not the objective function may be improved further.

Theorem: *Consider a feasible solution* $\mathbf{x}_B = \mathbf{B}^{-1}\mathbf{b}$ *to the set of constraints* $\mathbf{Ax} = \mathbf{b}$ *with the value of the objective function* $z = \mathbf{c}_B\mathbf{x}_B$. *If for any column* $\mathbf{P}_j$ *in* $\mathbf{A}$, *not in* $\mathbf{B}$, *the condition* $z_j - c_j < 0$ *holds, and if at least one* $y_{ij} > 0$, $i = 1, \ldots, M$, *then it is possible to obtain a new basic feasible solution with objective function* $\hat{z}$ *such that* $\hat{z} \geq z$.

PROOF. The value of the original objective function is

$$z = \mathbf{c}_B\mathbf{x}_B = \sum_{i=1}^{M} c_{Bi}x_{Bi} \qquad (3.29)$$

The value of the new objective function is

$$\hat{z} = \hat{c}_B \hat{x}_B = \sum_{i=1}^{M} \hat{c}_{Bi} \hat{x}_{Bi} \tag{3.30}$$

Note that $\hat{c}_{Bi} = c_{Bi}$ for $i \neq r$ and $\hat{c}_{Br} = c_j$. Using these prices and the transformation formulas given by equations (3.28), we may find the new value of the objective function,

$$\hat{z} = \sum_{\substack{i=1 \\ i \neq r}}^{M} c_{Bi}\left(x_{Bi} - x_{Br}\frac{y_{ij}}{y_{rj}}\right) + \frac{x_{Br}}{y_{rj}} c_j \tag{3.31}$$

Note that

$$c_{Br}\left(x_{Br} - \frac{x_{Br}y_{rj}}{y_{rj}}\right) = 0$$

Therefore adding the rth term to the summation above does not change the right side:

$$\hat{z} = \sum_{i=1}^{M} c_{Bi}\left(x_{Bi} - x_{Br}\frac{y_{ij}}{y_{rj}}\right) + \frac{x_{Br}}{y_{rj}} c_j \tag{3.32}$$

With algebra we find

$$\hat{z} = z + \frac{x_{Br}}{y_{rj}} (c_j - z_j) \tag{3.33}$$

$$\hat{z} = z + \theta(c_j - z_j) \tag{3.34}$$

where

$$\theta = \frac{x_{Br}}{y_{rj}}$$

By examining this expression we see that if $z_j - c_j < 0, \hat{z} \geq z$, and the theorem is proved. $c_j - z_j$ may be viewed as the change in z per unit increase in x_j, whereas nonbasic variables are zero and other basic variables adjust as they must to maintain a basic feasible solution. Note that if we are minimizing z, we shall want to substitute a vector $\mathbf{P}_j$ for which $z_j - c_j > 0$.

Unbounded Solutions

In the discussion above, we have assumed that if we inserted a vector $\mathbf{P}_j$ into the basis, there was at least one $y_{ij} > 0$, for $i = 1, \ldots, M$. We shall now examine what happens when all $y_{ij} \leq 0, i = 1, \ldots, M$, when we insert some vector $\mathbf{P}_j$ into the basis.

Suppose we have the basic feasible solution

$$\sum_{i=1}^{M} x_{Bi}\mathbf{P}_i = \mathbf{b}$$

Let us add and subtract $\lambda\mathbf{P}_j$ on the left side:

$$\sum_{i=1}^{M} x_{Bi}\mathbf{P}_i - \lambda\mathbf{P}_j + \lambda\mathbf{P}_j = \mathbf{b} \tag{3.35}$$

where λ is any scalar and $\mathbf{P}_j$ is the vector entering the basis. Note that $\mathbf{P}_j$ may be expressed as a linear combination of the basis vectors,

$$\mathbf{P}_j = \sum_{i=1}^{M} y_{ij}\mathbf{P}_i$$

Substituting this into equation (3.35) we find

$$\sum_{i=1}^{M} x_{Bi}\mathbf{P}_i - \lambda \sum_{i=1}^{M} y_{ij}\mathbf{P}_i + \lambda\mathbf{P}_j = \mathbf{b}$$

Rearranging we find

$$\sum_{i=1}^{M} (x_{Bi} - \lambda y_{ij})\mathbf{P}_i + \lambda\mathbf{P}_j = \mathbf{b} \tag{3.36}$$

Equation (3.36) has the form of a feasible solution to the linear programming problem in $M + 1$ variables. This solution is *not* basic. The objective function of this new feasible solution is

$$\hat{z} = \sum_{i=1}^{M} c_{Bi}(x_{Bi} - \lambda y_{ij}) + c_j\lambda$$

With algebra we find

$$\hat{z} = z + \lambda(c_j - z_j)$$

We can see that when $z_j - c_j < 0$ and all $y_{ij} \leq 0$ we can make λ arbitrarily large and the new objective function will grow without bound. Such a solution is called an *unbounded solution*. In the case of the minimization problem, we could make λ sufficiently small to allow the objective function to become as small as we please.

In conclusion, we see that when some $z_j - c_j < 0$ and all $y_{ij} \leq 0$, $i = 1, \ldots, M$, the linear programming has an unbounded solution. We should note that such solutions are not expected in real-life applications. If the reader is aware of a profit maximization problem where the objective function grows without bound, he is requested to write to the authors immediately with the details of the problem. Unbounded solutions usually occur through some mistake in problem formulation.

Optimality Conditions

Our discussion to this point has indicated when a basic solution may be changed so that the objective function is improved. We have yet to develop a way of determining when the iterative process may be stopped and the optimal solution has been reached. The following theorem will yield the criteria for optimality.

Theorem: *Given a basic feasible solution to the linear programming problem,* $\mathbf{x}_B = (x_{B1}, \ldots, x_{BM})$ *and* $z = z_0$ *such that* $z_j - c_j \geq 0$ *for every* $\mathbf{P}_j$ *in* $\mathbf{A}$, *then* z_0 *is the maximum value of the objective function and* $\mathbf{x}_B$ *is the optimum basic feasible solution.*

The results of this theorem are extremely important because it essentially rounds out the theoretical development of the simplex method. It may be helpful to review the development up to this point. We have shown that given a basic feasible solution that is not optimal, in the absence of degeneracy, we can continue to change a single vector in the basis at a time. No basis can ever be repeated, because the objective function increases at each step and the same basis cannot yield two different values of the objective function. This process can only take a finite number of steps and will terminate in one of two ways:

1. One or more $z_j - c_j < 0$, and for each $z_j - c_j < 0$, $y_{ij} \leq 0$ for all $i = 1, \ldots, M$. In this case we have shown there is an unbounded solution.
2. All $z_j - c_j \geq 0$ for all columns of $\mathbf{A}$. In this case we have shown that we have an optimal basic feasible solution.

Another important result of the theorem is that it states that the optimum solution occurs at a basic feasible solution and hence we need not worry about examining nonbasic solutions in the iterative process.

Degeneracy

Many of the developments in the theory up to this point have assumed the absence of degeneracy. In this section we would like to point out some of the difficulties caused by degeneracy as well as their practical significance. If we recall equation (3.33),

$$\hat{z} = z + \frac{x_{Br}}{y_{rj}}(c_j - z_j)$$

We can see that when degeneracy is present it is possible for the objective function to be unimproved when inserting a new vector into the basis. That is $\hat{z} = z$. This will occur when $x_{Br} = 0$ and $y_{rj} > 0$. If the value of the objective function can remain unchanged, we are not sure that a basis will not be repeated [3]. Consequently, we are not sure that the iterative process will terminate in a finite number of steps. That is, under degeneracy, it is possible to get into a loop or cycle and to continue to repeat a basis.

To resolve degeneracy we must show that a basis need not be repeated. This then would allow us to arbitrarily shift basic feasible solutions away from a degenerate solution. Although the mathematical arguments do exist to show that this is true, they will not be covered here. The practical reason for this is simple: A practical problem, or application, has never been formulated in which the basis repeats itself using the simplex technique.

Those wishing a more detailed discussion of the theory should see Hadley [3].

Alternative Optima

Although the optimal value of the objective function in a linear programming problem is unique, the set of basic variables yielding this optimal value need not be unique. There may be two or more basic feasible solutions that give the same value of the objective function.

Theorem: *If* $x_1, \ldots, x_k$ *are* k *different optimal basic feasible solutions to a linear programming problem, then any convex combination of* $x_1, \ldots, x_k$, *is also an optimal feasible solution.*

PROOF. Assume that $x_1, \ldots, x_k$ are optimal N-component vectors containing all variables, including the nonbasic ones. Consider any convex combination

$$\mathbf{x} = \sum_{i=1}^{k} \mu_i x_i$$

where $\mu_i \geq 0$ and $\sum_{i=1}^{k} \mu_i = 1$. Since all $\mu_i \geq 0$ and all $x_i \geq 0$, $x \geq 0$. Also since $Ax_i = b$ it follows that $Ax = b$. Therefore x is feasible but not necessarily basic. We still must show that x is optimal.

Note that $z_0 = cx_i$. Therefore,

$$cx = \sum_{i=1}^{k} \mu_i cx_i$$

$$= \sum_{i=1}^{k} \mu_i z_0 = z_0$$

Therefore x is also an optimal solution and the theorem is proved.

This theorem shows that if there are two or more optimal basic feasible solutions, there are an infinite number of optimal solutions. Note that not all these optimal solutions will be basic. The following theorem will give some indication of how we may identify alternative optima.

Theorem: *Given an optimal basic feasible solution to the linear programming problem and for some* P_j *not in the basis,* $z_j - c_j = 0, y_{ij} > 0$ *for one* $i = 1, \ldots, M$, *then* P_j *may be inserted into the basis to yield an alternative optimal solution.*

The proof of the theorem is left to the reader as an exercise.

Example: We now have developed enough theory to solve a linear programming problem using an iterative process. Consider the following problem: max $z = 3x_1 + 2x_2$ subject to

$$x_1 + x_2 \leq 4$$
$$x_1 - x_2 \leq 2$$
$$x_1, x_2 \geq 0$$

We shall now outline the step by step procedure for solving the problem.

The reader should recognize that the technique used is not quite the simplex method. Matrix methods are used so that the underlying mathematical operations contained in the method will be apparent. We shall develop more efficient procedures for hand computation later in the discussion.

STEP 1. Add slack variables to obtain the problem II formation: max $z = 3x_1 + 2x_2$ subject to

$$x_1 + x_2 + x_3 \qquad = 4$$
$$x_1 - x_2 \qquad + x_4 = 2$$
$$x_1, \ldots, x_4 \geq 0$$

In terms of our notation,

$$
\begin{array}{cccc}
\mathbf{P}_1 & \mathbf{P}_2 & \mathbf{P}_3 & \mathbf{P}_4 \\
\end{array}
$$
$$
\mathbf{A} = \begin{bmatrix} 1 & 1 & 1 & 0 \\ 1 & -1 & 0 & 1 \end{bmatrix} \qquad \mathbf{b} = \mathbf{P}_0 = \begin{bmatrix} 4 \\ 2 \end{bmatrix}
$$

STEP 2. Find initial basic feasible solution. The unit vectors

$$
\mathbf{P}_3 = \begin{bmatrix} 1 \\ 0 \end{bmatrix} \qquad \mathbf{P}_4 = \begin{bmatrix} 0 \\ 1 \end{bmatrix}
$$

form a basis for E^2. The initial basic feasible solution has the form

$$x_3 \mathbf{P}_3 + x_4 \mathbf{P}_4 = \mathbf{P}_0$$

$$4 \begin{bmatrix} 1 \\ 0 \end{bmatrix} + 2 \begin{bmatrix} 0 \\ 1 \end{bmatrix} = \begin{bmatrix} 4 \\ 2 \end{bmatrix}$$

STEP 3. Express vectors not in basis as function of vectors in basis:

$$\mathbf{P}_1 = \mathbf{P}_3 + \mathbf{P}_4$$
$$\mathbf{P}_2 = \mathbf{P}_3 - \mathbf{P}_4$$

Also

$$z_1 = 0(1) + 0(1) = 0 \qquad z_1 - c_1 = -3$$
$$z_2 = 0(1) + 0(-1) = 0 \qquad z_2 - c_2 = -2$$

STEP 4. Determine vectors to be removed and inserted. Assume we add P_1 to the basis. To determine the vector to be removed, we consider

$$\frac{x_3}{y_{31}} = \frac{4}{1} = 4 \qquad \frac{x_4}{y_{41}} = \frac{2}{1} = 2$$

$$\min_i \left\{ \frac{x_{Bi}}{y_{ij}}, y_{ij} > 0 \right\} = \frac{2}{1} = 2$$

Therefore we remove P_4 if we add P_1. Note, however, that we must examine all possibilities before we decide which vector should be removed and which vector should be inserted.

The change in the objective function if we add P_1 and remove P_4 is

$$\Delta z = \frac{x_r}{y_{rj}} (c_j - z_j) = 6$$

If we add P_2, we may only remove P_3 since $y_{42} \le 0$. In this case

$$\Delta z = \frac{x_r}{y_{rj}} (c_j - z_j) = \frac{4}{1} (2) = 8$$

The maximum change in the objective function is 8. Therefore we shall add P_2 and remove P_3.

STEP 5. Compute a new basic feasible solution. We know that $P_3 = P_2 + P_4$. If we substitute this into the initial basic feasible solution we find

$$4P_2 + 6P_4 = P_0$$

We now proceed as before, expressing vectors not in the basis as functions of vectors in the basis, computing $z_j - c_j$'s, and so on. The example will not be carried further but will be left as an exercise for the reader. Only one additional iteration is required for optimality. The optimal basic feasible solution has $x_1 = 3$, $x_2 = 1$.

3.7 Simplex Method: Computational Algorithm

The previous section has outlined the theoretical developments required for the simplex technique. This section is concerned with using these developments to develop an efficient algorithm for the solution of linear programming problems.

Vector to Enter Basis

In determining a vector to enter the basis, recall that we have developed the following criterion:

$$\frac{x_{Br}}{y_{rk}} (c_k - z_k) = \max_j \left\{ \frac{x_{Br}}{y_{rj}} (c_j - z_j), \qquad z_j - c_j < 0 \right\}$$

We have seen in the example above that to apply this criterion we must compute x_{Br}/y_{rj} for all j in which $z_j - c_j < 0$. These computations were cumbersome in the example and are even more so for a large number of P_j.

The simplex method embodies a slight variation of this method that introduces greater efficiency in computation. The criterion used is one where a vector P_k is chosen to enter the basis such that

$$z_k - c_k = \min_j \{(z_j - c_j), z_j - c_j < 0\} \tag{3.37}$$

Although this is not a method of steepest ascent, computational experience has shown little loss in computational efficiency with a greatly simplified algorithm. We should point out that, in most computer programs, a tie for $\min_j (z_j - c_j)$ is usually broken by choosing the vector with the smallest j index.

Additional Computational Formulas

Assume that for a given basis we insert vector P_k and remove vector P_r. For any P_j we have

$$P_j = \sum_{i=1}^{M} y_{ij} P_i \tag{3.38}$$

In the discussion of the previous section, equation (3.25) gives the expression of P_r as a function of P_i, $i = 1, \ldots, M, i \neq r$, and P_k:

$$P_r = -\sum_{\substack{i=1 \\ i \neq r}}^{M} \frac{y_{ik}}{y_{rk}} P_i + \frac{1}{y_{rk}} P_k$$

Substituting this expression into equation (3.38) we find, with algebra,

$$P_j = \sum_{\substack{i=1 \\ i \neq r}}^{M} \left(y_{ij} - \frac{y_{rj} y_{ik}}{y_{rk}}\right) P_i + \frac{y_{rj}}{y_{rk}} P_k \tag{3.39}$$

This expression expresses any vector P_j as a linear combination of the new basis vectors. That is,

$$P_j = \sum_{i=1}^{M} \hat{y}_{ij} \hat{P}_i$$

where $\hat{P}_i = P_i, i \neq r$, and $\hat{P}_r = P_k$,

$$\hat{y}_{ij} = y_{ij} - \frac{y_{rj} y_{ik}}{y_{rk}} \qquad i \neq r$$

$$\hat{y}_{rj} = \frac{y_{rj}}{y_{rk}} \tag{3.40}$$

Equations (3.40) constitute computational formulas for transformation from old to new y_{ij}'s. Still to be determined are transformation formulas for the new $z_j - c_j$'s. It is easy to see that

$$\hat{z}_j - c_j = \sum_{i=1}^{M} \hat{c}_{Bi} \hat{y}_{ij} - c_j \tag{3.41}$$

where $\hat{c}_{Bi} = c_{Bi}$, $i \neq r$, and $\hat{c}_{Br} = c_k$. If we substitute equation (3.40) into equation (3.41) we have

$$\hat{z}_j - c_j = \sum_{\substack{i=1 \\ i \neq r}}^{M} c_{Bi}\left(y_{ij} - \frac{y_{rj}y_{ik}}{y_{rk}}\right) + \frac{y_{rj}}{y_{rk}} c_k - c_j \tag{3.42}$$

If we note that

$$c_{Br}\left(y_{rj} - y_{rj}\frac{y_{rk}}{y_{rk}}\right) = 0$$

equation (3.42) may be written

$$\hat{z}_j - c_j = \sum_{i=1}^{M} c_{Bi}\left(y_{ij} - \frac{y_{rj}y_{ik}}{y_{rk}}\right) + \frac{y_{rj}}{y_{rk}} c_k - c_j \tag{3.43}$$

With algebra,

$$\hat{z}_j - c_j = z_j - c_j - \frac{y_{rj}}{y_{rk}}(z_k - c_k) \tag{3.44}$$

Flow Chart of Simplex Technique

The simplex technique is shown in Figure 3.4 in block diagram form. All the computational formulas needed to go through the algorithm have been developed in the last two sections.

Initial Basic Feasible Solution

The discussion up to this point has assumed that we have an initial basic feasible solution. In this section we consider general methods for obtaining an initial basis. Suppose that the original problem I formulation contained all $\leq$ constraints. In this case a slack variable is added to each constraint to obtain the problem II formulation.

In the problem II formulation, the matrix $\mathbf{A}$ for the set of constraints $\mathbf{Ax} = \mathbf{b}$ has the form

$$\mathbf{A} = (\mathbf{R}, \mathbf{I})$$

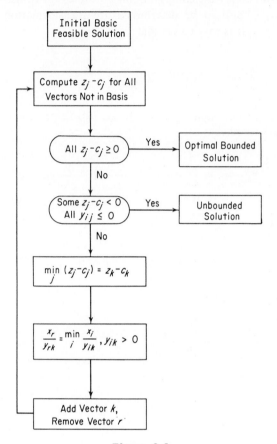

Figure 3.4.

where $\mathbf{I}$ is an mth-order identity matrix. Each column of $\mathbf{I}$ corresponds to a different constraint and a different slack variable. The ith column is a unit vector, $\mathbf{e}_i$, corresponding to the slack variable x_{R+i}. If we write

$$\mathbf{x} = \begin{bmatrix} \mathbf{x}_R \\ \mathbf{x}_S \end{bmatrix}$$

$\mathbf{x}_S$ contains M slack variables and $\mathbf{x}_R$ contains the original R variables. Setting $\mathbf{x}_R = \mathbf{0}$, we have

$$\mathbf{I}\mathbf{x}_S = \mathbf{b} \tag{3.45}$$

This is a basic feasible solution in the slack variables with

$$\mathbf{x}_S = \mathbf{b} \tag{3.46}$$

The solution is feasible since we have assumed $\mathbf{b} \geq \mathbf{0}$. Note that in this solution $\mathbf{B} = \mathbf{I}$ and $\mathbf{B}^{-1} = \mathbf{I}$. Using the definitions above,

$$\mathbf{Y}_j = \mathbf{B}^{-1}\mathbf{P}_j = \mathbf{I}\mathbf{P}_j = \mathbf{P}_j \tag{3.47}$$

$\mathbf{c}_B = \mathbf{0}$, since the prices associated with the slack variables are zero. Therefore, we also find

$$\begin{aligned} z_j - c_j = \mathbf{c}_B\mathbf{Y}_j - c_j = -c_j \\ z = \mathbf{c}_B\mathbf{x}_B = 0 \end{aligned} \tag{3.48}$$

Note that the arguments above hold whenever there is an identity matrix within the matrix $\mathbf{A}$. If some columns do not correspond to slack variables we find, as usual,

$$z_j - c_j = \mathbf{c}_B\mathbf{Y}_j - c_j = \mathbf{c}_B\mathbf{P}_j - c_j \tag{3.49}$$

We cannot assume that, in general, an identity matrix can be found in the matrix $\mathbf{A}$. Usually when the set of constraints contains greater than ($\geq$) or equality ($=$) constraints, an initial identity matrix cannot be found. In this situation there is no easy way of extracting an initial basis from the matrix $\mathbf{A}$. Our discussion now will be concerned with generating an initial identity matrix that will ultimately lead to a legitimate solution to the linear programming problem.

Given the original set of constraints $\mathbf{A}\mathbf{x} = \mathbf{b}$, consider a new set,

$$\mathbf{A}\mathbf{x} + \mathbf{I}\mathbf{x}_a = (\mathbf{A}, \mathbf{I})\begin{bmatrix} \mathbf{x} \\ \mathbf{x}_a \end{bmatrix} = \mathbf{b} \tag{3.50}$$

We have augmented the original variables with M additional variables, x_{ai}, that we shall call *artificial variables*. Corresponding to each x_{ai} there is a unit vector $\mathbf{e}_i$ in the augmented activity matrix.

Since an identity matrix appears in equation (3.50), we immediately have a basic feasible solution to the new set of constraints. Note, however, that this is *not* a feasible solution to the original set of constraints. Any solution to equation (3.50) that is also a feasible solution to the original set of constraints must have $\mathbf{x}_a = \mathbf{0}$. We must concern ourselves with developing a method of moving from the initial solution $\mathbf{x}_a = \mathbf{b}$ to a basic feasible solution for the original problem. Once this is accomplished, the simplex method can be used to find an optimum solution.

Since it is desirable to have $\mathbf{x}_a = \mathbf{0}$ in a feasible solution to the original constraints, we might reason that we could assign prices to each artificial variable which are so unfavorable that the objective function may be improved as long as any one artificial variable remains in the basis. If $\mathbf{z}$ is to be minimized we shall assign a very large positive value to the price of each artificial variable.

Let c_{ai} be the price of the artificial variable, x_{ai}. Then we shall assign the following prices:

$$c_{ai} = -M \qquad M > 0, \quad z \text{ to be maximized}$$
$$c_{ai} = M \qquad\ M > 0, \quad z \text{ to be minimized}$$

M is considered to be a very large number that is usually not specified for hand computations. It is viewed as being large enough so that the price of any nonartificial, or legitimate, variable is negligible when compared to it. In the use of a digital computer, a rule of thumb that may be used is that M is 1000 times the largest price corresponding to a legitimate variable [3].

It may not be necessary to add artificial variables to every constraint to generate an identity matrix within the matrix $\mathbf{A}$. For example, if $\mathbf{e}_i$ appeared in $\mathbf{A}$, then an artificial vector $\mathbf{e}$ would not be added to the augmented matrix.

The methods discussed above will allow us to generate an identity matrix for an initial basis in the solution of a linear programming problem. This is accomplished through the use of artificial variables that must be driven to zero to obtain a feasible solution to the original set of constraints. The simplex method will ultimately lead to an optimal basic feasible solution, if such a solution exists.[6]

Once an artificial vector leaves the basis it is never considered for re-entry. The reader is asked to prove this in the problems at the end of the chapter.

The method of artificial variables discussed in this section is sometimes called the "$-M$ technique." Its use was first suggested by Charnes [3]. In using this technique, there are several aspects that may lead to problems. Most of these are related to roundoff error and to accuracy of the optimal solution. These difficulties have led to the "two-phase method," which is more suitable for use on the digital computer. The development of this method will not be covered here but may be found in reference [2] or [3].

Inconsistency and Redundancy

Recall that we assumed, in our initial development of the simplex method, that $r(\mathbf{A}) = r(\mathbf{A}, \mathbf{b}) = M$. This assumes that there is a basic solution to the problem II formulation. When a slack variable is added to every constraint, it is clear that $r(\mathbf{A}) = r(\mathbf{A}, \mathbf{b}) = M$. Also if we start with an identity matrix in the activity matrix it is obvious that a basic solution exists. The following discussion will attempt to show that, if we start in the augmented system, with one or all artificial variables, we may determine, with the simplex method, whether the original constraints were consistent, and whether any one of the constraints is redundant.

---

[6] We shall see that it is not uncommon to convert one optimization problem into another as we have done above.

Assume there is no unbounded solution. Since no basis is ever repeated, we shall ultimately reach the optimality criterion, $z_j - c_j \geq 0$ for all j. Under these conditions, there are three cases to consider.

CASE 1. There are no artificial vectors in the basis. In this case, we know that an optimal basic feasible solution to the original set of equations has been found and that there is no inconsistency or redundancy.

CASE 2. There are one or more artificial vectors in the basis at a zero level. All artificial variables are zero, so we must have a feasible solution to the original problem. Therefore, the original constraints are consistent. In considering redundancy in this case we consider two alternatives:

(a) Assume that for some j, $y_{ij} \neq 0$, where i corresponds to a column of **B** containing an artificial variable, y_{ij} may be positive or negative. Note that to maintain feasibility when removing a vector $\mathbf{P}_r$ and inserting a vector $\mathbf{P}_k$, $x_r/y_{rk} \geq 0$. If an artificial vector is in the basis at a zero level, we can still remove it and maintain feasibility by inserting vector j. We may repeat this process until we obtain a degenerate basic feasible solution. Hence the constraints are not redundant.

(b) The only way the above procedure will not remove all artificial variables is where $y_{ij} = 0$ for all $\mathbf{P}_j$ and all i corresponding to columns of B having artificial variables. From this it is clear that the artificial vectors are not needed to express any column of **A** in terms of the basis vectors. Suppose that there are k artificial vectors in the basis at the zero level. Then every column of **A** can be written as the linear combination of $m - k$ linearly independent columns of **A**. Therefore, $r(\mathbf{A}) = m - k$, and k of the original constraints are redundant. It can be shown [3], that for those i in which $y_{ij} = 0$ for all j, those constraints are redundant.

CASE 3. There are one or more of the artificial vectors in the basis at a positive level. This indicates there was no feasible solution to the original problem. Otherwise, the artificial variables would be driven to zero. In this case there can either be (a) solutions, but no feasible ones, or (b) the constraints are inconsistent.

Simplex Tableau

Most practical applications of linear programming make use of the digital computer and existing computer programs. The operations performed in these programs are similar to the methods developed in this chapter. Hand computations are frequently needed for better understanding of the problems as well as serving as a check on the computer programs. The use of the matrix methods developed in the simplex method are quite cumbersome. This section is concerned with the use of a tableau and certain mnemonics to allow a greatly simplified hand computation procedure.

The tableau format for an initial basic feasible solution is shown in Table 3.1. The first column of the table indicates the vectors in the basis. The second column, under P_0, gives the value of x_B together with z, the value of the objective function. In the initial tableau, the first M columns, $P_1, \ldots, P_M$ and M rows contain the y_{ij}'s for the initial basis vectors. Note that it has the form of an identity matrix. This is consistent with equation (3.47). The last row under columns $P_1, \ldots, P_M$ contains the $z_j - c_j$'s for the basis vectors. The first m rows under columns $P_{M+1}, \ldots, P_N$ contain the y_{ij}'s for the vectors not in the basis. The last row under these columns contains the $z_j - c_j$'s for the vectors not in the basis.

TABLE 3.1. Initial Tableau for the Simplex Technique

Vectors in Basis	P_0	$P_1 \cdots P_i \cdots P_r \cdots P_M$	$P_{M+1} \cdots P_j \cdots P_k \cdots P_N$
P_1	x_1	$1 \cdots 0 \cdots 0 \cdots 0$	$\cdots y_{1j} \cdots y_{1k} \cdots$
P_i	x_i	$0 \cdots 1 \cdots 0 \cdots 0$	$\cdots y_{ij} \cdots y_{ik} \cdots$
P_r	x_r	$0 \cdots 0 \cdots 1 \cdots 0$	$\cdots y_{rj} \cdots y_{rk} \cdots$
P_M	x_M	$0 \cdots 0 \cdots 0 \cdots 1$	$\cdots y_{Mj} \cdots y_{Mk} \cdots$
—	z	$0 \cdots 0 \cdots 0 \cdots 0$	$\cdots z_j - c_j \cdots z_k - c_k \cdots$

If we decide to remove vector r and insert vector k, we apply computational formulas (3.32), (3.33), (3.40), and (3.44) and obtain the tableau given in Table 3.2. We shall now attempt to develop consistent computational rules that will not require us to remember all the detailed computational formulas. Note that the entire row corresponding to $\hat{P}_r = P_k$ may be found by dividing each member of the rth row of the first tableau by y_{rk}. The number y_{rk} is called the pivot element and is found at intersection of row corresponding to the vector leaving the basis and the column corresponding to the vector entering the basis. The row and column are shown by the dashed lines in Table 3.3. Appropriate values of the remaining basic variables, the objective function, $z_j - c_j$'s, and y_{ij}'s are also shown. We shall now discuss a rule that may be used to find all these values in the new tableau.

TABLE 3.2.   Second Tableau for the Simplex Method

Vectors in Basis		P_0	P_1	P_i	P_r	P_M	P_{M+1}	P_j	P_k	P_N
$\hat{P}_1$	$\hat{x}_1$	1 $\cdots$ 0 $\cdots$		$\hat{y}_{1r} \cdots$	0				0	
$\cdot$	$\cdot$	$\cdot$	$\cdot$	$\cdot$	$\cdot$			$\cdot$		
$\hat{P}_i$	$\hat{x}_i$	0 $\cdots$ 1 $\cdots$		$\hat{y}_{1r} \cdots$	0		$\hat{y}_{ij}$		0	
$\hat{P}_r$	$\hat{x}_r$	0 $\quad$ 0		$\hat{y}_{rr}$	0				1	
$\hat{P}_M$	$\hat{x}_M$	0 $\quad$ 0		$\hat{y}_{Mr}$	1				0	
		0 $\quad$ 0		$\hat{z}_r - c_r$	0		$\hat{z}_j - c_j$	1		

$$\hat{x}_i = x_i - \frac{x_r y_{ik}}{y_{rk}} \qquad \hat{x}_r = \frac{x_r}{y_{rk}} \qquad \hat{z}_j - c_j = (z_j - c_j) - \frac{y_{rj}(z_k - c_k)}{y_{rk}} \qquad \hat{y}_{ij} = y_{ij} - \frac{y_{ik} y_{rj}}{y_{rk}}$$

TABLE 3.3.   Computational Device for the Simplex Technique

Vectors in Basis		P_0	$P_1 \cdots P_i \cdots P_r \cdots P_M$	$P_{M+1} \cdots P_j \cdots P_k \cdots P_N$
P_1	x_1		1 $\cdots$ 0 $\cdots$ 0 $\cdots$ 0	$\cdots y_{1j} \cdots y_{1k} \cdots$
$\cdot$	$\cdot$		$\cdot$ $\cdot$ $\cdot$ $\cdot$	$\cdot$
P_i	x_i		0 $\cdots$ 1 $\cdots$ 0 $\cdots$ 0	$\cdots y_{ij} \longrightarrow y_{ik} \cdots$
P_r	x_r		0 $\cdots$ 0 $\cdots$ 1 $\cdots$ 0	$\cdots y_{rj} \cdots y_{rk} \cdots$
P_M	x_M		0 $\cdots$ 0 $\cdots$ 0 $\cdots$ 1	$\cdots y_{Mj} \cdots y_{Mk}$
—	z		0 $\cdots$ 0 $\cdots$ 0 $\cdots$ 0	$\cdots z_j - c_j \cdots$

Pivot Element

Table 3.1 is reproduced in Table 3.3 to provide assistance with the rule. To find $\hat{y}_{ij}$ we start out in row i, column j, of the old tableau. Write down y_{ij}. Move along row i to column k (corresponding to vector entering the basis). Write $y_{ij} - y_{ik}$. Go back to y_{ij}. Move down column j to row r (corresponding to the vector being removed). Write $y_{ij} - y_{ik}y_{rj}$. Find the pivot element, y_{rk}. Write

$$\hat{y}_{ij} = y_{ij} - \frac{y_{ik}y_{rj}}{y_{rk}}$$

This same device may be used for finding all $\hat{y}_{ij}$'s, $\hat{z}$, $\hat{z}_j - c_j$'s, and $\hat{x}_{Bi}$'s. To understand the technique we shall consider an example solved previously using matrix methods.

Example: We wish to solve the following linear programming problem: max $z = 3x_1 + 2x_2$ subject to

$$
\begin{aligned}
x_1 + x_2 + x_3 \qquad\quad &= 4 \\
x_1 - x_2 \qquad\quad + x_4 &= 2 \\
x_1, \ldots, x_4 &\geq 0
\end{aligned}
$$

The initial tableau is shown in Table 3.4. Using the simplex technique we decide to remove $\mathbf{P}_4$ and insert $\mathbf{P}_1$ into the basis. The pivot element is

TABLE 3.4.   Simplex Tableaux for Sample Problem

shown in tableau 1. Using the computational rule of thumb discussed above generates tableau 2. Sample computations are shown for a $\hat{y}_{ij}$ and a $\hat{z}_j - c_j$ for this tableau. The simplex technique next indicates that $\mathbf{P}_3$ should be removed and $\mathbf{P}_2$ inserted in the basis. Tableau 3 is obtained by applying the computational rules of thumb once again. By examining the row of $z_j - c_j$'s in this tableau we see that an optimal solution has been reached with $x_1 = 3$, $x_2 = 1$, and $z_0 = 12$. By comparing these tableaux with the matrix operations used on the example previously we see that the computational procedure has been greatly simplified.

Revised Simplex Method

The simplex method discussed above, although apparently suitable for hand computations, has proved inefficient for application on the digital computer. The storage of the information contained in the simplex tableau at each iteration has, on occasion, taxed the capacity of the machine. Also successive transformations on each tableau frequently cause problems with roundoff error.

The revised simplex method requires only that a new basis matrix inverse be computed directly at any time, thus doing away with the roundoff problem. Details of this algorithm are beyond the scope of this text. The interested reader is referred to Hadley [3] or Gass [2].

3.8   Duality Theory

The concept of a dual problem formulation has often proved useful in science and engineering. Circuit theory, economics, and game theory are examples of such areas. The dual linear programming problem has been, and continues to be, an important tool in the analysis of linear programming problems and related areas.

Consider a linear programming problem of the following form:

$$\max z = \mathbf{cx} \qquad (3.51)$$

subject to

$$\mathbf{Dx} \le \mathbf{d} \qquad (3.52)$$

$$\mathbf{x} \ge \mathbf{0} \qquad (3.53)$$

where $\mathbf{D} = [d_{ij}]$, $i = 1, \ldots, S$, $j = 1, \ldots, R$.

$$\mathbf{d} = \begin{bmatrix} d_1 \\ \vdots \\ d_S \end{bmatrix} \qquad \mathbf{x} = \begin{bmatrix} x_1 \\ \vdots \\ x_R \end{bmatrix} \qquad \mathbf{c} = (c_1, \ldots, c_R)$$

This problem will be called the *primal problem*. Corresponding to this primal problem there is a *dual problem*, which has the following form:

$$\min g = \mathbf{w}^T \mathbf{d} \qquad (3.54)$$

subject to

$$\mathbf{w}^T \mathbf{D} \geq \mathbf{c} \tag{3.55}$$

$$\mathbf{w}^T \geq \mathbf{0} \tag{3.56}$$

where $\mathbf{w}^T = (w_1, \ldots, w_S)$ is the vector of dual variables. This dual, for the case where the primal has all less than constraints, is sometimes called the *symmetric dual*. The reason for the reference to symmetry will be apparent later in the discussion. It should be noted that while the primal problem had R variables and S constraints, the dual has S variables and R constraints.

The primal–dual relationships may be remembered conveniently by using the following table:

$$
\begin{array}{c}
(x_1 \quad \ldots \quad x_R) \\
\begin{bmatrix} w_1 \\ \vdots \\ w_S \end{bmatrix}
\begin{bmatrix} d_{11} & \ldots & d_{1R} \\ \vdots & & \vdots \\ d_{S1} & \ldots & d_{SR} \end{bmatrix}
\leq
\begin{bmatrix} d_1 \\ \vdots \\ d_S \end{bmatrix} \\
\geq \\
(c_1 \quad \ldots \quad c_R)
\end{array}
\tag{3.57}
$$

The columns of the matrix are the activity vectors for the primal, and the rows are activity vectors for the dual. Primal constraints should be read across the table. Dual constraints should be read down the columns.

Example: Consider the following primal problem: max $z = x_1 + 2x_2$ subject to

$$
\begin{aligned}
2x_1 - 3x_2 &\leq 3 \\
-4x_1 + x_2 &\leq -4 \\
x_1, x_2 &\geq 0
\end{aligned}
$$

The dual problem may be found by reading down the columns of the activity matrix. The requirements vector for the primal becomes the price vector for the dual. The price vector for the primal becomes the requirements vector for the dual: min $g = 3w_1 - 4w_2$ subject to

$$
\begin{aligned}
2w_1 - 4w_2 &\geq 1 \\
-3w_1 + w_2 &\geq 2 \\
w_1, w_2 &\geq 0
\end{aligned}
$$

Theorem: *The dual of the dual is the primal.*

The theorem is self-explanatory. Proof is left to the reader as an exercise.

We now consider another form of a primal problem:

$$\max z = \mathbf{c}\mathbf{x} \tag{3.58}$$

subject to

$$\mathbf{Dx} = \mathbf{d} \tag{3.59}$$

$$\mathbf{x} \geq \mathbf{0} \tag{3.60}$$

Note that we may write the constraints of equation (3.59) as two inequalities,

$$\mathbf{Dx} \leq \mathbf{d} \qquad \mathbf{Dx} \geq \mathbf{d}$$

Equivalently, we may require

$$\mathbf{Dx} \leq \mathbf{d} \tag{3.61}$$

$$(-\mathbf{D})\mathbf{x} \leq (-\mathbf{d}) \tag{3.62}$$

Thus we may formulate a new primal consisting of equations (3.58), (3.61), (3.62), and (3.60). Using the definition of a symmetric dual, we can easily show that the dual is min $g = \mathbf{u}^T \mathbf{d} + \mathbf{v}^T(-\mathbf{d})$ subject to

$$\mathbf{u}^T \mathbf{D} + \mathbf{v}^T(-\mathbf{D}) \geq \mathbf{c}$$
$$\mathbf{u}^T, \mathbf{v}^T \geq \mathbf{0}$$

If we rewrite these equations we obtain min $g = (\mathbf{u} - \mathbf{v})^T \mathbf{d}$ subject to

$$(\mathbf{u} - \mathbf{v})^T \mathbf{D} \geq \mathbf{c}$$
$$\mathbf{u}, \mathbf{v} \geq \mathbf{0}$$

Let $\mathbf{w} = \mathbf{u} - \mathbf{v}$ and obtain the following dual problem:

$$\min g = \mathbf{w}^T \mathbf{d} \tag{3.63}$$

subject to

$$\mathbf{w}^T \mathbf{D} \geq \mathbf{c}$$
$$\mathbf{w}^T \text{ unrestricted}$$

It is important to note that $\mathbf{w}^T$ is unrestricted, because $\mathbf{u}^T$ and $\mathbf{v}^T$ are constrained to nonnegative values and hence their difference can be either positive or negative. We see that if the primal constraints are in equality form the dual variables are unrestricted in sign. The problem is called the *unsymmetric dual problem.*

As a special case of the symmetric dual problem consider the following primal:

$$\max z = \mathbf{cx} \tag{3.64}$$

subject to

$$\mathbf{Dx} \geq \mathbf{d}$$
$$\mathbf{x} \geq \mathbf{0}$$

We can rewrite the problem as follows:

$$\max z = \mathbf{cx} \tag{3.65}$$

subject to

$$(-\mathbf{D})\mathbf{x} \leq (-\mathbf{d})$$
$$\mathbf{x} \geq \mathbf{0}$$

By using the definition of the symmetric dual we may define the following dual problem:

$$\min g = \mathbf{u}^T(-\mathbf{d}) \tag{3.66}$$

subject to

$$\mathbf{u}^T(-\mathbf{D}) \geq \mathbf{c}$$
$$\mathbf{u} \geq \mathbf{0}$$

If we let $\mathbf{w} = -\mathbf{u}$, we obtain the equivalent problem:

$$\min g = \mathbf{w}^T\mathbf{d} \tag{3.67}$$

subject to

$$\mathbf{w}^T\mathbf{D} \geq \mathbf{c}$$
$$\mathbf{w}^T \leq \mathbf{0}$$

It is interesting to note that the form of the dual objective function and constraints are independent of the form of the primal constraints. The only thing that varies in the dual formulation is the condition on the dual variables, which depends on whether the primal constraints were greater than, less than, or equality constraints.

If the primal contains a mixture of constraints, it is not difficult to prove the dual has the following properties: (1) The objective function and constraints have the same form as above, (2) dual variables corresponding to less than primal constraints are constrained to be nonnegative, (3) dual variables corresponding to primal equality constraints are unrestricted in sign, and (4) dual variables corresponding to greater than primal constraints are restricted to nonpositive values.

Example: Consider the following primal problem:

$$\max z = 3x_1 + x_2 + x_3 - x_4 \tag{3.68}$$

subject to

$$
\begin{aligned}
x_1 + x_2 + 2x_3 + 3x_4 &\leq 5 \\
x_1 - x_2 \quad\quad\quad &= -1 \\
x_3 - \quad x_4 &\geq -1 \\
x_1, x_2, x_3, x_4 &\geq 0
\end{aligned}
$$

The dual problem is:

$$\min g = 5w_1 - w_2 - w_3 \tag{3.69}$$

subject to

$$
\begin{aligned}
w_1 + w_2 \quad\quad &\geq 3 \\
w_1 - w_2 \quad\quad &\geq 1 \\
2w_1 \quad + w_3 &\geq 1 \\
3w_1 \quad - w_3 &\geq -1
\end{aligned}
$$

$$w_1 \geq 0 \quad\quad w_2 \text{ unrestricted} \quad\quad w_3 \leq 0$$

With the definitions above it is possible to derive many useful relationships that may be used in solving linear programming problems. The relationships between the primal and dual continue to be useful in the development of mathematical programming algorithms. The following theorem, sometimes called the *fundamental dual theorem*, provides the basic foundation for duality in linear programming.

Theorem: (a) *The primal has an optimum finite solution if and only if the dual has an optimum finite solution, in which case* max z = min g. (b) *If the primal has an unbounded solution the dual has no feasible solution.* (c) *If the dual has an unbounded solution, the primal has no feasible solution.* (d) *Both problems may be unfeasible.*

The proof of the theorem is left to the problems at the end of the chapter and further reading [3]. Embodied in these arguments is an explicit definition of a solution to the dual which will prove useful.

Suppose we define, for an optimal basis **B**,

$$\mathbf{w}^T = \mathbf{c}_B \mathbf{B}^{-1} \tag{3.70}$$

The proof of part (a) of the theorem shows that equation (3.70) is an optimal feasible solution to the dual.

Recall that for slack and artificial variables

$$z_j - c_j = z_j = \mathbf{c}_B \mathbf{B}^{-1} \mathbf{P}_j$$

For the ith slack variable, $\mathbf{P}_i$ is a unit vector $\mathbf{e}_i$. Therefore,

$$\mathbf{c}_B \mathbf{B}^{-1} \mathbf{P}_i = \mathbf{c}_B \mathbf{B}^{-1} \mathbf{e}_i = w_i \tag{3.71}$$

where w_i is the ith dual variable. Thus the $z_j - c_j$'s for the slack vectors in an optimal solution to the primal are the values of the corresponding optimal dual variables.

If the primal contained greater than or equal to constraints, assume one artificial variable was added for each such constraint. For the ith artificial variable $\mathbf{P}_j$ is a unit vector $\mathbf{e}_i$. In the same way it is easy to show that the z_j's for the artificial vectors in an optimal solution to the primal are the corresponding optimal dual variables.

As an example of these relationships consider the optimal simplex tableau for the example of Section 3.7: $z_3 - c_3 = z_3 = w_1 = 3$ and $z_4 - c_4 = z_4 = w_2 = 1$. Thus we see that it is possible to read an optimal dual solution directly from the optimal primal tableau.

Complementary Slackness

We shall consider a further effort to relate the primal and dual formulations of the linear programming problem. The following two theorems show the intimate relation between primal and dual. Consider a primal of the form given by equations (3.51), (3.52), and (3.53).

Theorem: *A necessary and sufficient condition for any pair of feasible solutions to the primal and dual to be optimal is that*

$$w_i x_{R+i} = 0 \qquad i = 1, \ldots, S$$

where x_{R+i} is the ith slack variable in the primal, and

$$x_j w_{S+j} = 0 \qquad j = 1, \ldots, R$$

where w_{S+j} is the jth surplus variable for the dual.

The proof of the two theorems may be found in Hadley [3]. The first theorem indicates that if the ith primal constraint does not hold as an equality, then $w_i = 0$. The reason for the term complementary slackness can be seen if we write the primal and dual constraints in the following form:

$$\mathbf{Dx} \le \mathbf{d} \qquad \mathbf{x} \ge \mathbf{0}$$
$$\mathbf{w}^T \mathbf{D} \ge \mathbf{c}^T \qquad \mathbf{w} \ge \mathbf{0}$$

Assume that the constraints are numbered in the order shown. The theorem indicates that, at optimality, if the primal constraint holds as a strict inequality, then its complementary dual constraint holds as an equality. Conversely, if a dual constraint holds as a strict inequality, its complementary primal constraint holds as an equality.

Problems

1. Using the simplex method, solve the following linear programming problem. Do not use a tableau. Use only matrix algebra.

$$\max z = 5x_1 + 3x_2$$

subject to

$$3x_1 + 5x_2 \le 15$$
$$5x_1 + 2x_2 \le 10$$
$$x_1, x_2 \ge 0$$

2. Use the simplex tableau to solve the following linear programming problem.

$$\max z = 2x_1 + x_2 + 4x_3$$

subject to

$$x_1 + x_2 + x_3 \le 800$$
$$x_1 + x_2 + x_3 \le 400$$
$$x_1 + 2x_2 \ge 200$$
$$x_1, x_2, x_3 \ge 0$$

3. Use the simplex method to solve the following:

$$\max z = x_1 + x_2 + 3x_3 + 2x_4$$

subject to

$$x_1 + 3x_2 + x_3 + 4x_4 \leq 20$$
$$x_1 + 8x_2 + x_3 + x_4 \geq 2$$
$$-3x_1 + 2x_2 + 5x_3 - 10x_4 \geq 10$$
$$x_1, \ldots, x_4 \geq 0$$

4. Use the simplex tableau to solve the following problem. Is there a unique solution? Why?

$$\max z = 6x_1 + 4x_2$$

subject to

$$2x_1 + 3x_2 \leq 30$$
$$3x_1 + 2x_2 \leq 24$$
$$x_1 + x_2 \geq 3$$
$$x_1, x_2 \geq 0$$

5. Solve the following linear programming problem. Formulate the dual. Solve the dual. How many tableaux does each solution take? What rationale would you use in deciding to solve the dual or the primal?

$$\min z = 80x_1 + 60x_2 + 80x_3$$

subject to

$$x_1 + 2x_2 + 3x_3 \geq 4$$
$$2x_1 + 3x_3 \geq 3$$
$$2x_1 + 2x_2 + x_3 \geq 4$$
$$4x_1 + x_2 + x_3 \geq 6$$
$$x_1, x_2, x_3 \geq 0$$

6. Show a graphical example, in solutions space, of a linear programming problem with more than one optimal solution.

7. Linear programming problems may be displayed in a requirements space consisting of the activity and requirements vectors. In Problem 1, draw members of the basis and the requirements vector in a two-dimensional space for each iteration. What is the relationship of the requirements vector to the activity vectors in each case?

8. Consider the following equations:

$$x_1 + 2x_2 + x_3 + 3x_4 = 20$$
$$2x_1 + x_2 + x_3 + 2x_4 = 15$$

A feasible solution is $x_1 = 2$, $x_2 = 5$, $x_3 = 2$, and $x_4 = 2$. Reduce this feasible solution to a basic feasible solution.

9. Find the dual of the following problems:

(a) $\max z = 4x_1 + 6x_2 + 7x_3 + 2x_4$

subject to

$$x_1 + x_2 + x_4 \geq 5$$
$$2x_1 + x_3 + x_4 \geq 7$$
$$x_2 + 3x_3 + x_4 \geq 1$$
$$x_1, \ldots, x_4 \geq 0$$

$$(b) \quad \max z = 10x_1 + 5x_2 - 3x_3 + 4x_4$$

subject to

$$x_1 + 3x_2 + 4x_3 + 5x_4 \geq 21$$
$$2x_1 + 3x_2 + 4x_3 - 5x_4 \geq 5$$
$$4x_1 + 7x_2 - 2x_3 - 2x_4 = 12$$
$$x_1, \ldots, x_4 \geq 0$$

10. Consider the following linear programming problem:

$$\max z = 2x_1 + x_2$$

subject to

$$4x_1 + 3x_2 \leq 24$$
$$3x_1 + 5x_2 \leq 15$$
$$x_1, x_2 \geq 0$$

(a) Solve the problem graphically in solutions space.
(b) Use matrix methods with the simplex method to find the optimal solution; do not use a tableau.
(c) Draw all bases in part (b) in requirements space.

11. Using only the definition of a symmetric dual problem find the dual of the following:

$$\max z = \mathbf{cx}$$

subject to

$$\mathbf{Ax} = \mathbf{b}$$
$$\mathbf{x} \text{ unrestricted}$$

12. Discuss the situation where the following statement is not true: A solution to a linear programming problem (maximization) is optimal and finite if and only if $z_j - c_j \geq 0$.

13. Consider the primal problem

$$\max z = \mathbf{cx}$$

subject to

$$\mathbf{Ax} = \mathbf{b}$$
$$\mathbf{x} \geq 0$$

Suppose that we multiply the kth constraint by the scalar $\lambda \neq 0$. If $\mathbf{w}^T$ is an optimal solution to the dual of Problem 12, derive, in a rigorous manner, the optimal solution to the dual of the primal problem whose kth constraint is multiplied by λ.

14. Prove that the set of all feasible solutions to a linear programming problem is a convex set.

15. Show that, when using the simplex method, any vector that is removed at one iteration cannot re-enter the basis at the next iteration.

16. Prove that a necessary and sufficient condition for the primal to have an optimum finite solution is that the dual have an optimum finite solution where $\max z = \min g$.

17. Prove the following: If the primal has an unbounded solution, the dual has no feasible solution.

18. Prove the converse of Problem 17: If the dual has an unbounded solution, the primal has no feasible solution.

19. Give an example to show that both primal and dual problems may be unfeasible.

20. Find the optimal dual solution to Problem 1. Use only matrix algebra.

21. Is the dual solution corresponding to an initial primal solution necessarily feasible? Under what conditions would this be true?

22. Develop an argument showing where the dual $z_j - c_j$'s are found in a primal tableau.

23. What economic interpretation may be given to the dual variables? How does this relate to the Lagrange multiplier discussed in Chapter 2?

24. What are the Kuhn-Tucker conditions for Problem 1? How do these relate to the complementary slackness conditions?

25. Consider the following linear programming problem

$$\max z = 2x_1 + x_2$$

subject to

$$x_1 + x_2 \leq 4$$
$$3x_1 + x_2 \leq 10$$
$$x_1, x_2 \geq 0$$

(a) State the dual problem.
(b) Using your knowledge of duality, write a set of necessary and sufficient conditions for the problem to have an optimal solution.
(c) Write the Kuhn-Tucker conditions for the problem. Compare these conditions to those in (b).

References Cited and Bibliography

[1] Hadley, G. *Linear Algebra.* Reading, Mass.: Addison-Wesley, 1961.
[2] Gass, S. *Linear Programming*, 2nd ed. New York: McGraw-Hill, 1964.
[3] Hadley, G. *Linear Programming.* Reading, Mass.: Addison-Wesley, 1962.

CHAPTER **4**

Nonlinear Programming

4.1   Introduction

In Chapter 3 we considered optimization techniques for linear problems. Because of linearity we were able to develop a very efficient algorithm for handling such problems. Unfortunately no such general algorithms exist for solving all nonlinear optimization problems. However, for problems with certain identifiable structures efficient algorithms have been developed. In addition, it is often possible to transform the given nonlinear problem into one in which these structures become apparent.

The general statement of the nonlinear programming problem is: $\max f(\mathbf{x})$ subject to

$$g_i(\mathbf{x}) \begin{pmatrix} \leq \\ = \\ \geq \end{pmatrix} 0 \qquad i = 1, \ldots, M$$

$$\mathbf{x} \geq \mathbf{0}$$

Before we discuss algorithms for solving nonlinear programming problems, with at least one of the functions being nonlinear, we shall mention several algorithms for solving unconstrained problems. These algorithms are based on the direct approach to optimization. Recall that this approach involves making local observations of the objective function, and then based on the information gleaned from these observations moving in a direction that appears promising. This procedure is different from the indirect approach, which involves constructing conditions that must be satisfied at the optimal solution. The construction of such conditions was discussed in Chapter 2. In this chapter we shall discuss computational aspects of nonlinear optimization problems.

100

4.2   Direct Methods

A large number of direct methods have been developed for optimizing unconstrained functions. Many of the techniques require assumptions such as continuity, whereas others require existence of first and/or second derivatives. No attempt will be made to cover exhaustively the algorithms that have been developed. Rather we shall choose a few of the ones that appear most promising intuitively and attempt to discuss their relative merits and demerits. For a more complete discussion of various techniques we refer the reader to the book *Optimum Seeking Methods* by Wilde [1].

Before launching into the first of these algorithms it will be helpful to define various concepts that we shall need. The first concept is that of unimodality. Roughly speaking, unimodality means that there is only one peak. The function has only one mode. Consider, for example, the function $f(\cdot)$ of one variable x, $a \leq x \leq e$, which is pictured in Figure 4.1.

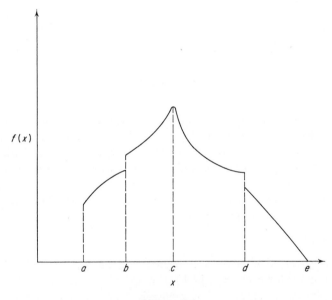

Figure 4.1.

The function has discontinuities at b and d, is continuous for all $b < x < d$, is differentiable everywhere in $b < x < d$ except at c, and has its maximum at c. This function is unimodal. As one can see, unimodality is a more general concept than convexity or concavity. A function that is concave is unimodal, but the converse is not necessarily true.

One must be careful in the definition of unimodality to specify if the function is unimodal with respect to a maximum or minimum. As an example, the function shown in Figure 4.1 is unimodal with respect to a maximum. However, it has a local minimum at a and a global minimum at e. Figure 4.2 shows a function that is unimodal with respect to a minimum.

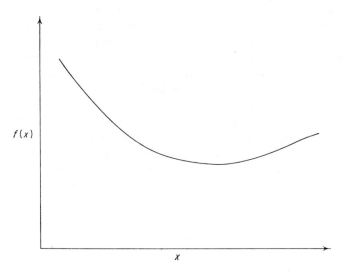

Figure 4.2.

A function may be unimodal in some interval while having several peaks in some larger interval. The function pictured in Figure 4.3 is unimodal with respect to a minimum in the interval $a \leq x \leq c$, unimodal with respect to a maximum for $b \leq x \leq d$, and unimodal with respect to a minimum when $c \leq x \leq e$.

We shall define unimodality with respect to a minimum. The corresponding definition for a maximum is similar.

Unimodality

A function, $f(\mathbf{x})$, defined for $\mathbf{x}$ in the interval $[\mathbf{a}, \mathbf{b}]$, is *unimodal* with respect to a minimum if for every $\mathbf{x}$ in $[\mathbf{a}, \mathbf{b}]$ there exists a curve from $\mathbf{x}$ to $\mathbf{x}^0$ along which the function decreases monotonically, where $\mathbf{x}^0$ is the value of $\mathbf{x}$ that minimizes $f(\mathbf{x})$.

It is clear why we are interested in unimodal functions. If we are assured that a given function is unimodal, we can derive direct methods that guarantee convergence to a point $\mathbf{x}^*$ and establish that the point $\mathbf{x}^*$ to which we converge yields the optimal solution, $\mathbf{x}^* = \mathbf{x}^0$. If a function has more than one peak, then the point to which we converge will depend on the starting point—a result that leaves something to be desired. An example of such a situation is shown in Figure 4.4.

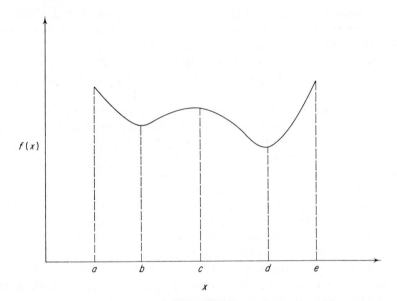

Figure 4.3.

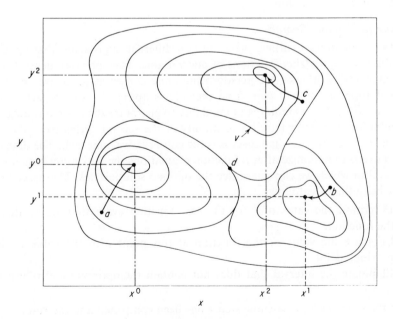

Figure 4.4.

If we begin our exploration at point b and follow a strictly rising path, we converge to (x^1, y^1), and if we start at c we converge to (x^2, y^2). Notice that if we start at point d it is possible that we might converge to any one of the three local maxima while following a strictly rising path. Clearly we would prefer to converge to the point (x^0, y^0), because it yields a higher value of the objective function than the other local maxima.

One might question whether it would be acceptable from a computational point of view to choose a large number of starting points for a given problem and select the best result from among all the outcomes. The reason we prefer to avoid such an approach whenever possible is that there is usually a cost associated with carrying out each exploration. Thus, if we are solving a problem on the computer and using direct methods to obtain the maximum, the number of computations and, therefore, the computing time is related to the number of different starting points. One might desire to minimize the number of function evaluations and still guarantee the attainment of the maximum. An alternative objective is to minimize with a given number of function evaluations the size of the region that contains the maximum. Naturally the strategy one chooses will dictate the outcome. Both of the above-mentioned objectives have been employed successfully.

Direct methods fall naturally into two categories. Those associated with optimizing functions of one variable and methods developed for functions of several variables. We shall concentrate first on those suitable primarily for single variables and discuss direct methods for functions of several variables in the succeeding section.

Single-Variable Search

As we mentioned earlier, there are two different approaches that appear useful when optimizing functions of one variable. The approach depends on the explorer's outlook—the person being more conservative (or pessimistic) would adopt a different plan from that of his optimistic counterpart. Each plan we shall discuss requires unimodality to guarantee the desired outcome. In addition, the latter requires continuity of the second derivative.

The first scheme we shall discuss is the conservative approach. The desired objective is to minimize after n function evaluations the maximum remaining interval in which we can guarantee the optimal solution lies. The procedure may be outlined as follows:

1. Determine the value of x for the next function evaluation and evaluate the function.
2. Compare the value of the function at this point with the value at the previous point.
3. Eliminate the interval that does not contain the optimum and return to step 1.

For the moment let us assume step 1 has been completed and the results are shown in Figure 4.5.

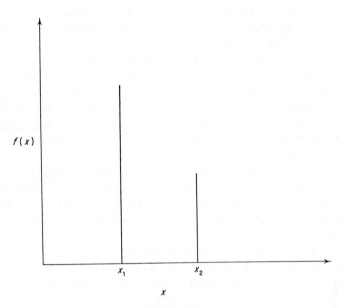

Figure 4.5.

If we are looking for a maximum the interval to the right of x_2 may be eliminated, since we have assumed the function is unimodal. Given the location of the two values of x, x_1, and x_2, the maximum may be contained in one of the three intervals, $x^* \leq x_1$, $x_1 \leq x^* \leq x_2$, and $x_2 \leq x^*$. Suppose

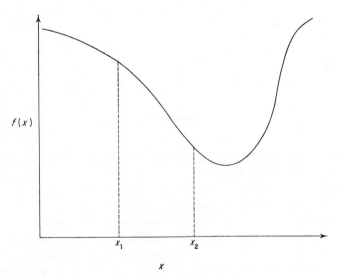

Figure 4.6.

we have the function evaluated at x_1 and x_2 and the outcome is as shown in
Figure 4.5. We can argue conclusively that the maximum does not lie in the
interval $x \geq x_2$. Suppose the maximum did occur at some x, say $x \geq x_2$.
Then the curve would be similar to the one in Figure 4.6.

Since we have assumed unimodality there exists a strictly rising curve from
every point x to the maximum. In particular, from point x_1 there is a monotonically increasing curve to x^*. However, we can see that the function
decreases to the right of x_1 and thus there is no strictly rising path to the
maximum. This contradicts our unimodality assumption. Thus the maximum
cannot lie to the right of x_2.

We have seen how to eliminate parts of the line segment to reduce the
interval in which we can guarantee the optimal solution lies. What we
desire to do is to make this interval "the interval of uncertainty," remaining
as small as possible after n function evaluations, that is, minimize the maximum interval of uncertainty.

To solve this problem we shall start with an interval of uncertainty, I, in
which we have one function evaluation at the point x_j. We now must decide
at which point x_{j+1} the next function evaluation is to be made.

Lemma: *The point x_{j+1} is placed symmetrically in the remaining interval.*

PROOF. There are two possible intervals of uncertainty, I to x_{j+1} and x_j
to I_1, where I_0 is the left end point of the interval and I_1 is the right point.
These possibilities are illustrated in Figure 4.7.

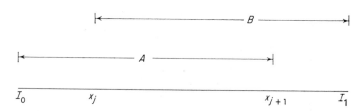

Figure 4.7.

The interval of uncertainty that remains will depend on the relative values
of $f(x_j)$ and $f(x_{j+1})$; that is, if $f(x_j) > f(x_{j+1})$, then A is the remaining interval
of uncertainty, because we have shown previously that x^* cannot be contained
in $[x_{j+1}, I_1]$ under these circumstances. Conversely, if $f(x_j) < f(x_{j+1})$, the
new interval becomes B. Unfortunately we cannot say a priori which will be
larger. Thus the maximum interval of uncertainty that remains is max $[A, B]$,
and we wish to choose x_{j+1} to minimize this maximum interval. We shall
show that at the optimal solution $A = B$. Suppose $B < A$, as shown in the
diagram, is the interval of uncertainty that remains if $f(x_j) < f(x_{j+1})$. If we

decrease x_{j+1} by ϵ then we can decrease the interval of uncertainty to $A - \epsilon$, and thus the placement of x_{j+1} is not optimal. A similar argument can be obtained for the other possibility when $x_{j+1} - I_0 < I_1 - x_j$. The only condition under which no improvement can be made is when $A = B$, $(x_{j+1} - I_0 = I_1 - x_j)$, and thus this arrangement is optimal.

We have now reduced the problem of minimizing the interval in which the optimal solution lies to one of locating the first point at which to evaluate the function. Each succeeding point is placed symmetrically in the remaining interval with respect to the point already contained in the interval. Thus we have transformed one optimization problem into another—a not uncommon occurrence.[1] Notice that the optimal solution to this problem depends on

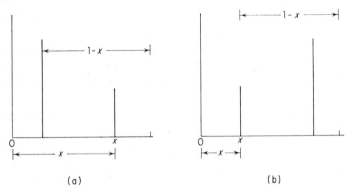

Figure 4.8.

the number of explorations (function evaluations) one is allowed to make. We shall develop the decision rule when we have two, three, and four evaluations to make. Hopefully a pattern will develop and we shall be able to generalize from these limited results to the general case.

Consider the problem of reducing the interval of uncertainty with only two explorations. As we mentioned above, *the problem is one of locating the first point, because the second is placed symmetrically*. We lose no generality if we normalize the original interval so that its length is 1. Suppose we locate the first point at $0.5^2 \leq x \leq 1$. The remaining point will be placed symmetrically in the remaining interval, at $1 - x$. The possible results are shown in Figure 4.8. The interval of uncertainty will be either $[0, x]$ or $[1 - x, 1]$, depending on the relative values of $f(x)$ evaluated for each of the two points. Since

---

[1] Recall that a similar result was obtained in Chapter 2 when we derived sufficient conditions for equality-constrained problems.

[2] No generality is lost if we require 0.5, because we can initiate the search x units away from either end.

we cannot conclude beforehand which result will occur, we choose the maximum of these, using our conservative criteria. What we would like to do is choose x to minimize this maximum:

$$\min_{0 \le x \le 1} \max [x, 1 - x]$$

The proper choice is clearly for x to be 0.5, because this minimizes the maximum. Notice that this result requires the placement of the first experiment at 0.5 and the second at $1 - 0.5$, which means that both are placed at the same point and no comparisons are possible. However, if we require that the distance between the two points be ϵ, we obtain the result that $x = 0.5 - (\epsilon/2)$ and the interval then becomes $0.5 + (\epsilon/2)$ instead of 0.5.

Now let us turn our attention to the case where three function evaluations are available. Suppose we place the first point at $x \le 0.5$.[3] After placing the second point, the remaining interval has length $1 - x$ with a point located x units away from one end of the interval. Since we must be symmetrical, the final point is placed x units away from the opposite end of the remaining interval. Thus the final interval will be the maximum of the two quantities $[x, 1 - 2x]$. We must choose x to minimize this maximum, which leads to $x = \frac{1}{3}$. Again we notice that our rule will call for two function evaluations to coincide—either at $\frac{1}{3}$ or $\frac{2}{3}$. If ϵ is small, we might just separate the two final points by ϵ, with the resulting interval of uncertainty being $\frac{1}{3} + \epsilon$.[4]

One might be tempted now to generalize and say that because, when $n = 2$ we located the first point at $\frac{1}{2}$ and when $n = 3$ the first point is located at $\frac{1}{3}$, then when four explorations are possible the first experiment should be at $\frac{1}{4}$. In fact, we can do better than this, as is illustrated below. Suppose we place the first point at x units from 0. The second point must be located $1 - x$ units from 0 by symmetry. The resulting interval of uncertainty is $1 - x$ (if $x \le 0.5$). The third point must be located x units away from one end point of the interval. The resulting interval of uncertainty is either $1 - 2x$ (if $x \le \frac{1}{3}$) or x (if $x \ge \frac{1}{3}$). If the interval is $1 - 2x$, we have an experiment located x units away from one end so by symmetry we locate the remaining experiment x units from the other end and the resulting interval is the largest of x and $1 - 3x$. If, on the other hand, the interval is x, we have a point located at $1 - 2x$. The final point is located symmetrically in the interval and the result is an interval that has maximum length of either $1 - 3x$ or $1 - 2x$. In the first case, the optimal choice is $x = 0.25$, but in the latter $x = 0.4$ is best. The resulting interval of uncertainty in each case is 0.25 and 0.2. Clearly the one that yields 0.2 is optimal and thus the location of the first point occurs at $x = 0.4$.

---

[3] No generality is lost if we require 0.5, because we can initiate the search x units away from either end.

[4] Wilde [1] contains a refinement of this approach that allows the final interval to be $\frac{2}{3}\epsilon$ smaller.

We have the results for three cases. When $n = 2$, $x = \frac{1}{2}$, for $n = 3$, $x = \frac{1}{3}$, and for $n = 4$, $x = \frac{2}{5}$. Notice that the numerator in the case when $n = 4$ is the sum of the numerators from the two previous cases, and the denominator is also the sum of the two preceding denominators. This sequence is called the Fibonacci sequence—where the current value is the sum of the two preceding ones.

The first eight Fibonacci numbers, F_n, are shown below:

n	0	1	2	3	4	5	6	7	8
F_n	1	1	2	3	5	8	13	21	34

There is an interesting relationship between the Fibonacci numbers and the location of the first experiment: If we have n observations the first should be located at $x = F_{n-1}/F_n$. We have shown this result for $n = 2$, 3, and 4. The extension to the general case becomes very cumbersome using this mode of proof—for an alternative presentation see Wilde's book *Optimum Seeking Methods*. Wilde also shows that the optimum final interval, h_n^*, is inversely related to the nth Fibonacci number,

$$h_n^* = \frac{1}{F_n} \tag{4.1}$$

when the original interval is of unit length.

A Curve-Fitting Approach

The second procedure we shall discuss is a very simple one but it is restricted to functions that are twice-differentiable. It involves approximating the function $f(x)$ by a quadratic equation,

$$f(x) = a + bx + cx^2 \tag{4.2}$$

We need three pieces of information to determine the values of the coefficients. For example, if we evaluate $f(x)$ at $x = 0$ we have obtained a value for a since

$$f(x = 0) = a + b(0) + c(0)^2 = a$$

If we evaluate $f(x)$ for two other values of x, the remaining coefficients, b and c, are easily obtained. An alternative to evaluating the function is to evaluate the first and second derivatives at $x = 0$. Thus

$$\left.\frac{df}{dx}\right|_{x=0} = b + 2c(0) = b \tag{4.3}$$

$$\left.\frac{d^2f}{dx^2}\right|_{x=0} = 2c \tag{4.4}$$

Once the coefficients are determined, we may differentiate the function $f(x)$, set the result to zero, and solve the equation for x:

$$\frac{df}{dx} = b + 2cx = 0, \quad x = -\frac{b}{2c} \tag{4.5}$$

If the quadratic expression for $f(x)$ is an accurate approximation, the value of x obtained will be a good approximation to the extreme point of the actual function. Under these circumstances only three function evaluations are required. If the function is not adequately approximated by the quadratic relationship, a cubic polynomial may be used. For example, if one finds that the point generated by setting the first derivative of the second-order approximation is not the desired extreme point, a cubic expression can be developed with only one more function evaluation and the three points obtained for constructing the quadratic approximation. These techniques are easily implemented, and good results have been obtained when they have been used.

In discussing multivariable search schemes we shall find that it is often desirable to solve multivariable problems by solving a sequence of single-variable problems. In fact, it will become obvious as we proceed through our discussion of approaches to nonlinear programming problems that we often reduce the problem to solving a sequence of easier problems. These reductions are carried out by a sequence of transformations and/or approximations that yield a tractable problem. This procedure closely parallels our thought processes in which we take an abstract problem and by making a series of identifications reduce the problem to something concrete, that is, something with which we are familiar.

Multivariable Search

In this section we turn our attention to multivariable search problems. A wide variety of techniques have been developed to attack problems of this nature. Substantial portions of several books have been devoted to descriptions of many of these techniques.[5] Our purpose here will be to describe a few of these methods. We have chosen those which appear to be the easiest to implement and are the most intuitively appealing. The interested reader may consult the bibliography for references to many of the other techniques.

Steepest Ascent

The first method we shall describe is called *steepest ascent*. This technique is based on obtaining the gradient[6] of the function at a point, searching for the maximum along this gradient, and then repeating this process until the gradient becomes sufficiently small. Since this procedure makes extensive use of the

---

[5] See, for example, Wilde [1], Hadley [2], Lavi and Vogl [3], and Graves and Wolfe [4].
[6] The gradient is a vector of first partial derivatives and is written

$$\text{gradient } f(\mathbf{x}) = \nabla f(x) = \text{grad} f(x) = [\partial f/\partial x_1, \ldots, \partial f/\partial x_N].$$

gradient it is also called *gradient search*. The reason for the name of steepest ascent is that if the space over which the function is defined is Euclidean, a move along the gradient gives the greatest increase in the value of the function. This result does not carry over into non-Euclidean spaces. An example of a non-Euclidean problem is an inventory problem where one independent variable is the amount of stock purchased. A move along the gradient might not give the best results even if the move were a very small one. The reason for this apparent contradiction is that in Euclidean space distance is uniquely defined, but when one works with variables such as amount of stock to purchase, temperature, pressure, etc., the distance depends only on the choice of scale and not on some predetermined measure.

Recall that from Taylor's theorem we have

$$\frac{f(\mathbf{x}_0 + a\mathbf{h}) - f(\mathbf{x}_0)}{a} = \sum_{j=1}^{N} \frac{\partial f(\cdot)}{\partial x_j}\bigg|_{\mathbf{x}^0 + \theta a\mathbf{h}} h_j \tag{4.6}$$

If we take the limit of this as $a \to 0$, we have an expression for the directional derivative of $f(\cdot)$ in the direction $\mathbf{h}$. In search procedures what we are attempting to do is to choose the vector $\mathbf{h}$ (the direction) so as to maximize the change in the function. Thus we should maximize

$$\sum_{j=1}^{N} \frac{\partial f(\cdot)}{\partial x_j} h_j$$

To have a meaningful result we restrict the values of h_j so that $\mathbf{h}^T\mathbf{h} = 1$. If this restriction were not imposed, the obvious result would be to choose $h_j = +\infty$ if $\partial f(\cdot)/\partial x_j > 0$, and if $\partial f/\partial x_j < 0$ we would choose $h_j = -\infty$. The determination of the optimal $\mathbf{h}$ is an optimization problem—one that we shall leave to the reader to solve. However, the result is

$$h_j^* = \frac{1}{c} \frac{\partial f(\mathbf{x}_0)}{\partial x_j} \tag{4.7}$$

where

$$c = \left\{ \sum_{j=1}^{N} \left[\frac{\partial f(\mathbf{x}_0)}{\partial x_j} \right]^2 \right\}^{1/2} \tag{4.8}$$

If we substitute this result back into the expression for the directional derivative we obtain

$$\sum_{j=1}^{N} \frac{\partial f(\cdot)}{\partial x_j} h_j^* = \frac{1}{c} \sum_{j=1}^{N} \left(\frac{\partial f}{\partial x_j} \right)^2 = \left[\sum_{j=1}^{N} \left(\frac{\partial f}{\partial x_j} \right)^2 \right]^{1/2} \tag{4.9}$$

Since each term in the sum is nonnegative the sum is nonnegative. This is an important result in establishing convergence of the gradient technique.

A direction in which to move has been established above. Now we must determine how far to move in this direction. Notice that any point on the gradient emanating from $\mathbf{x}_0$ can be represented as a function of one parameter, u. Since a line is a *one-dimensional subspace*, we require only one independent variable together with $\mathbf{x}_0$ to specify any point on the line,

$$\mathbf{x} = \mathbf{x}_0 + u\mathbf{h}^* \qquad (4.10)$$

This result may be illustrated in two dimensions. Consider the function whose contours are shown in Figure 4.9. The contours are curves along which the function is constant. Notice that the gradient at $\mathbf{x}_0$ is normal to the contour at $\mathbf{x}_0$. In fact, we constructed it this way. As we vary u from 0 through the range of positive values we generate the line shown.

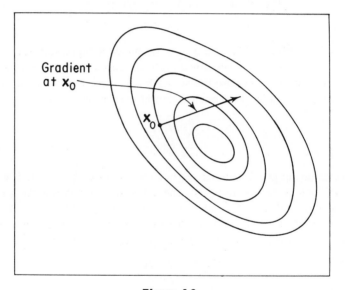

Figure 4.9.

The problem now becomes one of choosing the value of u to maximize the function along this line,

$$\max_{u} f(\mathbf{x}_0 + u\mathbf{h}^*)$$

If the function were linear, the optimal value of u would be equal to infinity. For nonlinear functions the result is not so obvious. In many cases we resort to using one of the one-dimensional search schemes to determine the optimal value of u. Once the desired value of u has been determined, the process is repeated; that is, the gradient at this point is generated and the maximum along this new line is found. This procedure continues until the gradient vanishes. For unimodal functions, the gradient vanishes at no more than one point and this point is the desired optimum solution.

Convergence of the process can be established fairly simply. However, it is not difficult to obtain problems for which the process converges to the maximum after an infinite number of steps. In many cases the rate of convergence to some $\mathbf{x}$ for which $|\partial f/\partial x_j| < \epsilon, j = 1, \ldots, N$, may be very slow. A simple heuristic argument for convergence is given below. For the purposes of the argument we will assume that the function has continuous first partial derivatives, is unimodal, and has a maximum in the interior of the region to be searched. Since the function is unimodal and has continuous first partial derivatives, it has a unique maximum and this maximum occurs at the point $\mathbf{x}^*$, where each first partial derivative vanishes,

$$\frac{\partial f(\mathbf{x}^*)}{\partial x_j} = 0 \qquad j = 1, \ldots, N \tag{4.11}$$

Furthermore, there are no other points $\mathbf{x}$ for which

$$\frac{\partial f(\mathbf{x})}{\partial x_j} = 0 \qquad j = 1, \ldots, N$$

The process described above generates a set of points $\mathbf{x}_1, \mathbf{x}_2, \ldots$, which satisfy the relationships

$$\mathbf{x}_{i+1} = \mathbf{x}_i + u_i \mathbf{h}_i^* \qquad i = 1, 2, \ldots \tag{4.12}$$

We also have that

$$f(\mathbf{x}_{i+1}) > f(\mathbf{x}_i) \qquad i = 1, 2, \ldots \tag{4.13}$$

if $\mathbf{h}_i \neq \mathbf{0}$.

There are two possibilities to consider. The first is that at some state in the process $\mathbf{h}^* = \mathbf{0}$. If this occurs we are at the maximum and the process terminates. The other possibility is that $\mathbf{h}^*$ does not vanish in a finite number of steps. In this situation we make use of the result that the function increases at each step and that it is bounded from above. This establishes convergence but not in a finite number of steps.

To illustrate this procedure consider the problem

$$\max f(x_1, x_2) = -10(x_1 - 5)^2 - (x_2 + 1)^2$$

This will be an artificial example, since the solution can be obtained very simply by solving the two linear equations generated by setting the partial derivatives equal to zero. However, it will serve to illustrate the principles involved.

Suppose we arbitrarily decide to initiate the search at the point $(0, 0)$. The function evaluated at this point is -251. The gradient is the vector whose components are the first partial derivatives of the function. Thus

$$\text{grad } f|_{(0,0)} = \left(\begin{array}{c} \dfrac{\partial f}{\partial x_1} \\[2mm] \dfrac{\partial f}{\partial x_2} \end{array} \right) \Bigg|_{(0,0)} = \begin{pmatrix} 100 \\ -2 \end{pmatrix}$$

$$\mathbf{h}^* = \frac{\text{grad } f}{|\text{grad } f|} = \frac{\begin{pmatrix} 100 \\ -2 \end{pmatrix}}{\sqrt{(10{,}004)}}$$

The next point to search is generated by

$$\mathbf{x}_1 = \mathbf{x}_0 + u\mathbf{h}^*$$
$$= \begin{pmatrix} 0 \\ 0 \end{pmatrix} + 100.02 \begin{pmatrix} 100 \\ -2 \end{pmatrix}$$

Thus

$$\mathbf{x}_1 = \begin{pmatrix} 100u \\ -2u \end{pmatrix} \cdot \frac{1}{100.02}$$

We now have a function of one variable u. We wish to find the value of u that maximizes the function. We discussed earlier how the approximation procedure might be used. We shall illustrate its use together with the gradient method below. The function $f(\cdot)$ will be approximated by a quadratic expression in u,

$$f(u) = a + bu + cu^2$$

We know that

$$f(u = 0) = a = f(\mathbf{x}_0)$$

We also have that

$$\left. \frac{df(u)}{du} \right|_{u=0} = b = \left. \frac{\partial f}{\partial x_1} \right|_{u=0} \frac{dx_1}{du} + \left. \frac{\partial f}{\partial x_2} \right|_{u=0} \frac{dx_2}{du}$$
$$= [-20(x_1 - 5)|_{u=0}\,(100) - 2(-2)(x_2 + 1)|_{u=0}] \cdot \tfrac{1}{100.02}$$
$$= 100.02$$

Finally, to evaluate c we need one more piece of information about $f(u)$. When $u = 10.002$,

$$\mathbf{x}^1 = \begin{pmatrix} 10 \\ -0.2 \end{pmatrix}$$

and $f(\mathbf{x}_1) = -250.64$. c may now be calculated as

$$c = \frac{-250.64 + 251 - 1000.4}{100.04} = \frac{-1000.04}{100.04} = -9.9864$$

To find u^* we set the derivative of $f(u)$ with respect to u to zero. Thus

$$\frac{df}{du} = b + 2cu = 0 \Rightarrow u^* = \frac{-b}{2c}$$

Evaluating u^* we find

$$u^* \simeq 0.0500018$$

Thus

$$\mathbf{x}_1 = \begin{pmatrix} 5.00018 \\ -0.00036 \end{pmatrix}$$

and $f(\mathbf{x}_1) = -0.81$.

We now calculate the gradient at this point:

$$\text{grad } f|_{5,-0.1} \approx \begin{pmatrix} 0 \\ -1.8 \end{pmatrix}$$

We again approximate $f(u)$ by a quadratic function in u. Thus

$$f(u) = a + bu + cu^2$$

where the constants a, b, and c are not necessarily the same as in the previous case.

$$f(u = 0) = f(\mathbf{x}_1) = a = -0.81$$

$$f'(u = 0) = \frac{\partial f}{\partial x_1}\frac{dx_1}{du} + \frac{\partial f}{\partial x_2}\frac{dx_2}{du} = \sqrt{1.8} = b$$

When $u = 1$,

$$f(u = 1) = -0.81 = a + b + c$$

Thus $c = -0.81 + 0.81 - \sqrt{1.8} = -\sqrt{1.8}$. The optimal value of u may be calculated from

$$u^* = -\frac{b}{2c} = -0.5$$

$$\mathbf{x}_2 = \mathbf{x}_1 + u \text{ grad } f$$

$$= \begin{pmatrix} 5.00018 \\ -0.100036 \end{pmatrix} + 0.5\begin{pmatrix} 0 \\ -1.8 \end{pmatrix} = \begin{pmatrix} 5.00018 \\ -1.00036 \end{pmatrix}$$

$$f(\mathbf{x}_2) = -25 \times 10^{-4}$$

Continuing this procedure we find that

$$\mathbf{x}_3 = \mathbf{x}_2 + u^* \text{ grad } f = \begin{pmatrix} 5 \\ -1.05 \end{pmatrix} + 0.5\begin{pmatrix} 0 \\ 0.1 \end{pmatrix} = \begin{pmatrix} 5 \\ -1 \end{pmatrix}$$

which we know is the optimal solution. Notice that we rounded off our calculations—if we had not rounded off, the optimal solution would not have been obtained in three steps.

Before leaving the discussion of the steepest ascent method, we wish to point out some of the disadvantages of this technique. One disadvantage that we mentioned earlier is that connected with functions defined on non-Euclidean spaces. In these cases any direction in which the function increases may be defined as the direction of steepest ascent by a proper choice of scale. Thus two searchers working with the same data but using different scales will generate a different sequence of points x_1, x_2, ... It is not difficult to imagine how drastically the choice of scales might affect the rate of convergence.[7] Another difficulty with the gradient method becomes apparent when

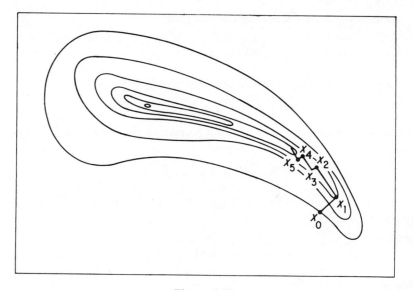

Figure 4.10.

dealing with functions that have pronounced ridges. An example of the slowness of convergence in such problems is illustrated in Figure 4.10. When the gradient technique encounters a ridge, it tends to take a large number of small steps before ascertaining the curvature of the function. Various modifications have been suggested to overcome the poor performance of the gradient method on ridged functions. Those interested in obtaining more information regarding these modification should consult references [1, 5, 17].

We now turn our attention to the method of Fletcher and Powell [6]. This technique appears to be the most efficient currently available for solving search problems that are quadratic. If the function is quadratic in N variables, the procedure converges to the optimal solution in exactly N iterations.

---

[7] See reference [5] for further discussion of this point.

The method also gives good results for functions that are more complex than a quadratic form.

The *Fletcher-Powell technique* is a modified or *deflected gradient* approach. The technique is intuitively appealing because it uses information that is generated at each iteration, whereas the gradient technique discards this useful information. The past information is used in a very ingenious way and involves constructing the Hessian of the function. When the function under consideration is quadratic, unimodal, and twice differentiable, the Hessian is constructed after N iterations of the procedure. When more complex functions are involved, the method generates a good approximation to the Hessian in the neighborhood of the extreme point. In the gradient method we construct a sequence of first-order approximations to the function while the Fletcher-Powell technique automatically generates a second-order approximation by using only first-order information. One would naturally expect the second-order approximation to yield better results.

Suppose we wish to maximize a quadratic function of several variables,

$$f(\mathbf{x}) = \mathbf{a}^T\mathbf{x} + \tfrac{1}{2}\mathbf{x}^T\mathbf{G}\mathbf{x} \qquad (4.14)$$

where

$$\mathbf{a} = \begin{pmatrix} a_1 \\ \vdots \\ a_N \end{pmatrix} \qquad \mathbf{x} = \begin{pmatrix} x_1 \\ \vdots \\ x_N \end{pmatrix} \qquad \mathbf{G} = \begin{pmatrix} g_{11} & \cdots & g_{1N} \\ \vdots & & \vdots \\ g_{N1} & \cdots & g_{NN} \end{pmatrix}$$

If the function is unimodal, the maximum occurs at the point where the gradient of $f(\cdot)$ vanishes:

$$\text{grad } f(\cdot) = \mathbf{a} + \mathbf{G}\mathbf{x} = 0$$

We can solve for $\mathbf{x}^*$ to obtain

$$\mathbf{x}^* = -\mathbf{G}^{-1}\mathbf{a}$$

However in the problem we wish to solve, we do not have sufficient information regarding $\mathbf{G}$ and $\mathbf{a}$. We must determine this required information from grad $f(\cdot)$ at several points. We shall do this while assuring that the function will increase at each iteration.

The procedure involves (1) obtaining the gradient, $\mathbf{d}_i$, at some point $\mathbf{x}_i$; (2) constructing a direction, $\mathbf{S}_i$, along which we desire to move; and (3) moving along this direction to some new point $\mathbf{x}_{i+1}$. This procedure is repeated until the gradient at some point becomes sufficiently small. We may express steps 2 and 3 more explicitly[8] as

$$\mathbf{S}_i = -\mathbf{H}_i\mathbf{d}_i \qquad (4.15)$$

---

[8] Ordinarily bold face lower case letters are used to indicate vectors; however, to be consistent with the current literature, we are using capital $\mathbf{S}$ to indicate the new direction.

where $\mathbf{H}_i$ is some negative definite matrix defined below, and

$$\mathbf{x}_{i+1} = \mathbf{x}_i + u_i^*\mathbf{S}_i \tag{4.16}$$

u_i^* is chosen to maximize $f(\mathbf{x}_i + u_i\mathbf{S}_i)$.

This procedure is very similar to the gradient method discussed previously. In fact, if $\mathbf{H}_i = -\mathbf{I}$ the direction is along the gradient. When $-\mathbf{H}_i$ is not the identity matrix, we move along a path deflected from the gradient. Thus the procedure is a *deflected gradient* technique.

The sequence of matrices $\mathbf{H}_i$ is generated by the difference equation

$$\mathbf{H}_{i+1} = \mathbf{H}_i + \mathbf{C}_i + \mathbf{B}_i \tag{4.17}$$

Since we have said the process converges in N steps,

$$\mathbf{H}_N = \mathbf{G}^{-1} \tag{4.18}$$

From this relationship we can deduce the part that $\mathbf{C}_i$ and $\mathbf{B}_i$ play in the process. If we add the terms from $i = 0$ to $i = N - 1$ in the defining equation for $\mathbf{H}_{i+1}$ we find

$$\sum_{i=0}^{N-1} \mathbf{H}_{i+1} = \sum_{i=0}^{N-1} \mathbf{H}_i + \sum_{i=0}^{N-1} \mathbf{C}_i + \sum_{i=0}^{N-1} \mathbf{B}_i \tag{4.19}$$

Simplifying this equation we find

$$\mathbf{H}_N - \mathbf{H}_0 = \sum_{i=0}^{N-1} \mathbf{C}_i + \sum_{i=0}^{N-1} \mathbf{B}_i$$

Since we require $\mathbf{H}_N = \mathbf{G}^{-1}$ we obtain

$$\mathbf{G}^{-1} = \mathbf{H}_0 + \sum_{i=0}^{N-1} \mathbf{C}_i + \sum_{i=0}^{N-1} \mathbf{B}_i$$

We shall construct the $\mathbf{B}_i$ so that as we proceed it cancels out the effect of the initial choice of $\mathbf{H}_0$,

$$\sum_{i=0}^{N-1} \mathbf{B}_i = -\mathbf{H}_0 \tag{4.20}$$

This means that

$$\sum_{i=0}^{N-1} \mathbf{C}_i = \mathbf{G}^{-1} \tag{4.21}$$

Thus as the process proceeds we are continually updating our information about the true form of $\mathbf{G}^{-1}$ and discarding the presumably erroneous information contained in the initial estimate of $\mathbf{G}^{-1}$, namely, $\mathbf{H}_0$.

We mentioned earlier that we obtain a second-order result based only on first-order information. This is done by using information about the gradients at two different points. Define

$$\mathbf{y}_i = \mathbf{d}_{i+1} - \mathbf{d}_i \tag{4.22}$$

This quantity is then used to generate the matrices $\mathbf{C}_i$ and $\mathbf{B}_i$. For example,

$$\mathbf{B}_i = \frac{-\mathbf{H}_i \mathbf{y}_i \mathbf{y}_i^T \mathbf{H}_i}{\mathbf{y}_i^T \mathbf{H}_i \mathbf{y}_i} \tag{4.23}$$

The procedure is now completely defined and follows the steps outlined below:

1. Choose an initial point $\mathbf{x}_0$, an initial guess of the inverse of the Hessian $\mathbf{H}_0$, and determine the gradient $\mathbf{d}_0$ at $\mathbf{x}_0$.
2. Calculate the direction $\mathbf{S}_0$ in which to move $\mathbf{S}_0 = -\mathbf{H}_0 \mathbf{d}_0$.
3. Determine u_0^*—the value of u_0 that maximizes $f(\mathbf{x}_0 + u_0 \mathbf{S}_0)$.
4. This yields the point $\mathbf{x}_1 = \mathbf{x}_0 + u_0^* \mathbf{S}_0$.
5. Calculate $\mathbf{C}_0$, $\mathbf{B}_0$, and from this $\mathbf{H}_1$.
6. Repeat steps 1 through 5 increasing all subscripts by 1 each time through the iteration until $\mathbf{d}_i^T \mathbf{d}_i \leq \epsilon$, where ϵ is some predetermined acceptable convergence parameter.

The initial estimate $\mathbf{H}_0$ of the inverse must be chosen to be negative definite and symmetric.

The process can be shown to converge in a manner similar to the argument presented previously for convergence of the gradient technique. We assume the function has a maximum on the interior of the region to be searched, and since the function increases at each iteration this maximum will be attained. A stronger convergence statement can be made when $f(\mathbf{x})$ is quadratic. The process will converge to $\mathbf{x}^*$ in N iterations when $f(\cdot)$ is quadratic. The proof of this quadratic convergence is given below and involves constructing a set of N conjugate vectors $\mathbf{S}_0, \ldots, \mathbf{S}_i, \ldots, \mathbf{S}_{N-1}$. Since $\mathbf{S}_i$ is the path we follow at the ith iteration, we reach the point after N steps, where $\mathbf{S}_N = 0$. Since $\mathbf{S}_N$ is a linear nonsingular transform on $\mathbf{d}_N$ this means $\mathbf{d}_N$ also vanishes and thus the maximum is attained in N steps.

The first step in the proof is to recognize that the difference in the gradients $\mathbf{y}_i$ is a particular linear transformation on $\mathbf{S}_i$.[9] This can be shown as follows:

$$\mathbf{y}_i = \mathbf{d}_{i+1} - \mathbf{d}_i$$

But $\mathbf{d}_i$ is the gradient at $\mathbf{x}_i$,

$$\mathbf{d}_i = \mathbf{a} + \mathbf{G}\mathbf{x}_i \tag{4.24}$$

---

[9] No continuity is lost if the reader prefers to bypass this proof on the first reading.

Therefore,

$$\mathbf{y}_i = \mathbf{a} + \mathbf{G}\mathbf{x}_{i+1} - \mathbf{a} - \mathbf{G}\mathbf{x}_i = \mathbf{G}\mathbf{x}_{i+1} - \mathbf{G}\mathbf{x}_i$$

This reduces to

$$\mathbf{y}_i = \mathbf{G}u_i^*\mathbf{S}_i \tag{4.25}$$

because

$$\mathbf{G}\mathbf{x}_{i+1} - \mathbf{G}\mathbf{x}_i = \mathbf{G}(\mathbf{x}_{i+1} - \mathbf{x}_i)$$

and

$$\mathbf{x}_{i+1} = \mathbf{x}_i + u_i^*\mathbf{S}_i$$

Next we must show that $\mathbf{S}_i$ and $\mathbf{d}_{i+1}$ are orthogonal. This is readily established by noting that the vector $\mathbf{S}_i$ is tangent to a contour of $f(\cdot)$ at the point $\mathbf{x}_{i+1}$ since $f(\mathbf{x}_{i+1})$ is the maximum of $f(\cdot)$ along the vector $\mathbf{S}_i$ emanating from $\mathbf{x}_i$. We have already established previously that the gradient at a point is perpendicular to the tangent of the function at that point and so $\mathbf{S}_i^T\mathbf{d}_{i+1} = 0$. The proof will now be completed by showing that the gradient at $\mathbf{x}_N$ is orthogonal to all previous paths taken (that is, $\mathbf{d}_N^T\mathbf{S}_i = 0$, $i = 0, 1, \ldots, N - 1$) and furthermore that the paths form a set of linearly independent nonnull vectors. From this we can conclude that $\mathbf{d}_N$ must be the null vector. Since the Hessian is negative definite, we know that there exists only one null gradient and at the point where the gradient vanishes we have the maximum. There are several intermediate steps in the proof that we shall develop below. We have shown that

$$\mathbf{y}_i = u_i^*\mathbf{G}\mathbf{S}_i$$

Premultiplying the equation above by $\mathbf{H}_{i+1}$ we obtain

$$u_i^*\mathbf{H}_{i+1}\mathbf{G}\mathbf{S}_i = \mathbf{H}_{i+1}\mathbf{y}_i$$
$$= \mathbf{H}_i\mathbf{y}_i + \mathbf{C}_i\mathbf{y}_i + \mathbf{B}_i\mathbf{y}_i \tag{4.26}$$

Defining

$$\mathbf{C}_i = \frac{u_i^*\mathbf{S}_i\mathbf{S}_i^T}{\mathbf{S}_i^T\mathbf{y}_i} \quad \text{and recalling that} \quad \mathbf{B}_i = \frac{-\mathbf{H}_i\mathbf{y}_i\mathbf{y}_i^T\mathbf{H}_i}{\mathbf{y}_i^T\mathbf{H}_i\mathbf{y}_i} \tag{4.27}$$

we obtain

$$u_i^*\mathbf{H}_{i+1}\mathbf{G}\mathbf{S}_i = \mathbf{H}_i\mathbf{y}_i + \frac{u_i^*\mathbf{S}_i\mathbf{S}_i^T\mathbf{y}_i}{\mathbf{S}_i^T\mathbf{y}_i} - \frac{\mathbf{H}_i\mathbf{y}_i\mathbf{y}_i^T\mathbf{H}_i\mathbf{y}_i}{\mathbf{y}_i^T\mathbf{H}_i\mathbf{y}_i}$$
$$= \mathbf{H}_i\mathbf{y}_i + u_i^*\mathbf{S}_i - \mathbf{H}_i\mathbf{y}_i$$
$$= u_i^*\mathbf{S}_i \tag{4.28}$$

Thus

$$\mathbf{H}_{i+1}\mathbf{G}\mathbf{S}_i = \mathbf{S}_i \tag{4.29}$$

We shall use this result in succeeding steps.

Next we shall consider the following two equations. Their validity will be established inductively:

$$S_i^T G S_j = 0 \qquad 0 \le i < j < k \qquad\qquad (4.30)$$

$$H_k G S_i = S_i \qquad 0 \le i < k \qquad\qquad (4.31)$$

Suppose $k = 2$. Then we must show that

$$S_0^T G S_1 = 0$$
$$H_2 G S_1 = S_1$$

The second equation has been developed previously. We have also shown above that

$$H_1 G S_0 = S_0$$

Premultiplying this by $-d_1^T$ we obtain

$$-d_1^T H_1 G S_0 = -d_1^T S_0$$

But we established earlier that d_1 was orthogonal to S_0 since S_0 was a contour tangent. Thus

$$-d_1^T H_1 G S_0 = 0 \qquad\qquad (4.32)$$

But

$$S_1 = -H_1 d_1$$

or transposing and recalling that G is symmetrical, we have

$$S_0^T G S_1 = 0 \qquad\qquad (4.33)$$

To complete the induction we assume the results are true for k and show they hold for $k + 1$. By definition of the gradient we have

$$d_k = a + G x_k$$

Recall that

$$\begin{aligned}
x_k &= x_{k-1} + u_{k-1}^* S_{k-1} \\
&= x_{k-2} + u_{k-2}^* S_{k-2} + u_{k-1}^* S_{k-1} \\
&= x_{i+1} + u_{i+1}^* S_{i+1} + \cdots + u_{k-1}^* S_{k-1}
\end{aligned} \qquad (4.34)$$

Thus

$$\begin{aligned}
d_k &= a + G x_k \\
&= a + G x_{i+1} + u_{i+1}^* G S_{i+1} + \cdots + u_{k-1}^* G S_{k-1} \\
&= d_{i+1} + u_{i+1}^* G S_{i+1} + \cdots + u_{k-1}^* G S_{k-1}
\end{aligned} \qquad (4.35)$$

Premultiplying this result by S_i^T we obtain

$$S_i^T d_k = S_i^T d_{i+1} + u_{i+1}^* S_i^T G S_{i+1} + \cdots + u_{k-1}^* S_i^T G S_{k-1} \qquad (4.36)$$

We have already established that the first term on the right is zero and we have assumed that the remaining terms are zero (from the induction step). Therefore,

$$\mathbf{S}_i^T \mathbf{d}_k = 0 \qquad 0 \le i < k \qquad\qquad (4.37)$$

But

$$\mathbf{S}_i^T = \mathbf{S}_i^T \mathbf{G} \mathbf{H}_k$$

(by assumption). Thus

$$\mathbf{S}_i^T \mathbf{G} \mathbf{H}_k \mathbf{d}_k = 0$$

Recall that $-\mathbf{H}_k \mathbf{d}_k = \mathbf{S}_k$, so that

$$\mathbf{S}_i^T \mathbf{G} \mathbf{S}_k = 0 \qquad 0 \le i < k$$

In the induction step we assumed

$$\mathbf{H}_k \mathbf{G} \mathbf{S}_i = \mathbf{S}_i$$

Premultiplying both sides by $\mathbf{y}_k^T$ we obtain

$$\begin{aligned}
\mathbf{y}_k^T \mathbf{H}_k \mathbf{G} \mathbf{S}_i &= \mathbf{y}_k^T \mathbf{S}_i \\
&= u_k \mathbf{S}_k^T \mathbf{G} \mathbf{S}_i \\
&= 0 \qquad\qquad 0 \le i < k
\end{aligned}$$

Now all the necessary tools are available for the induction proof.

$$\begin{aligned}
\mathbf{H}_{k+1} \mathbf{G} \mathbf{S}_i &= \mathbf{H}_k \mathbf{G} \mathbf{S}_i + \mathbf{C}_k \mathbf{G} \mathbf{S}_i + \mathbf{B}_k \mathbf{G} \mathbf{S}_i \\
&= \mathbf{S}_i + \frac{u_k \mathbf{S}_k \mathbf{S}_k^T \mathbf{G} \mathbf{S}_i}{\mathbf{S}_k^T \mathbf{y}_k} - \frac{\mathbf{H}_k \mathbf{y}_k \mathbf{y}_k^T \mathbf{H}_k \mathbf{G} \mathbf{S}_i}{\mathbf{y}_k^T \mathbf{H}_k \mathbf{y}_k} \\
&= \mathbf{S}_i + \mathbf{0} - \frac{\mathbf{H}_k \mathbf{y}_k \mathbf{y}_k^T \mathbf{S}_i}{\mathbf{y}_k^T \mathbf{H}_k \mathbf{y}_k} \\
&= \mathbf{S}_i - \frac{\mathbf{H}_k \mathbf{y}_k \mathbf{S}_k \mathbf{G} \mathbf{S}_i}{\mathbf{y}_k^T \mathbf{H}_k \mathbf{y}_k} \\
&= \mathbf{S}_i \qquad\qquad\qquad (4.38)
\end{aligned}$$

and the proof is completed.

We have shown that

$$\mathbf{S}_i^T \mathbf{G} \mathbf{S}_k = 0 \qquad 0 \le i < k \qquad \text{all } k = 1, 2, 3, \dots, N-1$$

Since $\mathbf{G}$ is negative definite, $\mathbf{S}_i$ and $\mathbf{S}_k$ are linearly independent. This result may be easily established as follows. Suppose one of the $\mathbf{S}_i$, say $\mathbf{S}_p$, is linearly dependent on $\mathbf{S}_k$,

$$\mathbf{S}_p = \alpha \mathbf{S}_k \qquad \alpha \ne 0$$

Thus

$$\alpha \mathbf{S}_k^T \mathbf{G} \mathbf{S}_k = 0$$

But

$$\mathbf{S}_k^T \mathbf{G} \mathbf{S}_k < 0$$

unless $S_k = 0$.[10] This implies that $\alpha = 0$, which means that S_p and S_k are linearly independent for all $p = 0, 1, \ldots, k - 1$, for $k = 1, \ldots, N - 1$. Thus all the paths followed are linearly independent. We have shown that d_N is orthogonal to $S_0, S_1, \ldots, S_{N-1}$, which form a set of N linearly independent vectors. The only vector satisfying these requirements is the null vector. Thus $d_N = 0$ and the maximum has been attained.

To illustrate the calculations required to employ the Fletcher-Powell method, suppose

$$f(x_1, x_2) = a^T x + \tfrac{1}{2} x^T G x$$

where

$$a = \begin{pmatrix} 5 \\ 2 \end{pmatrix} \qquad G = \begin{pmatrix} -9 & -2 \\ -2 & -6.25 \end{pmatrix}$$

To initiate the computations we choose

$$H_0 = \begin{pmatrix} -1 & 0 \\ 0 & -1 \end{pmatrix}$$

and a starting point of

$$x_0 = \begin{pmatrix} 0 \\ 0 \end{pmatrix}$$

$$d_0 = a + G x_0$$

$$= a = \begin{pmatrix} 5 \\ 2 \end{pmatrix}$$

$$S_0 = -H_0 d_0$$

$$= \begin{pmatrix} 1 & 0 \\ 0 & 1 \end{pmatrix} \begin{pmatrix} 5 \\ 2 \end{pmatrix} = \begin{pmatrix} 5 \\ 2 \end{pmatrix}$$

We must now determine u_0^* to maximize $f(x_0 + u_0 S_0)$. We demonstrated earlier how one might employ the quadratic approximation procedure to accomplish this maximization. Since it is not pertinent to this illustration we shall determine u_0^* analytically.

$$f(x_0 + u_0 S_0) = a^T (x_0 + u_0 S_0) + \tfrac{1}{2}(x_0^T + u_0 S_0^T) G (x_0 + u_0 S_0)$$

$$= 29 u_0 + u_0^2(-145)$$

$$\frac{df(x_0 + u_0 S_0)}{du} = 29 - 290 u_0 = 0 \Rightarrow u_0 = \frac{29}{290} = 0.1$$

Thus

$$x_1 = x_0 + u_0^* S_0$$

$$= \begin{pmatrix} 0 \\ 0 \end{pmatrix} + 0.1 \begin{pmatrix} 5 \\ 2 \end{pmatrix} = \begin{pmatrix} 0.5 \\ 0.2 \end{pmatrix}$$

---

[10] Since G is negative definite, $S_k^T G S_k < 0$ for all $S_k \neq 0$. We have assumed $S_k \neq 0$ because $S_k = -H_k d_k$, which is zero only if $d_k = 0$. But $d_k \neq 0$, or we have achieved the optimum.

Continuing we find

$$\mathbf{d}_1 = \mathbf{a} + \mathbf{Gx}_1$$

$$= \begin{pmatrix} 5 \\ 2 \end{pmatrix} + \begin{pmatrix} -9 & -2 \\ -2 & -6.25 \end{pmatrix} \begin{pmatrix} 0.5 \\ 0.2 \end{pmatrix}$$

$$= \begin{pmatrix} 5 \\ 2 \end{pmatrix} + \begin{pmatrix} -4.9 \\ -2.25 \end{pmatrix} = \begin{pmatrix} 0.1 \\ -0.25 \end{pmatrix}$$

$$\mathbf{y}_1 = \mathbf{d}_1 - \mathbf{d}_0 = \begin{pmatrix} 0.1 \\ -0.25 \end{pmatrix} - \begin{pmatrix} 5 \\ 2 \end{pmatrix} = \begin{pmatrix} -4.9 \\ -2.25 \end{pmatrix}$$

$$\mathbf{H}_1 = \mathbf{H}_0 + \mathbf{C}_0 + \mathbf{B}_0$$

$$= \begin{pmatrix} -1 & 0 \\ 0 & -1 \end{pmatrix} + \frac{\begin{pmatrix} 0.5 \\ 0.2 \end{pmatrix}(5 \quad 2)}{(5 \quad 2)\begin{pmatrix} -4.9 \\ -2.25 \end{pmatrix}} + \frac{\begin{pmatrix} -4.9 \\ -2.25 \end{pmatrix}(+4.9 \quad +2.25)}{(-4.9 \quad -2.25)\begin{pmatrix} 4.9 \\ 2.25 \end{pmatrix}}$$

$$= \begin{pmatrix} -1 & 0 \\ 0 & -1 \end{pmatrix} + \frac{\begin{pmatrix} 2.5 & 1 \\ 1 & 0.4 \end{pmatrix}}{-2.9} + \frac{\begin{pmatrix} 24.01 & 11.025 \\ 11.025 & 5.0625 \end{pmatrix}}{29.0725}$$

$$= \begin{pmatrix} -0.2602 & 0.3448 \\ 0.3448 & -0.8396 \end{pmatrix}$$

$$\mathbf{S}_1 = -\mathbf{H}_1\mathbf{d}_1 = \begin{pmatrix} -0.2602 & 0.3448 \\ 0.3448 & -0.8396 \end{pmatrix}\begin{pmatrix} 0.1 \\ -0.25 \end{pmatrix} = \begin{pmatrix} 0.1122 \\ -0.2444 \end{pmatrix}$$

Thus

$$\mathbf{x}_2 = \mathbf{x}_1 + u_1^*\mathbf{S}_1$$

$$= \begin{pmatrix} 0.5 \\ 0.2 \end{pmatrix} + u_1^*\begin{pmatrix} 0.1122 \\ -0.2444 \end{pmatrix}$$

$$f(\mathbf{x}_1 + u_1\mathbf{S}_1) = \mathbf{a}^T(\mathbf{x}_1 + u_1\mathbf{S}_1) + \tfrac{1}{2}(\mathbf{x}_1^T + u_1\mathbf{S}_1^T)\mathbf{G}(\mathbf{x}_1 + u_1\mathbf{S}_1)$$

$$\frac{df}{du} = \mathbf{a}^T\mathbf{S}_1 + \mathbf{S}_1^T\mathbf{Ax}_1 + u\mathbf{S}_1^T\mathbf{GS}_1 = 0$$

$$u = -\frac{\mathbf{a}^T\mathbf{S}_1 - \mathbf{S}^T\mathbf{Gx}_1}{\mathbf{S}_1^T\mathbf{GS}_1} = \frac{-0.0722 - 0}{-0.3769} = 0.19167$$

Continuing we find

$$\mathbf{x}_2 = \begin{pmatrix} 0.5 \\ 0.2 \end{pmatrix} + 0.19167\begin{pmatrix} 0.1122 \\ -0.2444 \end{pmatrix}$$

$$= \begin{pmatrix} 0.5215 \\ 0.1532 \end{pmatrix}$$

Calculating $\mathbf{d}_2$ yields

$$\mathbf{d}_2 = \mathbf{a} + \mathbf{G}\mathbf{x}_2$$

$$= \begin{pmatrix} 5 \\ 2 \end{pmatrix} + \begin{pmatrix} -9 & -2 \\ -2 & -6.25 \end{pmatrix} \begin{pmatrix} 0.5215 \\ 11532 \end{pmatrix}$$

$$= \begin{pmatrix} 5 \\ 2 \end{pmatrix} + \begin{pmatrix} -4.9999 \\ 2.0005 \end{pmatrix} = \begin{pmatrix} 0.0001 \\ -0.0005 \end{pmatrix}$$

which we shall consider a close approximation to $\mathbf{0}$.[11]

As we mentioned earlier, there are numerous algorithms for optimizing functions using a direct or search procedure. We shall not have space to discuss these algorithms; however, the interested reader should consult the references at the end of the chapter for leads to other algorithms. Among the most prominent procedures not covered here are the *direct*, or *pattern* [17], *search*, the *parallel-tangents* [5] *scheme*, the *conjugate gradient technique*, and Newton's method. Pattern search is particularly effective in following straight or slightly curving ridges. Parallel tangents exploits the notion that for an ellipsoidal function of two variables the line connecting the high point of two parallel contours passes through the maximum. This concept can be extended to functions of several variables and appears to be quite successful. Newton's method uses second-order information to obtain the solution, but this information is generated much less efficiently than in the Fletcher-Powell scheme.

As we shall point out later in this chapter, search techniques are extremely useful in solving nonlinear programming problems. The approach is to convert the constrained problem into an unconstrained problem and solve the new unconstrained problem by one of the direct methods discussed above. Direct methods have been developed for solving constrained problems. However their efficiency in solving problems with nonlinear constraints is questionable and in most cases it appears to be more efficient to solve the unconstrained problem which can be obtained from the original problem.

4.3 Quadratic Programming

We now turn our attention to problems slightly more complicated than those discussed in Chapter 3. The types of problems discussed in this section have the following structure:

$$\min f(\mathbf{x}) = \mathbf{c}^T\mathbf{x} + \tfrac{1}{2}\mathbf{x}^T\mathbf{G}\mathbf{x}$$

where

$$\mathbf{x} = \begin{pmatrix} x_1 \\ \vdots \\ x_N \end{pmatrix} \qquad \mathbf{c} = \begin{pmatrix} c_1 \\ \vdots \\ c_N \end{pmatrix} \qquad \mathbf{G} = \begin{pmatrix} g_{11} & \cdots & g_{1N} \\ \vdots & & \\ g_N & \cdots & g_{NN} \end{pmatrix} = (\mathbf{g}_1, \ldots, \mathbf{g}_N) \qquad (4.39)$$

---

[11] Roundoff error induced this discrepancy.

We shall assume **G** is symmetric and positive definite. The constraints have the following form:

$$\mathbf{A}\mathbf{x} \leq \mathbf{b}$$
$$\mathbf{x} \geq \mathbf{0}$$

where

$$\mathbf{A} = (\mathbf{a}_1, \ldots, \mathbf{a}_N) = \begin{pmatrix} a_{11} & \cdots & a_{1N} \\ \vdots & & \\ a_{M1} & \cdots & a_{MN} \end{pmatrix} \qquad \mathbf{b} = \begin{pmatrix} b_1 \\ \vdots \\ b_M \end{pmatrix} \qquad (4.40)$$

If **G** is null we have the standard linear programming problem. However, we have assumed **G** is positive definite. Suppose we construct the Kuhn-Tucker conditions for this problem. Introducing slack variables q_i^2 and r_j^2, the problem becomes:

$$\min f(\mathbf{x})$$
$$\text{subject to}$$
$$\mathbf{a}_i^T\mathbf{x} + q_i^2 = b_i \qquad i = 1, \ldots, M$$
$$-x_j + r_j^2 = 0 \qquad j = 1, \ldots, N \qquad (4.41)$$

We shall now proceed to form the Lagrange function

$$F(\mathbf{x}, \mathbf{g}, \mathbf{u}, \boldsymbol{\lambda}, \mathbf{r}) = f(\mathbf{x}) + \sum_{i=1}^{M} \lambda_i(\mathbf{a}_i^T\mathbf{x} + q_i^2 - b_i)$$

$$+ \sum_{j=1}^{N} u_j(-x_j + r_j^2) \qquad (4.42)$$

Forming the necessary conditions we find

$$\frac{\partial F(\cdot)}{\partial x_j} = \frac{\partial f}{\partial x_j} + \sum_{i=1}^{M} \lambda_i a_{ij} - u_j = 0 \qquad j = 1, \ldots, N \qquad (4.43)$$

$$\lambda_i(\mathbf{a}_i\mathbf{x} - b_i) = 0 \qquad (4.44)$$

$$u_i x_i = 0 \qquad (4.45)$$

$$\mathbf{A}\mathbf{x} = \mathbf{b} \qquad (4.46)$$

and finally **x**, $\boldsymbol{\lambda}$, and **u** must all be nonnegative.

Rewriting the first equation we find

$$\frac{\partial F}{\partial x_j} = c_j + \sum_{i=1}^{N} g_{ij}x_i + \sum_{i=1}^{M} \lambda_i a_{ij} - u_j = 0 \qquad j = 1, \ldots, N$$

Define $q_i^2 = y_i \geq 0$. With this definition $\mathbf{a}_i^T \mathbf{x} - b_i = -y_i$ and we can simplify the second condition to read $\lambda_i y_i = 0$. Thus the problem becomes

$$-u_j + c_j + \sum_{i=1}^{N} g_{ij} x_i + \sum_{i=1}^{M} \lambda_i a_{ij} = 0 \qquad j = 1, \ldots, N \qquad (4.47)$$

$$\mathbf{Ax} + \mathbf{Iy} = \mathbf{b}$$
$$\mathbf{x} \geq 0$$
$$\mathbf{y} \geq 0$$
$$\boldsymbol{\lambda} \geq 0$$
$$\mathbf{u} \geq 0$$

and finally $\lambda_i y_i = 0$, $i = 1, \ldots, M$, $u_j x_j = 0$, $j = 1, \ldots, N$. Notice one important result. With the exception of the last condition the Kuhn-Tucker conditions are linear. The problem is one of finding a solution to a set of linear equations and inequalities where the variables must be nonnegative and the $M + N$ complementary slackness conditions must be satisfied.

Wolfe suggested a solution procedure for this problem using the simplex algorithm with one slight modification. His suggestion involved introducing N nonnegative artificial variables v_j into the equations representing $\partial F/\partial x_j = 0$:

$$-u_j + c_j + \sum_{i=1}^{N} g_{ji} x_i + \sum_{i=1}^{M} \lambda_i a_{ij} - v_j = 0 \qquad (4.48)$$

Starting with an initial basic solution of $\mathbf{v} = \mathbf{c}$, $\mathbf{y} = \mathbf{b}$, and $\mathbf{x} = 0$, $\boldsymbol{\lambda} = 0$, we minimize

$$\sum_{i=1}^{N} v_i \qquad (4.49)$$

subject to

$$-\mathbf{u} + \mathbf{c} + \mathbf{g}_i \mathbf{x} + \mathbf{a}_i \boldsymbol{\lambda} - \mathbf{v} = 0 \qquad (4.50)$$

$$\mathbf{Ax} + \mathbf{y} = \mathbf{b} \qquad \mathbf{u}, \mathbf{x}, \mathbf{y}, \boldsymbol{\lambda}, \text{ and } \mathbf{v} \text{ nonnegative} \qquad (4.51)$$

and the complementary slackness conditions

$$\begin{aligned} \lambda_i y_i &= 0 \qquad i = 1, \ldots, M \\ u_j x_j &= 0 \qquad j = 1, \ldots, N \end{aligned} \qquad (4.52)$$

With one exception, this is a linear programming problem that can be solved by the simplex algorithm. We must modify the algorithm to include the complementary slackness conditions. Thus when deciding whether to introduce y_i into the basic solution, we must first ensure either that λ_i is not in the solution or that λ_i will be removed when y_i enters. This additional check is not difficult to incorporate into the simplex algorithm and has been successfully accomplished. Note that the problem has $2(M + N)$ variables and $N + M$ linear constraints together with $M + N$ complementary slackness conditions, $\lambda_i y_i = 0$ and $u_j x_j = 0$.

We shall now consider an example to illustrate the computations involved. Suppose we are given

$$\max f(x_1, x_2) = 10x_1 + 25x_2 - 10x_1^2 - x_2^2 - 4x_1x_2$$

subject to

$$x_1 + 2x_2 \le 10$$
$$x_1 + x_2 \le 9$$
$$x_1, x_2 \ge 0$$

Recall that when maximizing $f(\mathbf{x})$ the Lagrange multipliers must all be nonpositive. Since we wish to use the simplex technique, we shall convert this to a minimization problem by multiplying the objective function by -1. This operation changes the sign of the Lagrange multipliers. After performing this transformation and adding the slack variables we obtain

$$\min \hat{f}(x_1, x_2) = -f(x_1, x_2) = -10x_1 - 25x_2 + 10x_1^2 + x_2^2 + 4x_1x_2$$

subject to

$$x_1 + 2x_2 + q_1^2 - 10 = 0$$
$$x_1 + x_2 + q_2^2 - 9 = 0$$
$$-x_1 + r_1^2 = 0$$
$$-x_2 + r_2^2 = 0$$

To obtain the necessary conditions we construct the Lagrange function,

$$F(x_1, x_2, u_1, u_2, r_1, r_2, \lambda_1, \lambda_2, q_1, q_2)$$
$$= -10x_1 - 25x_2 + 10x_1^2 + x_2^2 + 4x_1x_2$$
$$+ \lambda_1(x_1 + 2x_2 + q_1^2 - 10) + \lambda_2(x_1 + x_2 + q_2^2 - 9)$$
$$+ u_1(-x_1 + r_1^2) + u_2(-x_2 + r_2^2)$$

The necessary and sufficient conditions are

$$\frac{\partial F}{\partial x_1} = -10 + 20x_1 + 4x_2 + \lambda_1 + \lambda_2 - u_1 = 0$$

$$\frac{\partial F}{\partial x_2} = -25 + 4x_1 + 2x_2 + 2\lambda_1 + \lambda_2 - u_2 = 0$$

Defining $y_i = q_i^2$ we have

$$\lambda_1 y_1 = 0$$
$$\lambda_2 y_2 = 0$$
$$u_1 x_1 = 0$$
$$u_2 x_2 = 0$$

Also

$$x_1 + 2x_2 + y_1 = 10$$
$$x_1 + x_2 + y_2 = 9$$

and finally

$$x_1, x_2, y_1, y_2, u_1, u_2, \lambda_1, \lambda_2 \ge 0$$

Introducing artificial variables v_1 and v_2 we can construct the following modified linear program: max $g(v_1, v_2) = -v_1 - v_2$ subject to

$$20x_1 + 4x_2 + \lambda_1 + \lambda_2 - u_1 + v_1 = 10$$
$$4x_1 + 2x_2 + 2\lambda_1 + \lambda_2 - u_2 + v_2 = 25$$
$$x_1 + 2x_2 + y_1 = 10$$
$$x_1 + x_2 + y_2 = 9$$

with all variables nonnegative and

$$x_1 u_1 = 0 \qquad \lambda_1 y_1 = 0$$
$$x_2 u_2 = 0 \qquad \lambda_2 y_2 = 0$$

The first tableau becomes

	b	v_1	v_2	x_1	x_2	λ_1	λ_2	u_1	u_2	y_1	y_2*
v_1	10	1	0	20	4	1	1	-1	0	0	0
v_2	25	0	1	4	2	2	1	0	-1	0	0
y_1	10	0	0	1	2	0	0	0	0	1	0
y_2	9	0	0	1	1	0	0	0	0	0	1
		0	0	-24	-6	-3	-2	+1	+1	0	0

> * This tableau is slightly different from that shown in Chapter 3. The headings $v_1, \ldots, y_2$ represent variables and not the vectors associated with them.

Introducing x_1 into the basic solution we obtain

	b	v_1	v_2	x_1	x_2	λ_1	λ_2	u_1	u_2	y_1	y_2
x_1	$\frac{1}{2}$	$\frac{1}{20}$	0	1	$\frac{1}{5}$	$\frac{1}{20}$	$\frac{1}{20}$	$-\frac{1}{20}$	0	0	0
v_2	23	$-\frac{1}{5}$	1	0	$\frac{6}{5}$	$\frac{9}{5}$	$\frac{4}{5}$	$\frac{1}{5}$	-1	0	0
y_1	9.5	$-\frac{1}{20}$	0	0	$\frac{9}{5}$	$-\frac{1}{20}$	$-\frac{1}{20}$	$\frac{1}{20}$	0	1	0
y_2	8.5	$-\frac{1}{20}$	0	0	$\frac{4}{5}$	$-\frac{1}{20}$	$-\frac{1}{20}$	$\frac{1}{20}$	0	0	1
		$\frac{6}{5}$	0	0	$-\frac{6}{5}$	$-\frac{9}{5}$	$-\frac{4}{5}$	$-\frac{1}{5}$	1	0	0

x_2 now enters the basic solution. Notice that neither λ_1 or λ_2 can enter, since y_1 and y_2 are both basic variables.

	b	v_1	v_2	x_1	x_2	λ_1	λ_2	u_1	u_2	y_1	y_2
x_2	$\frac{5}{2}$	$\frac{1}{4}$	0	5	1	$\frac{1}{4}$	$\frac{1}{4}$	$-\frac{1}{4}$	0	0	0
v_2	20	$-\frac{1}{2}$	1	-6	0	$\frac{3}{2}$	$\frac{1}{2}$	$\frac{1}{2}$	-1	0	0
y_1	5	$-\frac{1}{2}$	0	-9	0	$-\frac{1}{2}$	$-\frac{1}{2}$	$\frac{1}{2}$	0	1	0
y_2	6.5	$-\frac{1}{4}$	0	-4	0	$-\frac{1}{4}$	$-\frac{1}{4}$	$\frac{1}{4}$	0	0	1
		$\frac{3}{2}$	0	6	0	$-\frac{3}{2}$	$-\frac{1}{2}$	$-\frac{1}{2}$	1	0	0

u_1 is entered into the solution next:

	b	v_1	v_2	x_1	x_2	λ_1	λ_2	u_1	u_2	y_1	y_2
x_2	5	0	0	$\frac{1}{2}$	1	0	0	0	0	$\frac{1}{2}$	0
v_2	15	0	1	3	0	2	1	0	-1	-1	0
u_1	10	-1	0	-18	0	-1	-1	1	0	2	0
y_2	4	0	0	$\frac{1}{2}$	0	0	0	0	0	$-\frac{1}{2}$	1
		1	0	-3	0	-2	-1	0	1	1	0

The normal rule would call for x_1 to be entered at this point. However, since u_1 is in the solution, x_1 cannot be entered unless u_1 leaves. Thus we shall enter λ_1.

	b	v_1	v_2	x_1	x_2	λ_1	λ_2	u_1	u_2	y_1	y_2
x_2	5	0	0	$\frac{1}{2}$	1	0	0	0	0	$\frac{1}{2}$	0
λ_1	7.5	0	$\frac{1}{2}$	$\frac{3}{2}$	0	1	$\frac{1}{2}$	0	$-\frac{1}{2}$	$-\frac{1}{2}$	0
u_1	17.5	-1	$\frac{1}{2}$	$\frac{33}{2}$	0	0	$-\frac{1}{2}$	1	$-\frac{1}{2}$	$\frac{3}{2}$	0
y_2	4	0	0	$\frac{1}{2}$	0	0	0	0	0	$-\frac{1}{2}$	1
		1	1	0	0	0	0	0	0	0	0

Since both v_1 and v_2 are out of the solution, the computation is complete. The optimal solution is $x_1 = 0$, $x_2 = 5$, $y_1 = 0$, $y_2 = 4$, $\lambda_1 = 7.5$, $\lambda_2 = 0$, $u_1 = 17.5$, and $u_2 = 0$, which satisfies the complementary slackness conditions and the restrictions on the signs of the Lagrange multipliers.

Beale's Algorithm

Other approaches to quadratic programming problems have been suggested. Beale [7] has developed an approach that does not use the Kuhn-Tucker conditions in the solution procedure. His approach involves partitioning the variables into basic and nonbasic variables at each stage and writing the objective function in terms of the nonbasic variables. For example, consider the constraints $\mathbf{Dz} \leq \mathbf{b}$. These constraints can be rewritten $\mathbf{Ax} = \mathbf{b}$, where

$$\mathbf{x} = \begin{pmatrix} \mathbf{z} \\ \mathbf{y} \end{pmatrix} \qquad \mathbf{A} = (\mathbf{D}, \mathbf{I})$$

We can arbitrarily select M of the variables to be basic variables with the remaining N becoming nonbasic variables.[11] Performing this partitioning we can write

$$\mathbf{x}_B = \mathbf{B}^{-1}\mathbf{b} - \mathbf{B}^{-1}\mathbf{R}\mathbf{x}_{NB} \qquad (4.53)$$

---

[11] See Section 3.3.

where $\mathbf{x}_B$ denotes the vector of basic variables and $\mathbf{x}_{NB}$ denotes the nonbasic variables, which are zero. $\mathbf{B}$ is the submatrix of $\mathbf{A}$ associated with $\mathbf{x}_B$ and $\mathbf{R}$ is the columns of $\mathbf{A}$ associated with $\mathbf{x}_{NB}$. Upon substituting this result into the objective function we obtain a function of $\mathbf{x}_{NB}$ only. Then we see that by increasing the value of any of the nonbasic variables the value of the objective function can be improved. Notice that the constraints on the new problem become

$$\mathbf{B}^{-1}\mathbf{R}\mathbf{x}_{NB} \leq \mathbf{B}^{-1}\mathbf{b} \qquad (4.54)$$

since $\mathbf{x}_B \geq \mathbf{0}$. Thus any component of $\mathbf{x}_{NB}$ can increase only until $\partial f(\mathbf{x}_{NB})/\partial x_{NBi}$ vanishes *or* one or more components of $\mathbf{x}_B$ are reduced to zero. Notice that we face the possibility of having more than M nonzero variables at any step in the iteration. This will occur when the new point generated at some step occurs where the $\partial f/\partial x_{NBj}$ vanishes. Geometrically this means that we are no longer at an extreme point of the convex set formed by the constraints and thus no longer have a basic solution with respect to the original constraint set. When this occurs we simply define a new variable, y_i, where

$$y_i = \frac{\partial f}{\partial x_{NBi}}$$

and a new constraint $y_i = 0$. We now have $M + 1$ nonzero variables and $M + 1$ constraints, which is a basic solution to the expanded set of constraints. The procedure is repeated until no improvements in the objective function may be obtained by increasing one of the nonbasic variables. This technique will converge in a finite number of steps. Proof of convergence is contained in Beale's paper [7].

We shall use as an example the same problem solved by the modified simplex algorithm. Consider

$$\max f(x_1, x_2) = 10x_1 + 25x_2 - 10x_1^2 - x_2^2 - 4x_1 x_2$$

subject to

$$\begin{aligned} x_1 + 2x_2 + x_3 &= 10 \\ x_1 + x_2 + x_4 &= 9 \\ x_1, x_2, x_3, x_4 &\geq 0 \end{aligned}$$

Selecting x_1 and x_2 arbitrarily to be the basic variables we obtain

$$\begin{aligned} x_1 &= 8 + x_3 - 2x_4 \\ x_2 &= 1 - x_3 + x_4 \end{aligned}$$

where

$$\mathbf{x}_B = \begin{pmatrix} x_1 \\ x_2 \end{pmatrix} \qquad \mathbf{x}_{NB} = \begin{pmatrix} x_3 \\ x_4 \end{pmatrix}$$

Expressing $f(\cdot)$ in terms of $\mathbf{x}_{NB}$ we find

$$f(x_3, x_4) = 10(8 + x_3 - 2x_4) + 25(1 - x_3 + x_4) - 10(8 + x_3 - 2x_4)^2$$
$$- (1 - x_3 + x_4)^2 - 4(8 + x_3 - 2x_4)(1 - x_3 + x_4)$$
$$\frac{\partial f}{\partial x_3} = 10 - 25 - 20(8 + x_3 - 2x_4) + 2(1 - x_3 + x_4)$$
$$- 4(1 - x_3 + x_4) + 4(8 + x_3 - 2x_4)$$

Evaluating this partial derivative at $\mathbf{x}_{NB} = 0$ we find

$$\frac{\partial f(\mathbf{x}_{NB})}{\partial x_3} = -145$$

Thus the objective function will decrease if x_3 is increased. This runs contrary to our wishes to increase the objective function. The partial derivative with respect to x_4 yields a more promising alternative:

$$\frac{\partial f(\mathbf{x}_{NB})}{\partial x_4} = -20 + 25 - 20(-2)(8 + x_3 - 2x_4) - 2(1 - x_3 + x_4)$$
$$+ 8(1 - x_3 + x_4) - 4(8 + x_3 - 2x_4)$$

At the point $\mathbf{x}_{NB} = 0$ we find

$$\frac{\partial f(\mathbf{x}_{NB})}{\partial x_4} = 299$$

Thus increasing x_4 will improve the objective function. We must now determine how much x_4 should or may increase. The maximum value x_4 is allowed to attain is determined by checking two quantities. They are (1) the value of x_4 for which $\partial f(\mathbf{x}_{NB})/\partial x_4$ vanishes, and (2) the largest value x_4 can attain without driving one of the basic variables negative. x_4 will be the minimum of these two. If x_4 is increased to a value greater than 4, x_1 will become negative, since

$$x_1 = 8 + x_3 - 2x_4$$

and $x_3 = 0$. The partial derivative vanishes at $x_4 = \frac{299}{66}$. Taking the minimum of $(4, \frac{299}{66})$ we find $x_4 = 4$, and the new basic variables are x_4 and x_2. We initiate a new iteration by solving for x_2 and x_4 in terms of x_1 and x_3. Thus

$$x_2 = 5 - \tfrac{1}{2}(x_1 + x_3)$$
$$x_4 = 4 + \tfrac{1}{2}(x_3 - x_1)$$

In this case

$$\mathbf{x}_B = \begin{pmatrix} x_2 \\ x_4 \end{pmatrix} \qquad \mathbf{x}_{NB} = \begin{pmatrix} x_1 \\ x_3 \end{pmatrix}$$

Expressing $f(\cdot)$ in terms of $\mathbf{x}_{NB}$ yields

$$f(x_1, x_3) = 10x_1 + 25[5 - \tfrac{1}{2}(x_1 + x_3)] - 10x_1^2$$
$$- [5 - \tfrac{1}{2}(x_1 + x_3)]^2 - 4x_1[5 - \tfrac{1}{2}(x_1 + x_3)]$$

$$\left.\frac{\partial f}{\partial x_1}\right|_{\mathbf{x}_{NB}=0} = -\frac{35}{2}$$

$$\left.\frac{\partial f}{\partial x_3}\right|_{\mathbf{x}_{NB}=0} = -\frac{15}{2}$$

Thus neither nonbasic variable can be introduced to increase $f(\cdot)$ and the optimal solution has been attained. The solution is $x_1 = x_3 = 0$, and $x_2 = 5$, $x_4 = 4$.

Theil and Van der Panne Algorithm

The final technique to be discussed for quadratic programming is the Theil and Van der Panne algorithm [8]. A foundation for this algorithm was developed in the problems in Chapter 3. It is based on the notion that an optimal solution $\mathbf{x}^0$ to

$$\max f(x) = \mathbf{cx} + \mathbf{x}^T\mathbf{Gx}$$

subject to

$$\mathbf{Ax} \le \mathbf{b}\,^{12}$$

where at the optimal solution

$$\begin{aligned} \mathbf{a}_i^T\mathbf{x}^0 &= b_i & i &= 1,\ldots,p \\ \mathbf{a}_i^T\mathbf{x}^0 &< b_i & i &= p+1,\ldots, M \end{aligned} \tag{4.55}$$

will also be an optimal solution to

$$\max f(\mathbf{x}) = \mathbf{cx} + \mathbf{x}^T\mathbf{Gx}$$

subject to

$$\mathbf{a}_i^T\mathbf{x} = b_i \qquad i = 1,\ldots,p$$

The algorithm has some intuitive appeal, especially for engineers. We have found that many engineers when faced with a constrained optimization problem will develop an approach much akin to this algorithm. The procedure is outlined below. The reader is asked to develop the necessary proofs in the problem set.

The first step in the algorithm is to solve the unconstrained problem,

$$\max f(\mathbf{x}) = \mathbf{cx} + \mathbf{x}^T\mathbf{Gx}$$

Call the optimal solution to this problem $\mathbf{x}_1^0$. If $\mathbf{Ax}_1^0 \le \mathbf{b}$, then $\mathbf{x}_1^0 = \mathbf{x}^0$, the optimal solution to the original quadratic programming problem. Suppose, however, that at $\mathbf{x}_1^0$

$$\mathbf{a}_i^T\mathbf{x}_1^0 > b_i \qquad i = 1,\ldots,p$$

---

[12] In this formulation we have incorporated $\mathbf{x} \ge 0$ in $\mathbf{Ax} \le \mathbf{b}$.

One then solves p problems of the form

$$\max f(\mathbf{x}) = \mathbf{c}\mathbf{x} + \mathbf{x}^T\mathbf{G}\mathbf{x}$$

subject to $\mathbf{a}_i^T\mathbf{x} = b_i$. The solutions to these problems are denoted by $\mathbf{x}_{2i}^0$, $i = 1, \ldots, p$. If for some $j \leq p$, $\mathbf{x}_{2j}^0$ is feasible to the original problem, it is the optimal solution to this problem. If $\mathbf{x}_{2i}^0 \neq \mathbf{x}^0$ for some i, then for each solution $\mathbf{x}_{2i}^0$ a subset of the remaining constraints is violated,

$$\mathbf{a}_j^T\mathbf{x}_{2j}^0 > b_j \qquad j \in V(\mathbf{x}_{2j}^0) \tag{4.56}$$

where $V(\mathbf{x})$ is the set of indices associated with the constraints violated at $\mathbf{x}$. One then solves a sequence of problems holding two constraints as equalities. If the optimal solution to any of these problems is feasible and if the solution to the problems obtained by holding only one constraint active violates the relaxed constraint, the solution is optimal.

The procedure is described more precisely below. Consider problems holding K constraints active,

$$\mathbf{a}_i^T\mathbf{x} = b_i \qquad i = 1, \ldots, K$$

and that at least one constraint of the original problem is violated by each solution to the previous set of problems,[13]

$$V(\mathbf{x}_K^0) \neq \varnothing \qquad \text{all } K \tag{4.57}$$

Then to each set of constraints held active to obtain the solution $\mathbf{x}_K^0$ append one of the constraints in the set $V(\mathbf{x}_K^0)$ and solve this new problem. The solution to one of these new problems, $\mathbf{x}_{K+1}^0$, will be the optimal solution to the original problem if and only if

1. $\mathbf{A}\mathbf{x}_{K+1}^0 \leq \mathbf{b}$;
2. the optimal solution to the set of $K + 1$ problems generated by deleting, one at a time, one of the constraints violates this constraint.

An example is given below to help the reader grasp the essentials of this algorithm. The example is the one solved previously both by the modified simplex and Beale's algorithm. Recall that we had

$$\max f(x_1, x_2) = 10x_1 + 25x_2 - 10x_1^2 - x_2^2 - 4x_1x_2$$

subject to

(1) $x_1 + x_2 \leq 9$		(3) $x_1 \geq 0$
(2) $x_1 + 2x_2 \leq 10$		(4) $x_2 \geq 0$

The Theil-Van der Panne approach is to solve the unconstrained problem first;

$$\max f(x_1, x_2) = 10x_1 + 25x_2 - 10x_1^2 - x_2^2 - 4x_1x_2$$

---

[13] $\varnothing$ denotes the null set.

Solving this problem we have

$$\frac{\partial f}{\partial x_1} = 10 - 20x_1 - 4x_2 = 0$$

$$\frac{\partial f}{\partial x_2} = 25 - 4x_1 - 2x_2 = 0$$

The solution to these two equations is $x_1 = -\frac{40}{12}$, $x_2 = \frac{115}{6}$. This point violates constraints 1, 2, and 3. Thus

$$\{j\} = V(\mathbf{x}_1^0) = \{1, 2, 3\}$$

This point is illustrated in Figure 4.11.

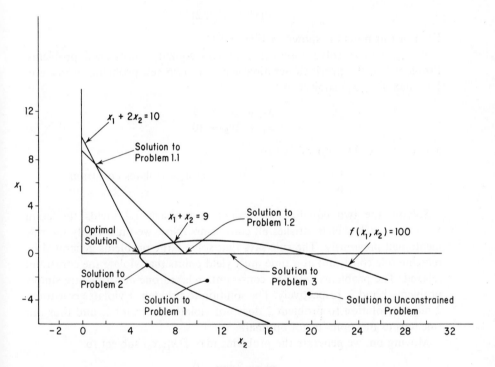

Figure 4.11.

The algorithm now calls for us to solve three new problems. They are

1. max $f(x_1, x_2)$ subject to $x_1 + x_2 = 9$.
2. max $f(x_1, x_2)$ subject to $x_1 + 2x_2 = 10$.
3. max $f(x_1, x_2)$ subject to $x_1 = 0$.

Solving the first problem yields

$$x_2 = \frac{159}{14} = 11\frac{5}{14} \qquad x_1 = -\frac{33}{14} = -2\frac{5}{14}$$

which violates constraints 2 and 3 and $V(\mathbf{x}_{21}^0) = \{2, 3\}$. The solution to problem 2 yields the point

$$x_2 = \frac{365}{66} \qquad x_1 = 10 - 2x_2 = \frac{660 - 730}{66} = \frac{-70}{66}$$

This violates constraint 3, $x_1 \geq 0$. Thus

$$\{j\} = V(\mathbf{x}_{22}^0) = \{3\}$$

Problem 3 $(x_1 = 0)$ becomes

$$\max f(x_2) = 25x_2 - x_2^2$$

The solution is $x_2 = 12\frac{1}{2}$, which violates constraints 1 and 2. Therefore,

$$V(\mathbf{x}_{23}^0) = \{1, 2\}$$

Each of this points is shown in Figure 4.11.

We now must solve a sequence of two equality-constrained problems. Problem 1 in the previous iteration generates two new problems, which are:
1.1. max $f(x_1, x_2)$ subject to

$$\begin{aligned} x_1 + x_2 &= 9 \\ x_1 + 2x_2 &= 10 \end{aligned}$$

and 1.2. max $f(x_1, x_2)$ subject to

$$\left.\begin{aligned} x_1 + x_2 &= 9 \\ x_1 &= 0 \end{aligned}\right\} \Rightarrow x_2 = 9 \qquad \begin{aligned} &\text{(which clearly violates constraint} \\ &\qquad\qquad x_1 + 2x_2 \leq 10) \end{aligned}$$

Solving the two equality constraints in problem 1.1 yields the point $x_1 = 8$, $x_2 = 1$, which satisfies all constraints. Now we must apply the rule mentioned previously. The rule says that solving the problems generated by relaxing one constraint at a time must yield points that violate the constraint relaxed. The problems with the constraints relaxed one at a time are simply problems 1 and 2, respectively. The solution to problem 1 violates constraint 2 but the solution to problem 2 does not violate constraint 1, and thus our rule tells us this point is not optimal.

Moving on, we generate the problem: max $f(x_1, x_2)$ subject to

$$\begin{aligned} x_1 + 2x_2 &= 10 \\ x_1 &= 0 \end{aligned}$$

by appending to the set of equality constraints one of those violated in the solution to problem 2. Since the only one violated was 3, this is the only new problem generated from problem 2. The solution to the equation occurs at

$$x_1 = 0 \qquad x_2 = 5$$

Applying the rule to check for optimality we obtain the problems max $f(x_1, x_2)$ subject to $x_1 + 2x_2 = 10$ and max $f(x_1, x_2)$ subject to $x_1 = 0$.

But these are problems 2 and 3, respectively. The solution to problem 2 violates constraint 3 and the solution to 3 violates constraint 2. Thus the rule is satisfied and the point $x_1 = 0$, $x_2 = 5$, is optimal.

4.4   Transformations

We now turn our attention to ways of transforming a constrained optimization problem into an unconstrained problem (or problems). We have already developed one such procedure by the use of the Lagrange multiplier concept. We have shown that extreme points of a constrained objective function correspond to stationary points of the Lagrange function. One way to generate extreme points is to find all points where the first derivatives of the Lagrange function vanish. Under the proper assumptions regarding finiteness of the objective function at every feasible solution and the nonsingularity of all Jacobians of the constraints the desired optimum will be generated. However, when faced with a nonlinear objective function subject to nonlinear constraints, the solution to the necessary conditions may be very difficult to obtain.

There are other ways of transforming constrained problems into unconstrained problems. The most promising one is the penalty function technique or *sequential unconstrained minimization technique* (SUMT) [9, 10]. Consider the problem: min $f(\mathbf{x})$ subject to

$$g_i(\mathbf{x}) \le 0 \qquad i = 1, \ldots, M$$

It is more convenient for our purposes to consider problems where the constraint inequalities are reversed. Clearly no generality is lost by considering the problem: min $f(\mathbf{x})$ subject to

$$h_i(\mathbf{x}) \ge 0 \qquad i = 1, \ldots, M$$

where $h_i(\mathbf{x}) = -g_i(\mathbf{x})$. The SUMT technique involves constructing the functions

$$P(\mathbf{x}, r_K) = f(\mathbf{x}) + r_k \sum_{i=1}^{M} \frac{1}{h_i(\mathbf{x})} \qquad k = 1, 2, \ldots, \quad r_K > 0 \qquad (4.58)$$

and minimizing the $P(\cdot)$ function for a decreasing sequence of values of r_K. We shall show for a convex programming problem which has a feasible interior point to the constraints that the solutions, $\mathbf{x}(r_k)$, corresponding to r_K converge to the optimal solution $\mathbf{x}^0$ as $k \to \infty$ if $r_k \to 0$ as $k \to \infty$.

Since $f(\mathbf{x})$ and $g_i(\mathbf{x})$ are convex (with at least one being strictly convex) the $P(\cdot)$ function is strictly convex for $r_k > 0$. Thus the minimum of $P(\mathbf{x}, r_k)$ occurs at the point where

$$\frac{\partial P}{\partial x_j} = 0 \qquad j = 1, \ldots, N \qquad (4.59)$$

and furthermore this point is unique. Since we assume that P is twice differentiable, the value of $\mathbf{x}$ which solves this set of equations can be expressed as $\mathbf{x}(r_K)$.[14]

To show that the sequence of $\mathbf{x}(r_k)$ converges to $\mathbf{x}^0$ (the solution to the original optimization problem) we use the argument advanced by Fiacco and McCormick [10]. We can choose some $\epsilon > 0$ such that for some $\hat{\mathbf{x}}^*$ in the interior of the constraint set

$$f(\hat{\mathbf{x}}^*) - f(\mathbf{x}^0) < \frac{\epsilon}{2} \tag{4.60}$$

This is possible since (1) $f(\mathbf{x}) \geq f(\mathbf{x}^0)$ for all feasible $\mathbf{x}$, and (2) $f(\cdot)$ is continuous. Next select some K, say K^*, such that $r_{K^\bullet} < \min_i (1/2M)[h_i(\mathbf{x}^*)]\epsilon$. By definition of $f(\mathbf{x}^0)$ we have

$$f(\mathbf{x}^0) \leq \min_{\mathbf{x}} P(\mathbf{x}, r_K) = P[\mathbf{x}(r_K), r_K] \tag{4.61}$$

The first inequality follows because

$$P(\mathbf{x}, r_K) = f(\mathbf{x}) + r_K \sum_{i}^{M} \frac{1}{h_i(\mathbf{x})} \tag{4.62}$$

and $r_K \sum_{i=1}^{M} [1/h_i(\mathbf{x})] > 0$. But

$$P[\mathbf{x}(r_K), r_K] \leq P[\mathbf{x}(r_{K^\bullet}), r_K] \tag{4.63}$$

because $\mathbf{x}(r_K)$ minimized $P[\mathbf{x}(r_K), r_K]$. With our choice of K^* we may write

$$f(\mathbf{x}^0) \leq P[\mathbf{x}(r_K), r_k] \leq P\ [\mathbf{x}(r_{K^\bullet}), r_K] < P[\mathbf{x}(r_{K^\bullet}), r_{K^\bullet}]$$

The last step follows since $r_K < r_{K^\bullet}$. Therefore,

$$P[\mathbf{x}(r_{K^\bullet}), r_K] = f[\mathbf{x}(r_{K^\bullet})] + r_K \sum_{i=1}^{M} \frac{1}{h_i[\mathbf{x}(r_{K^\bullet})]}$$

$$\leq f[\mathbf{x}(r_{K^\bullet})] + r_{K^\bullet} \sum_{i=1}^{M} \frac{1}{h_i[\mathbf{x}(r_{K^\bullet})]}$$

$$= P[\mathbf{x}(r_{K^\bullet}), r_{K^\bullet}] \tag{4.64}$$

The inequality is easily proved by (1) subtracting $f[\mathbf{x}(r_{K^\bullet})]$ from both sides, and (2) noting that $\sum \{1/h_i[\mathbf{x}(r_{K^\bullet})]\} > 0$. The final step involves recalling that

$$P[\mathbf{x}(r_{K^\bullet}), r_{K^\bullet}] \leq P(\mathbf{x}^*, r_{K^\bullet}) = f(\mathbf{x}^*) + r_{K^\bullet} \sum_{i=1}^{M} \frac{1}{h_i(\mathbf{x}^*)} \tag{4.65}$$

---

[14] The proof is based on an application of the implicit function theorem discussed in Chapter 2.

Tracing back through the inequalities presented above we have

$$f(\mathbf{x}^0) \le P[\mathbf{x}(r_K), r_K] \le P[\mathbf{x}(r_{K^\cdot}), r_{K^\cdot}] \le f(\mathbf{x}^*) + r_{K^\cdot} \sum_{i=1}^{M} \frac{1}{h_i(\mathbf{x}^*)}$$

But from continuity and the choice of $\mathbf{x}^*$ we know

$$(1) \quad f(\mathbf{x}^*) < f(\mathbf{x}^0) + \frac{\epsilon}{2}$$

$$(2) \quad r_{K^\cdot} < \min_j \frac{\epsilon}{2M}[h_j(\mathbf{x}^*)]$$

Using these two results in the right side of the inequality we have

$$f(\mathbf{x}^0) \le P[\mathbf{x}(r_K), r_K] < f(\mathbf{x}^0) + \frac{\epsilon}{2} + \frac{\epsilon}{2} = f(\mathbf{x}^0) + \epsilon \qquad (4.66)$$

Thus as $K \to \infty$, $P[\mathbf{x}(r_K), r_K]$ must converge to $f(\mathbf{x}^0)$. As a result of this convergence and the fact that $r_K \to 0$ as $K \to \infty$, we have that

$$(1) \quad \lim_{K \to \infty} f[\mathbf{x}(r_K)] = f(\mathbf{x}^0) \qquad (4.67)$$

$$(2) \quad \lim_{K \to \infty} r_K \sum_{i=1}^{M} \frac{1}{h_i[\mathbf{x}(r_K)]} = 0 \qquad (4.68)$$

We have now converted the problem of solving a nonlinear (in general) constrained problem into a sequence of unconstrained minimization problems. The accumulation point of the sequence of minimums of the unconstrained problems is the value of the objective function to the constrained problem. The procedure is to choose a value of $r_K < r_{K-1}$ and solve the minimization problem

$$\min_{\mathbf{x}} P(\mathbf{x}, r_K)$$

and then advance K by 1 and repeat.

Notice that for all $r_K > 0$ the solution $\mathbf{x}(r_K)$ will be in the interior of the constraint set. Thus the requirement that the interior be nonempty. If there did not exist a feasible $\mathbf{x}$ for which

$$h_i(\mathbf{x}) > 0 \qquad i = 1, \ldots, M$$

the first $P(\cdot)$ function would not be finite for any $r_K > 0$, because $\sum [1/h_i(\mathbf{x})]$ would be unbounded.

To illustrate the calculations we shall consider the example developed by Fiacco and McCormick [10],

$$\min f(x_1, x_2) = \frac{(x_1 + 1)^3}{3} + x_2$$

subject to

$$h_1(x_1, x_2) = x_1 - 1 \geq 0$$
$$h_2(x_1, x_2) = x_2 \geq 0$$

Forming the penalty function we obtain

$$P(x_1, x_2, r) = \frac{(x_1 + 1)^3}{3} + x_2 + r\left(\frac{1}{x_1 - 1} + \frac{1}{x_2}\right)$$

In more complicated problems which would require numerical solutions we would now choose a sequence of $r_k > 0$ so that $r_{k+1} < r_k$ and minimize the $P(\cdot)$ function for each r. However, in this case we can obtain the solution analytically for any general r. Thus

$$\frac{\partial P(\cdot)}{\partial x_1} = (x_1 + 1)^2 - \frac{r}{(x_1 - 1)^2} = 0$$

$$\frac{\partial P(\cdot)}{\partial x_2} = 1 - \frac{r}{x_2^2} = 0$$

The solution to these equations is $x_1 = (r^{1/2} + 1)^{1/2}$ and $x_2 = r^{1/2}$. Substituting these results into the $P(\cdot)$ function yields

$$P(r) = \frac{[(r^{1/2} + 1)^{1/2} + 1]^3}{3} + r^{1/2} + \frac{r}{(r^{1/2} + 1)^{1/2} - 1} + \frac{r}{r^{1/2}}$$

$$\lim_{r \to 0} P(r) = \frac{2^3}{3} = \frac{8}{3}$$

and the values of x_1^0 and x_2^0 are

$$x_1^0 = \lim_{r \to 0} (r^{1/2} + 1)^{1/2} = 1 \qquad x_2^0 = \lim_{r \to 0} r^{1/2} = 0$$

So far we have indicated only that $P[\mathbf{x}(r_K), r_K]$ converges to $f(\mathbf{x}^0)$ in the limit. One could conceivably spend a great deal of computation time minimizing the sequence of $P(\cdot)$ functions with very little improvement in $f(\mathbf{x})$ during the course of a large number of iterations. However, using duality theory a lower bound on $f(\mathbf{x}^0)$ can be developed. Using this lower bound together with the current value of $f[\mathbf{x}(r_K)]$ as an upper bound, we can obtain upper and lower limits for $f(\mathbf{x}^0)$. If sufficiently tight bounds can be obtained at some stage the computations may be terminated.

The lower bounds are developed as follows. Given the primal problem (assumed to be a convex program) minimize $f(\mathbf{x})$ subject to

$$h_i(\mathbf{x}) \geq 0 \qquad i = 1, \ldots, M$$

there exists a dual problem which is

$$\max F(\mathbf{x}, \boldsymbol{\lambda}) = f(\mathbf{x}) + \sum_{i=1}^{M} \lambda_i h_i(\mathbf{x})$$

subject to

$$\frac{\partial F}{\partial x_j} = 0 \quad j = 1, \ldots, N \text{ and } \lambda_i \geq 0 \quad i = 1, \ldots, M$$

If we define

$$\lambda_i(r_K) = \frac{r_k}{h_i^2[\mathbf{x}(r_K)]} \quad i = 1, \ldots, M \tag{4.69}$$

then $\lambda_i(r_K) > 0$. This point also satisfies the dual constraints $\partial F/\partial x_j = 0$, because at $\mathbf{x}(r_K)$,

$$\frac{\partial P}{\partial x_j}\Big|_{\mathbf{x}(r_K)} = \frac{\partial f(\cdot)}{\partial x_j} - r_K \sum_{i=1}^{M} \left\{ \frac{\frac{\partial h_i}{\partial x_j}\Big|}{[h_i(\cdot)]^2}\Big|_{\mathbf{x}(r_K)} \right\} = \frac{\partial F}{\partial x_j}\Big|_{\mathbf{x}(r_K)}$$

$\partial P/\partial x_j|_{\mathbf{x}(r_K)}$ vanishes since $\mathbf{x}(r_K)$ minimized $P(\mathbf{x}, r_K)$.

We have shown previously that for some K there is an ϵ such that

$$f(\mathbf{x}^0) \leq f[\mathbf{x}(r_K)] < f(\mathbf{x}^0) + \epsilon$$

and

$$0 < r_K \sum_{i=1}^{M} \frac{1}{h_i[\mathbf{x}(r_K)]} < \epsilon$$

Rearranging the last term yields

$$-\epsilon < -r_K \sum_{i=1}^{M} \frac{1}{h_i[\mathbf{x}(r_K)]} < 0$$

Combining the two inequalities yields

$$f(\mathbf{x}^0) - \epsilon < f[\mathbf{x}(r_K)] - r_K \sum_{i=1}^{M} \frac{1}{h_i[\mathbf{x}(r_K)]} < f(\mathbf{x}^0) + \epsilon \tag{4.70}$$

Thus

$$f[\mathbf{x}(r_K)] - r_K \sum_{i=1}^{M} \frac{1}{h_i[\mathbf{x}(r_K)]} \leq f(\mathbf{x}^0) \leq f[\mathbf{x}(r_K)] \tag{4.71}$$

But the left side is simply the dual function (if we properly define λ_i). Thus a lower bound on $f(\mathbf{x}^0)$ is the current value of the dual-objective function. The upper bound is the current value of $f(\cdot)$ at the Kth iteration. If at some iteration the difference between the upper and lower bound, which is

$$r_K \sum_{i=1}^{M} \frac{1}{h_i[\mathbf{x}(r_K)]}$$

is sufficiently small, the computations may be terminated.

We have shown how to convert the constrained problem into a sequence of unconstrained problems and how to develop convergence criteria for this sequence of minima. Now we must point the way for solution procedures to the unconstrained problem. At first glance we might be tempted to point out that this solution is obtained by setting the partial derivatives of the $P(\cdot)$ function equal to zero. However, if the original problem was nonlinear, the P function will be nonlinear also (except under certain specialized conditions) and we would again be faced with solving a system of simultaneous, nonlinear equations

$$\frac{\partial P}{\partial x_j} = 0 \quad j = 1, \ldots, N$$

Here we rely on the direct optimization procedure discussed earlier in this chapter. The Fletcher-Powell and gradient procedures have both been used with good success to determine the minima of the $P(\cdot)$ functions. Fiacco and McCormick point out that when the problem is convex, a second-order gradient procedure works very well. The Fletcher-Powell method has also been used very successfully with nonquadratic functions. The union of these two concepts appears to be one of the most effective approaches to nonlinear programming problems.

Notice that we have dealt only with problems where the constraints were inequalities. A similar procedure to solve problems with equality constraints has been developed which involves a modification of the $P(\cdot)$ function. For those equality constraints we introduce terms of the form

$$\left(\frac{1}{r_K}\right) \sum_{i=M+1}^{p} [h_i(\mathbf{x})]^2$$

Notice that as $r_K \to 0$ this term will become unbounded unless $\sum [h_i(\mathbf{x})] \to 0$ also. Using this approach, however, we lose the convenient lower bound we developed for the inequality-constrained case.

Other types of penalty functions might be considered. One example is to choose $\ln h_i(\mathbf{x})$ instead of $1/h_i(\mathbf{x})$. There is no doubt that rates of convergence will depend on the choice of the form of penalty function used.

The final topic of this section is a discussion of scheme for the choice of the initial $\mathbf{x}$ to minimize $P(\mathbf{x}, r_K)$. Some work has been reported which indicates that an extrapolation procedure may be useful to estimate $\mathbf{x}(r_K)$. Thus given $\mathbf{x}(r_{K-2})$, $\mathbf{x}(r_{K-1})$, r_{K-2}, r_{K-1}, and the next value of r, r_K, it is not unreasonable to choose as an initial guess of $\mathbf{x}_K$ the value obtained from

$$\hat{\mathbf{x}}(r_K) = a + br_K$$

[$\hat{\mathbf{x}}(r_K)$ indicates an estimate of $\mathbf{x}(r_K)$], where a and b are determined from the information about $\mathbf{x}(r_{K-2})$ and $\mathbf{x}(r_{K-1})$. In practice a slightly more general procedure is to use information at the last three optimal solutions $\mathbf{x}(r_{K-3})$, $\mathbf{x}(r_{K-2})$, and $\mathbf{x}(r_{K-1})$ to fit a quadratic equation to the data.

4.5   Geometric Programming

Next we shall focus our attention on a nonlinear programming technique initially derived from inequalities rather than the calculus and its extensions. The name geometric programming arose because the geometric-arithmetic mean inequality was the basis of the development. We shall first consider the unconstrained problem and to do this we shall derive the inequality using the classical optimization theory developed in Chapter 2. Then using the inequality we shall indicate how these relationships may be used to obtain optimal solutions to nonlinear problems. We shall see that when the problem has a specialized structure, the solution may be obtained simply by solving a set of linear equations. This rather startling result will hopefully stimulate additional research into the theory of inequalities. Conceivably a similar result may be obtained for variational problems using analogous inequalities from functional analysis.

Suppose we wish to maximize

$$f(\mathbf{x}) = \prod_{n=1}^{N} x_n$$

subject to

$$\sum_{n=1}^{N} x_n = c < \infty$$

$$x_n \geq 0 \qquad n = 1, \ldots, N$$

The maximum will clearly not occur where any of the $x_j = 0$ for $f(\mathbf{x})$ is also zero at this point. For the moment let us ignore these inequalities (in the spirit of the Theil-Van der Panne arguments) and solve the simpler problem

$$\max f(\mathbf{x}) = \prod_{n=1}^{N} x_n$$

subject to

$$\sum_{n=1}^{N} x_n = c < \infty$$

Forming the Lagrange function yields

$$F(\mathbf{x}, \lambda) = f(\mathbf{x}) + \lambda \left(\sum_{n=1}^{N} x_n - c \right)$$

The necessary conditions are

$$\frac{\partial F}{\partial x_j} = \prod_{\substack{n=1 \\ n \neq j}}^{N} x_n + \lambda = 0 \qquad j = 1, \ldots, N$$

Solving for λ we find

$$\lambda = -\prod_{\substack{n=1 \\ n \neq j}}^{N} x_n$$

But j can be any integer from 1 to N and so we can write

$$\lambda = -\prod_{\substack{n=1 \\ n \neq k}}^{N} x_n$$

Equating these two results we obtain

$$x_1 x_2 \cdots x_{j-1} x_{j+1} \cdots x_N = x_1 x_2 \cdots x_{k-1} x_{k+1} \cdots x_N$$

Since we have assumed $x_j \neq 0$ we obtain

$$x_k^0 = x_j^0 = a \qquad \text{for all } j, k = 1, \ldots, N$$

where a is some constant. But

$$\sum_{n=1}^{N} x_n = c = \sum_{n=1}^{N} a = Na$$

Thus

$$x_j^0 = a = \frac{c}{N} \qquad j = 1, \ldots, N$$

and

$$f(\mathbf{x}^0) = \prod_{n=1}^{N} \frac{c}{N} = \left(\frac{c}{N}\right)^N$$

We have established that

$$\max f(\mathbf{x}) = \left(\frac{c}{N}\right)^N$$

It follows then that

$$f(\mathbf{x}) \leq \left(\frac{c}{N}\right)^N \tag{4.72}$$

where $c = \sum_{n=1}^{N} x_n$. Therefore,

$$f(\mathbf{x}) = \prod_{n=1}^{N} x_n \leq \left(\frac{\sum_{n=1}^{N} x_n}{N}\right)^N \tag{4.73}$$

Taking the Nth root of each side yields

$$\left(\prod_{n=1}^{N} x_n\right)^{1/N} \leq \frac{1}{N} \sum_{n=1}^{N} x_n \tag{4.74}$$

with equality only when $x_n = c/N$. This is the geometric-arithmetic mean inequality.

We have obtained an upper bound on $f(\mathbf{x})$ or, looking at the problem differently, a lower bound on $(1/N) \sum_{n=1}^{N} x_n$:

$$\frac{1}{N} \sum_{n=1}^{N} x_n \geq \left(\prod_{n=1}^{N} x_n \right)^{1/N}$$

Optimization problems may be approached from either viewpoint. We again encounter the dual relationship discussed previously. The dual problem will, in many cases, be the easier to solve.

A more general form of the inequality is[15]

$$\sum_{n=1}^{N} \delta_n x_n \geq \prod_{n=1}^{N} x_n^{\delta_n}$$

where δ_n are nonnegative weights whose sum is 1. Zener, Duffin, and Peterson [14] used this result to derive the geometric programming relationships. However, we shall pursue an argument more closely related to classical optimization theory. This approach was suggested by Wilde and Beightler [12]. Consider the problem

$$\min f(\mathbf{x}) = \sum_{j=1}^{P} c_j P_j(\mathbf{x})$$

with $c_j > 0$ and $P_j(\mathbf{x})$ has the form

$$P_j(\mathbf{x}) = \prod_{i=1}^{N} x_i^{a_{ij}}$$

where a_{ij} may be any real number. Zener called the $P_j(\cdot)$ posynomials because they are positive and closely related to polynomials.

This problem can be approached by taking the partial derivatives with respect to each x_k and requiring the result to equal zero. Thus

$$\frac{\partial f(\mathbf{x})}{\partial x_k} = \sum_{j=1}^{P} c_j \frac{\partial P_j(\mathbf{x})}{\partial x_k} = 0 \qquad k = 1, \ldots, N$$

But[16]

$$\frac{\partial P_j(\mathbf{x})}{\partial x_k} = \frac{a_{kj}}{x_k} P_j(\mathbf{x})$$

---

[15] The δ's in this section should not be confused with the Kronecker delta.
[16] Recall we require each x_k to be positive.

Putting this result into the previous equation yields

$$\frac{1}{x_k} \sum_{j=1}^{P} a_{kj} c_j P_j = 0$$

Since each $x_k > 0$ and each $c_j > 0$, $f(\mathbf{x}^0)$ will be positive. Thus we may divide $\partial f(\mathbf{x})/\partial x_k$ by $f(\mathbf{x}^0)$,

$$\sum_{j=1}^{P} \frac{a_{kj} c_j P_j}{f(\mathbf{x}^0)} = 0 \qquad k = 1, \ldots, N$$

Let us now make a simple transformation of variables. Define

$$\delta_j = \frac{c_j P_j}{f(\mathbf{x}^0)} \qquad j = 1, \ldots, P \tag{4.75}$$

Using this definition and the necessary condition we find that

$$\sum_{j=1}^{P} a_{kj} \delta_j = 0 \qquad k = 1, \ldots, N \tag{4.76}$$

By virtue of the definition of δ_j we obtain

$$\sum_{j=1}^{P} \delta_j = \frac{1}{f(\mathbf{x}^0)} \sum_{j=1}^{P} c_j P_j \tag{4.77}$$

which must equal 1 at the optimal solution.

Summarizing the results we have

$$\sum_{j=1}^{P} \delta_j = 1 \qquad \text{(normality)}$$

$$\sum_{j=1}^{P} a_{kj} \delta_j = 0 \qquad k = 1, \ldots, N \text{ (orthogonality)}$$

It is more convenient to work in matrix notation. Define

$$\mathbf{A} = \begin{bmatrix} 1 & \cdots & 1 \\ a_{11} & \cdots & a_{1P} \\ \vdots & & \vdots \\ a_{N1} & \cdots & a_{NP} \end{bmatrix} \qquad \mathbf{\delta} = \begin{bmatrix} \delta_1 \\ \vdots \\ \delta_P \end{bmatrix} \qquad \mathbf{b} = \begin{bmatrix} 1 \\ 0 \\ \vdots \\ 0 \end{bmatrix}$$

Thus we require from the normality and orthogonality conditions

$$\mathbf{A}\mathbf{\delta} = \mathbf{b} \tag{4.78}$$

We have now reduced the original, highly nonlinear problem to one of finding the correct set of δ which solves these linear, nonhomogeneous equations. Recall that

1. There will be no solution if $r(\mathbf{A}, \mathbf{b}) > r(\mathbf{A})$, where $(\mathbf{A}, \mathbf{b})$ denotes the matrix $\mathbf{A}$ augmented by $\mathbf{b}$,

$$(\mathbf{A}, \mathbf{b}) = \begin{bmatrix} 1 & \cdots & 1 & b_0 \\ a_{11} & \cdots & a_{1P} & b_1 \\ \vdots & & \vdots & \\ a_{N1} & \cdots & a_{NP} & b_N \end{bmatrix}$$

2. There will be a unique solution if $\mathbf{A}$ is square and

$$r(\mathbf{A}, \mathbf{b}) = r(\mathbf{A})$$

3. There will be an infinite number of solutions if

$$P > N + 1 \quad \text{or} \quad r(\mathbf{A}) < P$$

When condition 1 exists there is no vector $\mathbf{x} > \mathbf{0}$ for which $f(\mathbf{x})$ achieves a minimum. There is a unique minimum when condition 2 is satisfied. When condition 3 is the result, additional work must be done to find the global minimum.

Notice that when condition 2 is satisfied we simply solve for δ by

$$\delta = \mathbf{A}^{-1}\mathbf{b} \tag{4.79}$$

Thus the optimal solution is obtained (in terms of the δ) by carrying out simple algebraic manipulations.

Let us simplify the expression for min $f(\mathbf{x})$. We know that at the optimal solution

$$f(\mathbf{x}^0) = \frac{c_j P_j}{\delta_j} = \frac{c_j \prod_{n=1}^{N} x_n^{a_{jn}}}{\delta_j}$$

Raising both sides to the power δ_j and taking the product we find

$$\prod_{j=1}^{P} f(\mathbf{x}^0)^{\delta_j} = \prod_{j=1}^{P} \left(\frac{c_j \prod_{n=1}^{N} x_n^{a_{jn}}}{\delta_j} \right)^{\delta_j} \tag{4.80}$$

The left side reduces to $f(\mathbf{x}^0)$ because $\sum \delta_j = 1$, and

$$\prod_{j=1}^{P} f(\mathbf{x}^0)^{\delta_j} = [f(\mathbf{x}^0)]^{\sum \delta_j} = f(\mathbf{x}^0)$$

Since all products are finite, the order of multiplication may be reversed on the right side to yield

$$\prod_{j=1}^{P} \left[\left(\frac{c_j}{\delta_j} \right) \prod_{n=1}^{N} x_n^{a_{jn}} \right]^{\delta_j} = \prod_{j=1}^{P} \left(\frac{c_j}{\delta_j} \right)^{\delta_j} \prod_{j=1}^{P} \left(\prod_{n=1}^{N} x_n^{a_{jn}} \right)^{\delta_j}$$

$$= \prod_{j=1}^{P} \left(\frac{c_j}{\delta_j} \right)^{\delta_j} \prod_{n=1}^{N} x_n^{\Sigma_j \, a_{jn} \delta_j}$$

$$= \prod_{j=1}^{P} \left(\frac{c_j}{\delta_j} \right)^{\delta_j} \prod_{n=1}^{N} x_n^{0}$$

$$= \prod_{j=1}^{P} \left(\frac{c_j}{\delta_j} \right)^{\delta_j} \qquad (4.81)$$

Thus

$$\min f(\mathbf{x}) = f(\mathbf{x}^0) = \prod_{j=1}^{P} \left(\frac{c_j}{\delta_j} \right)^{\delta_j}$$

and therefore

$$f(\mathbf{x}) \geq \prod_{j=1}^{P} \left(\frac{c_j}{\delta_j} \right)^{\delta_j} \qquad (4.82)$$

where the δ_j must satisfy the orthogonality and normality conditions derived earlier.

When there is a unique solution for $\boldsymbol{\delta}$ (condition 2 is satisfied) the problem is solved except for calculating the values of the x_n from

$$c_j \prod_{n=1}^{N} x_n^{a_{jn}} = \delta_j f(\mathbf{x}^0) \qquad (4.83)$$

When condition 3 is satisfied we must have

$$\max \prod_{j=1}^{P} \left(\frac{c_j}{\delta_j} \right)^{\delta_j}$$

subject to $\mathbf{A}\boldsymbol{\delta} = \mathbf{b}$, since

$$\min f(\mathbf{x}) = \max \prod_{j=1}^{P} \left(\frac{c_j}{\delta_j} \right)^{\delta_j}$$

Example: Consider the economic-lot-size problem where we wish to find the optimal inventory level to minimize

$$f(q) = c_1 q + \frac{c_2}{q}$$

In this example

$$\begin{aligned} P_1 &= q & a_{11} &= 1 \\ P_2 &= q^{-1} & a_{12} &= -1 \end{aligned}$$

We have 2 δ's, one for each term. Forming the normality condition we obtain $\delta_1 + \delta_2 = 1$. The orthogonality condition

$$\sum_{j=1}^{2} a_{1j}\delta_j = 0$$

yields

$$1\cdot\delta_1 + (-1)\cdot\delta_2 = 0 \qquad \text{or} \qquad \delta_1 - \delta_2 = 0$$

From this we deduce that

$$\delta_1 = \delta_2 = \tfrac{1}{2}$$

$$f(q^0) = \left(\frac{c_1}{\delta_1}\right)^{\delta_1}\left(\frac{c_2}{\delta_2}\right)^{\delta_2} = \left(\frac{c_1}{1/2}\right)^{1/2}\left(\frac{c_2}{1/2}\right)^{1/2}$$

$$= 2\sqrt{c_1 c_2}$$

and from the defining equation for δ_1 we have

$$\delta_1 f(q^0) = c_1 P_1 = c_1 q$$

Thus

$$q^0 = \frac{\delta_1 f(q^0)}{c_1} = \sqrt{\frac{c_2}{c_1}}$$

We shall now investigate the case when we wish to minimize an objective function that is a sum of Zener-Duffin posynomials subject to equality constraints of the same form: min $f(\mathbf{x})$ subject to

$$g_i(\mathbf{x}) = \sum_{k=1}^{P(i)} c_{ik} P_{ik}(\mathbf{x}) = 1 \qquad i = 1, \ldots, M$$

$P(i)$ denotes the number of terms in the ith constraint and

$$P_{ik}(\mathbf{x}) = \prod_{n=1}^{N} x_n^{a_{ikn}}$$

Although the notation is clumsy, the concept is the same as we have investigated previously. We form the Lagrange function

$$F(\mathbf{x}, \lambda) = f(\mathbf{x}) + \sum_{i=1}^{M} \lambda_i[g_i(\mathbf{x}) - 1]$$

and require

(1) $$\frac{\partial F}{\partial x_l} = 0 = \frac{\partial f(\mathbf{x})}{\partial x_l} + \sum_{i=1}^{M} \lambda_i \frac{\partial g_i(\mathbf{x})}{\partial x_l} \qquad l = 1, \ldots, N$$

(2) $$\frac{\partial F}{\partial \lambda_i} = 0 = g_i(\mathbf{x}) - 1 \qquad\qquad i = 1, \ldots, M$$

Notice that our constraints have the form $g_i(\mathbf{x}) = 1$. Actually, as long as the right side is positive we may obtain this form by a simple linear transformation.

The case when $g_i(\mathbf{x}) = 0$ is not admissible, because our solution space requires $\mathbf{x} > 0$. When the right side is negative, solution procedures have been obtained. However, the arguments are outside the scope of this book. The interested reader may consult references [13] and [14].

Let us investigate condition (1) in more detail.

$$\frac{\partial F}{\partial x_l} = 0 = \sum_{j=1}^{P} \frac{c_j a_{lj} P_j(\mathbf{x})}{x_l} + \sum_{i=1}^{M} \lambda_i \left[\sum_{k=1}^{P(i)} \frac{c_{ik} a_{ikl} P_{ik}(\mathbf{x})}{x_l} \right]$$

We may again introduce variables δ_j and δ_{ik} as follows. Define

$$\delta_j = \frac{c_j P_j}{f(\mathbf{x}^0)} \qquad \delta_{ik} = \frac{\lambda_i c_{iK} P_{iK}}{f(\mathbf{x}^0)} \tag{4.84}$$

Notice again that

$$\sum_{j=1}^{P} \delta_j = 1 \tag{4.85}$$

Furthermore, we have the orthogonality conditions

$$\sum_{j=1}^{P} a_{lj}\delta_j + \sum_{i=1}^{M} \sum_{k=1}^{P(i)} a_{ikl}\delta_{ik} = 0 \qquad l = 1, \ldots, N \tag{4.86}$$

This condition comes from substituting the definitions of δ_j and δ_{iK} into $\partial F/\partial x_l = 0$.

In the unconstrained case the δ_j were all positive, since

$$\delta_j = \frac{c_j P_j}{f(\mathbf{x}^0)} > 0 \tag{4.87}$$

In the equality-constrained case the δ_j are again positive. However, the δ_{iK} may be negative, because we do not require λ_i to be nonnegative. It is desirable to have all $\delta_{iK} > 0$ to formulate a dual function. Notice that if we reverse the order of formulating the Lagrange function, the signs of the Lagrange multipliers will change. Therefore, if we encounter a problem where one of the λ_{iK} is negative, we can reverse its sign simply by writing that term in the Lagrange function as

$$\lambda_q[1 - g_q(\mathbf{x})]$$

We are again, in certain cases, able to formulate a highly nonlinear problem as one of solving a system of linear equations,

$$\sum_{j=1}^{P} \delta_j = 1 \qquad \text{(normality)}$$

$$\sum_{j=1}^{P} a_{lj}\delta_j + \sum_{i=1}^{M} \sum_{k=1}^{P(i)} a_{ikl}\delta_{ik} = 0 \qquad l = 1, \ldots, N \text{ (orthogonality)}$$

When these equations have a unique solution, the optimal solution of the original problem has been obtained. All that is required is that $f(\mathbf{x}^0)$ and $\mathbf{x}$ be calculated from the definitions of the δ_j and δ_{iK}. In the case when there are an infinite number of solutions we must again resort to maximizing the dual function which is given by

$$h(\mathbf{\delta}) = \prod_{j=1}^{P} \left(\frac{c_j}{\delta_j}\right)^{\delta_j} \prod_{i=1}^{M} \left[\prod_{k=1}^{P(i)} \left(\frac{c_{ij}}{\delta_{ij}}\right)^{\delta_{ij}}\right] \prod_{i=1}^{M} V_i^{V_i} \tag{4.88}$$

where

$$V_i = \sum_{k=1}^{P(i)} \delta_{ik} \tag{4.89}$$

subject to the orthogonality and normality restrictions.

Although the above function may seem to be very difficult to work with, it appears to be much simpler to handle than the original problem because the constraints are now linear. In addition, we may choose to work with the log of the dual function which is linear in the variable $y_j = \ln \delta_j$ and $y_{ik} = \ln \delta_{ij}$.

The same conditions and dual function are obtained when there are inequality constraints of the form $g_i(\mathbf{x}) \leq 1$. The proof of the orthogonality conditions is left as an exercise for the reader. The dual function is again obtained through the use of inequalities. Those interested should consult the references at the end of the chapter for further insight into how one arrives at the dual function given above [13, 14].

We can use the dual problem mentioned above to obtain bounds on the optimal solution. Since

$$f(\mathbf{x}) \geq f(\mathbf{x}^0) \geq h(\mathbf{\delta}) \tag{4.90}$$

we can choose any feasible $\mathbf{x}$, say $\mathbf{x}'$, and any feasible $\mathbf{\delta}$, say $\mathbf{\delta}'$, and know the optimal solution is bounded by

$$f(\mathbf{x}') \geq f(\mathbf{x}^0) \geq h(\mathbf{\delta}') \tag{4.91}$$

This gives us a convenient stopping rule in the case when there is no unique solution to the orthogonality and normality conditions and we approach the problem using some direct method to maximize the dual.

As an example of geometric programming, consider the problem

$$\min f(x_1, x_2) = 2x_1 x_2^{-3} + 4x_1^{-1} x_2^{-2} + \tfrac{3.2}{3} x_1 x_2$$

subject to $10 x_1^{-1} x_2^2 = 1$. The corresponding dual function is

$$h(\mathbf{\delta}) = \left(\frac{2}{\delta_1}\right)^{\delta_1} \left(\frac{4}{\delta_2}\right)^{\delta_2} \left(\frac{32}{3\delta_3}\right)^{\delta_3} \left(\frac{0.1}{\delta_4}\right)^{\delta_4} (\delta_4)^{\delta_4}$$

and the constraints are

$$\delta_1 + \delta_2 + \delta_3 = 1$$
$$\delta_1 - \delta_2 + \delta_3 - \delta_4 = 0$$
$$-3\delta_1 - 2\delta_2 + \delta_3 + 2\delta_4 = 0$$

Expressing each δ_i in terms of δ_1 we find

$$\delta_2 = 1 - \tfrac{4}{3}\delta_1$$
$$\delta_3 = \tfrac{1}{3}\delta_1$$
$$\delta_4 = \tfrac{8}{3}\delta_1 - 1$$

Thus

$$h(\delta) = h(\delta_1) = \left(\frac{2}{\delta_1}\right)^{\delta_1}\left(\frac{4}{1 - \tfrac{4}{3}\delta_1}\right)^{1 - 4/3\delta_1}\left(\frac{32}{\delta_1}\right)^{1/3\delta_1}(0.1)^{8/3\delta_1 - 1}$$

Working with $\ln[h(\delta_1)]$, which is a monotonic function of $h(\delta_1)$, we have

$$K(\delta_1) = \ln[h(\delta_1)] = \delta_1 \ln\frac{2}{\delta_1} + (1 - \tfrac{4}{3}\delta_1)\ln\frac{4}{1 - \tfrac{4}{3}\delta_1}$$

$$+ \frac{\delta_1}{3}\ln\frac{32}{\delta_1} + \left(\frac{8}{3}\delta_1 - 1\right)\ln 0.1$$

$$\frac{dK(\delta_1)}{d\delta_1} = \ln\frac{2}{\delta_1} + 2 - \frac{16\delta_1}{3} + \ln\frac{32}{\delta_1} + \frac{8}{3}\ln 0.1$$

which vanishes at $\delta_1 = 0.662$. Thus

$$\delta_2 = 0.217$$
$$\delta_3 = 0.221$$
$$\delta_4 = 0.766$$

Using these values we can now calculate x_1, x_2, and $f(\mathbf{x})$ from the definition of the δ_i:

$$\delta_1 = \frac{c_1 P_1}{f(\mathbf{x}^0)} = \frac{2x_1 x_2^{-3}}{f(\mathbf{x}^0)}$$

$$\delta_2 = \frac{c_2 P_2}{f(\mathbf{x}^0)} = \frac{4x_1^{-1}x_2^{-2}}{f(\mathbf{x}^0)}$$

$$\delta_3 = \frac{c_3 P_3}{f(\mathbf{x}^0)} = \frac{32}{3}\frac{x_1 x_2}{f(\mathbf{x}^0)}$$

$$\delta_4 = \frac{\lambda_1 c_4 P_4}{f(\mathbf{x}^0)} = \frac{\lambda_1 10 x_1^{-1}x_2^2}{f(\mathbf{x}^0)}$$

Dividing δ_1 by δ_3 we have

$$\frac{\delta_1}{\delta_3} = 3 = \frac{3}{16}x_2^{-4}$$

or $x_2^4 = \tfrac{1}{16}$, which implies that $x_2 = \tfrac{1}{2}$. From the constraint we know that

$$0.1x_1(\tfrac{1}{2})^{-2} = 1 \quad \text{or} \quad x_1 = 2.5$$

These values are consistent with the values obtained using the definitions of δ_2 and δ_4.

4.6   Nondifferentiable Problems

The final topic of this chapter is a discussion of selected alternative approaches to problems containing functions that are not differentiable. There are numerous examples of such problems. Problems in which the set of feasible solutions must be positive integers is one example. Consider the engineering design problem in which one must specify the number of tubes for a heat exchanger or the number of plates for a distillation column. The problem of determining the optimal number of new box cars a railroad should purchase or the number of cows the dairy herd should contain are other obvious examples of integer problems.

In this section we shall discuss two procedures for determining solutions to such nondifferentiable problems. The first is an extension of the Lagrange multiplier concept, and the second is a procedure known as "branch and bound," which is an intelligent partial enumeration scheme similar to the Fibonacci search procedure discussed earlier. The two techniques are applicable to certain nonlinear integer problems as well as linear ones. By linear integer problems we mean problems that are linear except for the requirement that the variables be integers. Nonlinear integer problems are those where functions of the variables are nonlinear, independent of the requirement that the solution space include only integers. The cutting plane method of Gomory [15] for linear integer problems will not be discussed in this chapter.

Generalized Lagrange Multiplier Technique

The first method we shall discuss is a generalization of the Lagrange multiplier technique. This extension is due to Everrett [16]. His main theorem is proved below.

Theorem: *Let* $\lambda = (\lambda_1, \ldots, \lambda_M)$ *be an ordered M tuple of nonpositive real numbers and S be any arbitrary set of real vectors. Then if* $\mathbf{x}^0 \in S$ *maximizes*

$$F(\mathbf{x}, \lambda) = f(\mathbf{x}) + \sum_{i=1}^{M} \lambda_i g_i(\mathbf{x})$$

for all $\mathbf{x} \in S$, $\mathbf{x}^0$ *maximizes* $f(\mathbf{x})$ *for all* $\mathbf{x} \in S$ *such that* $g_i(\mathbf{x}) \leq g_i(\mathbf{x}^0)$.

The set S may be the set of all positive integers or any other arbitrary set. This theorem says if we can find the proper $\lambda \leq \mathbf{0}$, and find an $\mathbf{x}^0$ which maximizes $F(\mathbf{x}, \lambda)$ for that particular λ, we have solved the problem

$$\max_{\mathbf{x} \in S} f(\mathbf{x})$$

subject to

$$g_i(\mathbf{x}) \le g_i(\mathbf{x}^0)$$

PROOF. Since $\mathbf{x}^0$ maximized $F(\mathbf{x}, \boldsymbol{\lambda})$ for a given $\boldsymbol{\lambda} \le 0$, we can write

$$F(\mathbf{x}^0, \boldsymbol{\lambda}) = f(\mathbf{x}^0) + \sum_{i=1}^{M} \lambda_i g_i(\mathbf{x}^0) \ge f(\mathbf{x}) + \sum_{i=1}^{M} \lambda_i g_i(\mathbf{x})$$

Rearranging we find

$$f(\mathbf{x}^0) \ge f(\mathbf{x}) + \sum_{i=1}^{M} \lambda_i[g_i(\mathbf{x}) - g_i(\mathbf{x}^0)]$$

But from the theorem $g_i(\mathbf{x}) \le g_i(\mathbf{x}^0)$ and $\lambda_i \le 0$ so that

$$\sum_{i=1}^{M} \lambda_i[g_i(\mathbf{x}) - g_i(\mathbf{x}^0)] \ge 0$$

Hence $f(\mathbf{x}^0) \ge f(\mathbf{x})$, which is the desired result.

Next we shall prove a theorem concerning the monotonicity of the Lagrange multipliers with the right side of the constraints.

Theorem: *Let $\boldsymbol{\lambda}_1$ produce solution $\mathbf{x}_1$ and $\boldsymbol{\lambda}_2$ yield solution $\mathbf{x}_2$. Assume*

$$g_i(\mathbf{x}_1) = g_i(\mathbf{x}_2) \qquad i = 1, \ldots, M; \quad i \ne K$$

and further

$$g_K(\mathbf{x}_1) > g_K(\mathbf{x}_2)$$

Then

$$\lambda_{2K} \le \frac{f(\mathbf{x}_1) - f(\mathbf{x}_2)}{g_K(\mathbf{x}_2) - g_K(\mathbf{x}_1)} \le \lambda_{1K}$$

PROOF

$$F(\mathbf{x}_1, \boldsymbol{\lambda}_1) \ge F(\mathbf{x}_2, \boldsymbol{\lambda}_1)$$

since $\mathbf{x}_1$ by definition maximizes $F(\mathbf{x}, \boldsymbol{\lambda}_1)$. Hence

$$f(\mathbf{x}_1) + \sum_{i=1}^{M} \lambda_{1i} g_i(\mathbf{x}_1) \ge f(\mathbf{x}_2) + \sum_{i=1}^{M} \lambda_{1i} g_i(\mathbf{x}_2)$$

Rearranging we find

$$f(\mathbf{x}_1) - f(\mathbf{x}_2) \ge \lambda_{1K}[g_K(\mathbf{x}_2) - g_K(\mathbf{x}_1)]$$

Since $g_K(\mathbf{x}_1) > g_K(\mathbf{x}_2)$, the coefficient of λ_{1K} is negative, and dividing both sides by it reverses the inequality. Therefore,

$$\frac{f(\mathbf{x}_1) - f(\mathbf{x}_2)}{g_K(\mathbf{x}_2) - g_K(\mathbf{x}_1)} \le \lambda_{1K}$$

A similar argument yields the remainder of the proof and this result is left for the reader to prove.

Let us now indicate how one might solve integer problems using the theorems we have presented above. Consider the problem

$$\max_{\mathbf{x} \in S} f(\mathbf{x})$$

where S is the set of all nonnegative vectors whose components must be integers. In addition we have the following constraints which must be satisfied:

$$g_i(\mathbf{x}) \le b_i \qquad i = 1, \ldots, M$$

If we can find a set of $\hat{\boldsymbol{\lambda}} \le \mathbf{0}$ such that for $\hat{\boldsymbol{\lambda}}$, $\mathbf{x}^0$ maximized $F(\mathbf{x}, \hat{\boldsymbol{\lambda}})$ and further that $g_i(\mathbf{x}^0) = b_i$, then $\mathbf{x}^0$ maximized $f(\mathbf{x})$ subject to $g_i(\mathbf{x}) \le b_i$. Notice that this is a sufficient but not a necessary condition. The optimal solution may occur on the interior of the constraint set and yet we cannot, using these theorems, prove optimality. However, there are many examples where the constraints are satisfied exactly at the optimal solution and this theorem has applications to problems of this type.

The computation procedure is to (1) choose a $\boldsymbol{\lambda} \le \mathbf{0}$, (2) find an $\mathbf{x} \in S$ that maximizes $F(\mathbf{x}, \boldsymbol{\lambda})$, (3) calculate for that $\mathbf{x}$ the value of $g_i(\mathbf{x})$. If $g_i(\mathbf{x}) = b_i$, $i = 1, \ldots, M$, an optimal solution to the original problem has been found. If not, another $\boldsymbol{\lambda}$ is chosen and the procedure repeated.

In other words, at each iteration we solve some problem. However, the problem that is solved may not have the desired right-hand sides for the constraints. We then modify the $\boldsymbol{\lambda}$ to give us a solution to a problem that is closer to the one we desire to solve.

We have some guides in choosing successive values of $\boldsymbol{\lambda}$, because b_K is monotonically increasing as λ_K increases if all other λ_i, $i \ne K$, are held constant.

Finally, we should point out that there may not exist a $\boldsymbol{\lambda}$ that yields the desired right-hand side to the constraints. In other words, we may not be able to find a $\boldsymbol{\lambda}$ that generates the desired problem. These phenomena, known as gaps, arise because of nonconvexity of the constraint set. Everrett [16] discusses several methods for overcoming these gaps and the interested reader should consult the original article for a discussion of the concepts. He also points out that his experience with a variety of production and allocation problems indicates that problems of this type have rarely contained these gaps at the optimal solution.[17]

---

[17] A discussion of the computational feasibility of this technique is contained in Everrett's paper [16].

As an example of Everrett's technique consider the problem of finding a maximum of $f(\mathbf{x})$ subject to the constraints

$$g_1(\mathbf{x}) = 2x_1 + 4x_2 + 5x_3 \leq 10$$
$$g_2(\mathbf{x}) = x_1 + 3x_2 \qquad \leq 5$$

and $x_i = 0, 1, \ldots, i = 1, 2, 3$, where

$$f(\mathbf{x}) = 13x_1 + 6.2x_2 + 10x_3 - 56.25x_3^2 - x_1^2 - 10x_2^2$$

This problem has the optimal noninteger solution of $x_1 = 4.95$, $x_2 = 0$, and $x_3 = 0.02$. Forming the modified Lagrange function we obtain

$$F(\mathbf{x}, \boldsymbol{\lambda}) = f(\mathbf{x}) + \lambda_1 g_1(\mathbf{x}) + \lambda_2 g_2(\mathbf{x})$$

which we wish to maximize over all $\mathbf{x}$, where each x_i must be a nonnegative integer. As an initial choice of λ_1 and λ_2, let $\lambda_1 = \lambda_2 = -2$. Hence

$$\begin{aligned}
F(x_1, x_2, x_3, \lambda_1, \lambda_2) &= 13x_1 + 6.2x_2 + 10x_3 - 56.25x_3^2 - x_1^2 - 10x_2^2 \\
&\quad + (-2)(2x_1 + 4x_2 + 5x_3) + (-2)(x_1 + 3x_2) \\
&= 7x_1 - x_1^2 - 7.8x_2 - 10x_2^2 - 56.25x_3^2
\end{aligned}$$

Since the coefficient of terms in x_2 and x_3 are both negative, the value of these variables that maximize $F(\cdot)$ are $x_2 = x_3 = 0$. x_1 may be either 3 or 4. We shall choose $x_1 = 3$. For this choice

$$g_1(3, 0, 0) = 6$$
$$g_2(3, 0, 0) = 3$$

These are not the desired values for the right-hand side of the constraints. However, we know b_1 is monotonically increasing as λ_1 increases if λ_2 is held constant. Therefore, our next choice will be

$$\lambda_1 = -1 \qquad \lambda_2 = -2$$

which yields

$$F(x_1, x_2, x_3, -1, -2) = 9x_1 - x_1^2 - 3.8x_2 - 10x_2^2 + 5x_3 - 56.25x_3^2$$

Again we must maximize this over the set of nonnegative integers. The solution occurs at

$$x_1 = 4 \qquad x_2 = x_3 = 0$$

which yields

$$g_1(4, 0, 0) = 8$$
$$g_2(4, 0, 0) = 4$$

We must modify the $\boldsymbol{\lambda}$ again. This time let us increase λ_2 to -1. The Lagrange function becomes

$$F(x_1, x_2, x_3, \lambda_1, \lambda_2) = 10x_1 - x_1^2 - 0.8x_2 - 10x_2^2 + 5x_3 - 56.25x_3^2$$

which has its maximum at $x_1 = 5$, $x_2 = x_3 = 0$. At this point

$$g_1(5, 0, 0) = 10$$
$$g_2(5, 0, 0) = 5$$

which are the desired right-hand sides. We are guaranteed that this solution is optimal by the main theorem of Everrett. At this point.

$$f(\mathbf{x}) = 40$$

Notice that the set of λ which yields this solution is not unique. For example, $\lambda_1 = 0$, $\lambda_2 = -3$, would also generate the point $x_1 = 5$, $x_2 = 0$, $x_3 = 0$. However we are guaranteed that the value of $f(\mathbf{x})$ will be no greater than 40 for any $\mathbf{x}$ such that

$$g_1(\mathbf{x}) \leq 10 \qquad g_2(\mathbf{x}) \leq 5$$

In this case the optimal solution is the same as is obtained if the answer to the noninteger problem was rounded off to the nearest integer. However, this is not true in general. There are many examples that contradict this assumption and one should beware of adopting this strategy for any general problem. Even in linear integer programs this solution procedure might very well yield erroneous results.

Branch and Bouhd

The final topic we wish to pursue in this section is branch and bound methods. These techniques are intelligent partial enumeration procedures for nonlinear programming problems. Although this technique has been used effectively to solve traveling salesman problems, quadratic assignment problems, covering problems, and other integer or mixed integer problems, we shall restrict our attention to integer and mixed integer nonlinear programs.

Branch and bound algorithms are iterative schemes for solving problems. The approach may be best illustrated by example. Consider the following mixed integer linear programming problem:

$$\max f(\mathbf{x}) = 8x_1 + 5x_2 + 7x_3$$

subject to

$$1.5x_1 + 3x_2 \leq 5$$
$$x_1 + 7x_2 + 2x_3 \leq 24$$
$$x_1 = 0, 1, 2, 3, 4, 5 \qquad \text{and} \qquad x_2, x_3 \geq 0$$

As a first approximation to the solution we shall treat x_1 as a continuous variable. If, by chance, the solution to this problem yields an integer solution we have solved the problem. If not, the solution to the continuous problem will serve as an upper bound on the value of the optimal solution to our problem. The tableaux are presented below:

VIB	P_1	P_2	P_3	P_4	P_5	
P_4	1.5	3		1		5
P_5	1	7	2		1	24
	-8	-5	-7	0	0	0

P_1	1	2	0	$\frac{2}{3}$	0	$\frac{10}{3}$
P_5	0	5	2	$-\frac{2}{3}$	1	$\frac{62}{3}$
	0	11	-7	$\frac{16}{3}$	0	$\frac{80}{3}$

P_3 must now be introduced.

P_1	1	2	0	$\frac{2}{3}$	0	$\frac{10}{3}$
P_3	0	$\frac{5}{2}$	1	$-\frac{1}{3}$	$\frac{1}{2}$	$\frac{62}{6}$
	0	$\frac{57}{2}$	0	$\frac{9}{3}$	$\frac{7}{2}$	$\frac{594}{6}$

which is the optimal solution to the continuous problem. This solution does not yield an integer value for x_1 and thus is not feasible for the given problem. However, it does give us an upper bound on $f(x^0)$, since we know $f(x^0) \leq \frac{594}{6}$. This is the bound in "branch and bound."

Now we must branch. The value of x_1 that solved the continuous approximation was $3\frac{1}{3}$. Since x_1 must be an integer, we can say that at the optimal solution to the original problem x_1 must lie in one of the two mutually exclusive regions

$$x_1 \geq 4 \quad \text{or} \quad x_1 \leq 3$$

Now we have generated two new continuous problems from the original problem as illustrated in Figure 4.12. The two new problems are shown below.

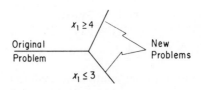

Figure 4.12.

$$(1)$$
$$\max f(x) = 8x_1 + 5x_2 + 7x_3$$

subject to

$$1.5x_1 + 3x_2 \quad\quad \le \ 5$$
$$x_1 + 7x_2 + 2x_3 \le 24$$
$$x_1 \ge 4,\, x_2,\, x_3 \ge \ 0$$

$$(2)$$
$$\max f(x) = 8x_1 + 5x_2 + 7x_3$$

subject to

$$1.5x_1 + 3x_2 \le \ 5$$
$$x_1 + 7x_2 + 2x_3 \le 24$$
$$x_1 \quad\quad\quad\quad\quad \le \ 3$$
$$x_1,\, x_2,\, x_3 \ge \ 0$$

In this simple example we can see immediately that problem 1 has no feasible solution. The solution to problem 2 is $x_1 = 3$, $x_2 = 0$, $x_3 = 10.5$, which is feasible to the original problem, and since we have no other branches to investigate it is also optimal.

In the more general case we may have many new problems generated. Suppose we have a mixed-integer linear programming problem with 20 variables, 10 of which must be integer. Suppose further that the optimal solution to the continuous problem yields noninteger values for 5 of the variables which must be integers. In this case the tree that results might appear similar to the one shown in Figure 4.13. Assume the continuous problem gave a solution

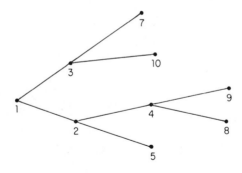

Figure 4.13.

for $x_1 = 2.78$. Then the first step is to create two new problems with $x_1 \le 2$ and $x_1 \ge 3$. Other branches are generated by placing similar constraints on variables that do not have the desired integer property. We can make the following simple observation. As we proceed branching and bounding we may find several feasible solutions to the original problem. Call these feasible solutions $x^1, \ldots, x^p$. Choose the x^K which has the property that it is the $\mathbf{x}$ for which $f(x)$ is maximum over all p feasible, solutions. Then since (1) on any branch, the value of the solution cannot increase (because we are adding constraints to preceding problems and thus reducing the feasible region with each branching) and (2) since we have a feasible solution x^K for which

$$f(\mathbf{x}^K) \ge f(\mathbf{x}^i) \quad\quad i = 1, \ldots, p$$

the branches corresponding to the $p - 1$ feasible solutions may be terminated and no new problems need be generated from these terminated branches. Once we reach a point where we can terminate all branches we have obtained the optimal solution.

Branching and bounding can be used to solve problems that would be convex programming problems except for the integer restriction. Consider the problem solved previously by Everrett's method:

$$\max f(\mathbf{x}) = 13x_1 + 6.2x_2 + 10x_3 - x_1^2 - 10x_2^2 - 56.25x_3^2$$

subject to

$$2x_1 + 4x_2 + 5x_3 \leq 10$$
$$x_1 + 3x_2 \qquad \leq 5$$
$$x_j \text{ a nonnegative integer} \qquad j = 1, 2, 3$$

Ignoring the integer restriction we obtain the solution $x_1 = 4.95$, $x_2 = 0$, $x_3 = 0.02$. Starting from this point with the branch and bound technique and arbitrarily branching on x_3 we obtain two new problems:

$$\max f(\mathbf{x}) = 13x_1 + 6.2x_2 + 10x_3 - x_1^2 - 10x_2^2 - 56.25x_3^2$$

subject to

$$2x_1 + 4x_2 + 5x_3 \leq 10$$
$$x_1 + 3x_2 \qquad \leq 5$$
$$x_1, x_2 \geq 0, x_3 \geq 1$$

and

$$\max f(\mathbf{x}) = 13x_1 + 6.2x_2 + 10x_3 - x_1^2 - 10x_2^2 - 56.25x_3^2$$

subject to

$$2x_1 + 4x_2 + 5x_3 \leq 10$$
$$x_1 + 3x_2 \qquad \leq 5$$
$$x_1, x_2, x_3 \geq 0, x_3 \leq 0$$

The solution to the first problem is

$$x_1 = 2.5, x_2 = 0, x_3 = 1 \qquad \text{and} \qquad f(\mathbf{x}^1) = -20$$

and the solution to the second problem is

$$x_1 = 5, x_2 = 0, x_3 = 0 \qquad \text{and} \qquad f(\mathbf{x}^2) = 40$$

We now can terminate the branch corresponding to the first problem, because $f(\mathbf{x}^2) > f(\mathbf{x}^1)$. There will be no new problems generated from branch 1 that will yield solutions greater than -20. Since we already have a feasible solution that yields a better solution than -20 and no solution generated from branch 1 will be greater than -20, branch 1 may be terminated. Branch 2 yields a solution with the desired property, so no other solutions are generated from it. Thus all branches are terminated and $x_1 = 5, x_2 = x_3 = 0$ is the optimal solution.

Problems

1. Solve the following problem by geometric programming

$$\min f(\mathbf{x}) = 5\frac{x_1}{x_2} + 10x_1^2 x_2 + 3\frac{1}{x_1}$$

2. Suppose you are given a linear programming problem:

$$\min f(\mathbf{x}) = \mathbf{cx}$$

subject to

$$\mathbf{Ax} = \mathbf{b}$$
$$\mathbf{x} > \mathbf{0}$$

Assuming $\mathbf{c} \geq \mathbf{0}$, $\mathbf{b} = 1$, $\mathbf{A} \geq \mathbf{0}$. Can geometric programming be used to obtain a solution? Why or why not?

3. Set up the necessary conditions to solve the following problem by geometric programming.

$$\min f(\mathbf{x}) = 3x_1/x_2 + x_2^2/x_1 + x_1^2 x_2$$

subject to

$$\tfrac{1}{4}x_1^2/x_2 + \tfrac{1}{9}x_2 x_1 = 1$$
$$2(1/x_1^2) + 4(x_2/x_1^3) = 2$$

4. Solve the following by geometric programming.

$$\min f(\mathbf{x}) = \frac{x_1 x_2}{x_3^2} + 2\frac{x_3}{x_1 x_2} + 5x_3$$

5. Show that for a geometric programming problem to have a feasible solution, each variable must appear in the denominator of at least one posynomial. Can a given variable appear only in the denominator of posynomials and still yield a feasible solution?

6. Show that if the numerator of $P_n(\mathbf{x})$ = the denominator of $P_k(\mathbf{x})$ [where $P_i(\mathbf{x})$ is the ith posynomial in a geometric programming problem] and the variables appearing in the numerator of $P_n(\mathbf{x})$ appear in no other posynomials except the denominator of $P_k(\mathbf{x})$, at least one redudant necessary equation results.

7. Solve the following problem using the branch and bound method:

$$\max f(\mathbf{x}) = -2x_1^2 + x_1 x_2 - 3x_2^2 + 4x_1$$

subject to

$$x_1 + x_2 \leq \tfrac{5}{4}$$
$$2x_1 + 4x_2 \leq 3$$
$$x_1, x_2 = 0, 1, 2, 3, \ldots$$

8. Using the branch and bound method solve

$$\max f(\mathbf{x}) = 3x_3^2 + 3x_1x_2 - 4x_2^2 + 3x_1 + x_2$$

subject to

$$
\begin{aligned}
3x_1 + x_2 + 4x_3 &\leq 11 \\
x_1 + 2x_2 + 2x_3 &\leq 8 \\
x_2 + x_1 &\geq 3 \\
x_1, x_2, x_3 &= 0, 1, 2, 3, \ldots
\end{aligned}
$$

9. Use the branch and bound method to solve

$$\min 3x_1^2 + 2x_1x_2 + 3x_2^2$$

subject to

$$
\begin{aligned}
x_1 + 3x_2 &\geq 1 \\
2x_1 + x_2 &\leq 5 \\
x_1 &\geq 0 \\
x_1, x_2 &= 0 \text{ or } 1
\end{aligned}
$$

10. Prove that the continuous solution to a branch and bound problem serves as an upper bound for the integer (or mixed integer) solution.

11. Use quadratic programming to minimize $x^2 + xy + 2y^2$ subject to

$$
\begin{aligned}
3x + 2y &\geq 3 \\
x + y &\leq 3 \\
x &\geq 0 \\
y &\geq 0
\end{aligned}
$$

12. Maximize

$$
\begin{aligned}
&-1.5x^2 - y^2 - 2.5z^2 \\
&+2xy + xz + yz
\end{aligned}
$$

subject to

$$
\begin{aligned}
3x + 5y + 2z &\geq 0 \\
3x + 5z &\leq 15 \\
x, y, z &\geq 0
\end{aligned}
$$

13. Under what conditions can λ_k and $y_k = u_k^2$ be in the basic solution of a quadratic programming problem at the same time?

14. Consider the following simplified version of Stigler's nutrition problem. It has been found desirable in constructing diets to require that certain nutritional standards be satisfied. For example, the daily diet for an average man should include at least 70 grams of protein, 0.8 grams of calcium, and 2.7. milligrams of vitamin B_1. There are several foods that can be used to satisfy these requirements. We shall select five of these. Their content of the requirements are continued in Table 4.1.

TABLE 4.1.   Content of Nutrient/100 lb of Food j

Food	Vitamin B (milligrams)	Protein (grams)	Calcium (grams)
1	0	2.51	1.5
2	25.1	1001.00	2.1
3	38.4	25.00	0.3
4	75.2	7.75	16.1
5	10.3	40.00	2.8

The cost of these foods is a quadratic function of the amount purchased. This relationship arises because after a certain amount is used, strategic reserves are depleted, and the food must be purchased on the open market. The market reacts to decreasing supply by increasing prices. Hence the following cost function is assumed:

$$f(\mathbf{x}) = \mathbf{cx} + \tfrac{1}{2}\mathbf{x}^T\mathbf{Gx}$$
$$\mathbf{c} = (1.5, \quad 2.1, \quad 0.5, \quad 10.2, \quad 7.8)$$

where c_i is the cost in dollars of food i. The quadratic form is given by the matrix $\tfrac{1}{2}\mathbf{G}$.

$$\tfrac{1}{2}\mathbf{G} = \begin{pmatrix} 10 & 0.2 & 0 & 0.1 & 0 \\ 0.2 & 0.1 & 0 & 0 & 0 \\ 0 & 0 & 0.01 & 0.2 & 0 \\ 0.1 & 0 & 0.2 & 12 & 0 \\ 0 & 0 & 0 & 0 & 15 \end{pmatrix}$$

$g_{ij} = \$/\text{lb}_{ij}$ used in diet. Find the annual minimum cost diet that satisfies the constraints using

(a) Wolfe's algorithm.
(b) Beale's algorithm.
(c) The Theil-Van der Panne algorithm.
(d) Suppose the requirement on vitamin B_1 was increased to 2.9 milligrams. Estimate how the total cost would change.

15. The famous traveling salesman problem may be described as follows. The salesman—starting at city A—wishes to plan his route on his trip through

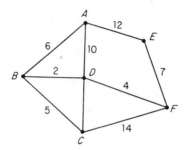

the region so as to minimize the total distance traveled. He must stop at each city in the territory exactly once during the tour. For the six-city problem shown, find by branch and bound techniques the minimum-cost tour starting and finishing at A that passes through each city only once. The distances are shown on the lines connecting the cities.

16. The assignment problem is a well-known problem in operations research. It may be stated as follows. Given n jobs and m men, assign the men to jobs so as to maximize the total return. The return is given by

$$\sum_{i=1}^{m} \sum_{j=1}^{n} p_{ij} x_{ij}$$

where p_{ij} is the return obtained if man j is assigned to job i and $x_{ij} = 1$ if man j is assigned to job i and 0 otherwise.

(a) Formulate the assignment problem as an integer program.
(b) Solve the problem by branch and bound techniques for five machines and four men, where

$$p_{ij} = i^2 + j^2 - ij$$

17. Solve Problem 14 by the sequential unconstrained minimization techniques using the Fletcher-Powell technique to solve the unconstrained problem. Do two iterations completely.

18. Draw contours of the following function and indicate the path taken by the steepest descent method and the Fletcher-Powell technique from the following starting points:

(a) $x_1 = 1, x_2 = 0$.
(b) $x_1 = 1, x_2 = 1$.
(c) $x_1 = -0.1, x_2 = -2$.

$$f(\mathbf{x}) = \mathbf{c}\mathbf{x} + \tfrac{1}{2}\mathbf{x}^T \mathbf{G}\mathbf{x}$$

where

$$\mathbf{c} = (2, -1) \qquad \mathbf{G} = \begin{pmatrix} 4 & 2 \\ 2 & 1 \end{pmatrix}$$

References Cited and Bibliography

[1] Wilde, D. J. *Optimum Seeking Methods*. Englewood Cliffs, N.J.: Prentice-Hall, 1964.
[2] Hadley, G. L. *Non-Linear and Dynamic Programming*. Reading, Mass.: Addison-Wesley, 1964.
[3] Lavi, A., and T. P. Vogl. *Recent Advances in Optimization Techniques*. New York: Wiley, 1966.
[4] Graves, R. L., and P. Wolfe. *Recent Advances in Mathematical Programming*. New York: McGraw-Hill, 1963.
[5] Shah, B. V., R. J. Buehler, and O. Kempthorne. "The Method of Parallel Tangents," *Tech. Rep. No. 2, Office of Naval Research Contract Nonr.-530(05)*, Iowa State University Statistical Laboratory, Ames, April 1961.

[6] Fletcher, R., and M. J. D. Powell. "A Rapidly Convergent Descent Method for Minimization," *Computer J.*, Vol. 7, 163–168 (1964).

[7] Beale, E. M. L. "On Quadratic Programming," *Naval Research Logistics Quarterly*, Vol. 6, 227–243 (1959).

[8] Theil, H., and C. Van der Panne. "Quadratic Programming as an Extension of Classical Quadratic Maximization," *Management Sci.*, Vol. 7, 1–20 (1960).

[9] Carroll, C. W. "The Created Response Surface Technique for Optimizing Nonlinear Restrained Systems," *Operations Res.*, Vol. 9, 169–184 (1961).

[10] Fiacco, A. V., and G. P. McCormick. "The Sequential Unconstrained Minimization Technique for Nonlinear Programming, A Primal-Dual Method," *Management Sci.*, Vol. 10, 2, 360–366 (1964).

[11] Zener, C. "A Mathematical Aid in Optimizing Engineering Designs," *Proc. Natl. Acad. Sci. U.S.*, Vol. 47, 537–539 (1961).

[12] Wilde, D. J., and C. S. Beightler. *Foundations of Optimization.* Englewood Cliffs, N.J.: Prentice-Hall, 1967.

[13] Wilde, D. J., and U. Passy. Private communication, Aug. 1965.

[14] Zener, C., R. J. Duffin, and E. L. Peterson. *Geometric Programming.* New York: Wiley, 1966.

[15] Gomory, R. E. "An Algorithm for Integer Solutions to Linear Programming," *Princeton-IBM Mathematics Research Project, Tech. Rep. No. 1,* (Nov. 1958).

[16] Everrett, A. "Generalized Lagrange Multiplier Method for Solving Problems of Optimum Allocation of Resources," *Operations Res.*, Vol. 11, 399–417 (1963).

[17] Hooke, R., and T. A. Jeeves. "Direct Search Solution of Numerical and Statistical Problems," *J. Assoc. Computing Machinery*, Vol. 8, 2, 212–229 (April 1961).

Bibliography of Search Techniques

[1] Anderson, R. L. "Recent Advances in Finding Best Operating Conditions," *J. Am. Statist. Assoc.*, Vol. 48, 789–798 (1953).

[2] Arrow, K. J. "A Gradient Method for Approximating Saddle Points and Constrained Maxima," The RAND Corp., Santa Monica, Calif., 1951, Paper P-223.

[3] Baer, R. M. "Note on an Extremum Locating Algorithm," *Computer J.*, Vol. 5, 193 (1962).

[4] Beightler, C. S., J. D. Crawford, and D. J. Wilde. "Differential Quadratic Programming: 1. The Differential Algorithm," *University of Texas Tech. Rept.* (Feb. 1963).

[5] Booth, A. D. "An Application of the Method of Steepest Descents to the Solution of Systems of Nonlinear Simultaneous Equations," *Quart. J. Mech. Appl. Math.*, Vol. 2, Pt. 4, 460–468 (1949).

[6] Box, G. E. P. "Evolutionary Operation: A Method of Increasing Industrial Productivity," *Appl. Statist.*, Vol. 6, 81–101 (1957).

[7] Box, G. E. P., and K. B. Wilson. "On the Experimental Attainment of Optimum Conditions," *J. Roy. Statist. Soc.*, Vol. 13 (B) 1–45 (1951).

[8] Bromberg, M. S. "Maximization and Minimization of Complicated Multi-variable functions," *AIEE Trans. Commun. Electron,* Vol. 58, 725–730 (1962).

[9] Brooks, S. H. "A Discussion of Random Methods for Seeking Maxima," *Operations Res.,* Vol. 6, 244–251 (1958).

[10] Brooks, S. H. "A Comparison of Maximum-Seeking Methods," *Operations Res.,* Vol. 7, 430–457 (1959).

[11] Brooks, S. H., and M. R. Mickey. "Optimum Estimation of Gradient Direction in Steepest Ascent Experiments," *Biometrics,* Vol. 17, 48–56 (1961).

[12] Brown, R. R. "Gradient Method for the Computer Solution of Systems Optimization Problems," *Wright Air Development Center, Tech. Note 57-159* (1957).

[13] Brown, R. R. "A Generalized Computer Procedure for the Design of Optimum Systems, Parts 1 and 11," *AIEE Trans. Commun. Electron.,* Vol. 78, Pt. 1, 285–293 (1959).

[14] Buehler, R. J., B. V. Shah, and O. Kempthorne. "Some Further Properties of the Method of Parallel Tangents and Conjugate Gradients," *Iowa State University Statist. Lab. Tech. Rept. No. 3* (1961).

[15] Buehler, R. J., B. V. Shah, and O. Kempthorne. "Some Properties of Steepest Ascent and Related Procedures for Finding Optimum Conditions," *Iowa State University Statist. Lab.* (1961).

[16] Bryson, A. E. "A Gradient Method for Optimizing Multistage Allocation Processes," *Proceedings of the Harvard Symposium on Digital Computers and Their Applications* (A. G. Oettinger, ed.). Harvard University Press, Cambridge, 1962, pp. 125–213.

[17] Bryson, A. E., and W. F. Denham. "A Steepest-Ascent Method for Solving Optimum Programming Problems," *J. Appl. Mech.,* Vol. 29, 247–257 (1962).

[18] Chanmugam, J., and G. E. P. Box. "Automatic Optimization of Continuous Processes," *Dept. of Statist., University of Wisconsin Tech. Rept. No. 1* (1960).

[19] Curry, H. G. "The Method of Steepest Descent for Nonlinear Minimization Problems," *Quart. Appl. Math.,* Vol. 2, 250–261 (1944).

[20] Davidon, W. C. "Variable Metric Method for Minimization," *Argonne Natl. Lab. ANL-5990 Rev.,* University of Chicago (1959).

[21] Dickinson, J. R. "The Use of Gradient Methods in Optimizing," *Can. G. E. Civilian Atomic Power Dept., Rept. R-59, CAP 26* (1959).

[22] Fedbaum, A. A. "Automatic Optimalizer," *Autom. Remote Control,* Vol. 19, No. 8 (1958).

[23] Finkel, R. W. "The Method of Resultant Descents for the Minimization of an Arbitrary Function," Preprint of paper presented at the *14th National Meeting of Association of Computing Machinery,* 1959, Paper 71.

[24] Fletcher, R., and C. M. Rieves. "Function Minimization by Conjugate Gradients," *Computer J.,* Vol 7, 149–154 (1964).

[25] Forsyth, G., and T. S. Motzkin. "Acceleration of the Optimum Gradient Method Preliminary Report," *Bull. Am. Math. Soc.,* Vol. 57 (1951).

[26] Gelfand, I. M., and M. L. Tselin. "The Principle of Nonlocal Search in Automatic Optimization Systems," *Soviet Phys. Doklady, English Transl.,* Vol. 6, 295–298 (1961).

[27] Gibson, J. E., K. S. Fu, and J. C. Hill. "Hill Climbing Using Piecewise Cubic Approximation," Control and Information Systems Lab., Purdue University, Paper TR-EE64-7.

[28] Glass, H., and I. Cooper. "Sequential Search: A Method for Solving Constrained Optimizing Problems," *J. Assoc. Computing Machinery*, Vol. 12, 71–82 (1965).

[29] Harkins, A. "The Use of Parallel Tangents in Optimization," Optimization Techniques, *Chem. Eng. Progr. Symp. Ser. 50*, Vol. 60, 35–40 (1964).

[30] Hestines, M. R., and E. Stiefel. "Method of Conjugate Gradients for Solving Linear Systems," *J. Res. Natl. Bur. Std.*, Vol. 49, 409–436 (1952).

[31] Hemsworth, F. R. "Empirical Methods of Optimization," *Trans. Inst. Chem. Engrs.*, 40 (1962), pp. 345–349.

[32] Kelly, H. J. "Method of Gradients," *Optimization Techniques with Applications to Aerospace Systems* (G. Leitman, ed.), New York: Academic Press, 1962, Chap. VI.

[33] Kelly, J. E. "The Cutting-Plane Method for Solving Convex Programs," *SIAM Journal 8*, 703–712 (Dec. 1960).

[34] Klingman, W. R., and D. M. Himmelblau. "Nonlinear Programming with the Aid of a Multiple-Gradient Summation Technique," *J. Assoc. Computing Machinery*, Vol. 11, 400–415 (1964).

[35] Levenberg, K. "A Method for the Solution of Certain Non-Linear Problems in Least Squares," *Quart. Appl. Math.*, Vol. 2, 164–168 (1944).

[36] Mugele, R. A. "A Nonlinear Digital Optimizing Program for Process Control Systems," *Proceedings of the Western Joint Computer Conference*, 1962, pp. 15–62.

[37] Mugele, R. A. "Nonlinear Optimization and Dynamic Control of Gas Pipe Lines," *Pipe Line News*, Vol. 36, 31 (1964).

[38] Powell, M. J. D. "An Iterative Method for Finding Stationary Values of a Function of Several Variables," *Computer J.*, Vol. 5, 147–151 (1962).

[39] Powell, M. J. D. "An Efficient Method for Finding the Minimum of a Function of Several Variables without Calculating Derivatives," *Computer J.*, Vol. 7, 155–162 (1964).

[40] Powell, M. J. D. "A Method for Minimizing a Sum of Squares of Non-Linear Functions without Calculating Derivatives," Appl. Math. Group, Theoretical Physics Dev., *Atomic Energy Research Establishment, Rept. A ERE-TP 161* (1964).

[41] Pugh, E. L. "Gradient Techniques for Nonlinear Programming," System Development Corp., Santa Monica, Calif., *Tech. Memo. TM-695* (Feb. 1962).

[42] Rosen, J. B. "The Gradient Projection Method for Non-linear Programming, Part I," *J. SIAM*, Vol. 8, 181–217 (1960).

[43] Rosen, J. B. "The Gradient Projection Method for Non-linear Programming, Part II," *J. SIAM*, Vol. 9, 414–432 (1961).

[44] Rosenbrock, H. H. "Automatic Method for Finding the Greatest or Least Value of a Function," *Computer J.*, Vol. 3, 175–184 (1960).

[45] Satterthwaite, F. E. "REVOP or Random Evolutionary Operation," *Statistical Engineering Institute, Boston Univ. Rept. 10/10/59* (1959).

[46] Shah, B. V., R. J. Buckler, and O. Kempthorne. "Some Algorithms for Minimizing a Function of Several Variables," *J. SIAM*, Vol. 12, 74–92 (1964).

[47] Umland, A. W., and W. N. Smith. "The Use of Lagrange Multiplier With Response Surfaces," *Technometrics*, Vol. 1, 289–292 (1959).

[48] Wilde, D. J. "Differential Calculus in Nonlinear Programming," *Operations Res.*, Vol. 10, No. 6, 764–773 (Nov. 1962).

[49] Wilson, R. B. "Solver." An unpublished computer program available by writing the author at the Graduate School of Business Administration, Stanford University.

[50] Witte, B. F. W., and W. R. Holst. "Two New Direct Minimum Search Procedures for Functions of Several Variables," paper presented at the *1964 Spring Joint Computer Conference in Washington, D.C.*, April 21–23.

[51] Wood, C. F. "Application of 'Direct Search' to the Solution of Engineering Problems," *Westinghouse Res. Labs. Sci. Paper 6-41210-1-P1* (1960).

[52] Wood, C. F. "Recent Developments in Direct Search Techniques," *Westinghouse Res. Rept. 62-159-522-R1* (1962).

[53] Wood, C. F. "Review of Design Optimization Techniques," *Westinghouse Res. Labs. Sci. Paper 64-8C4-361-P1* (Aug. 1964).

[54] Zellnick, H. E., N. E. Sondak, and R. J. Davis. "Gradient Search Optimization," *Chem. Eng. Progr.*, Vol. 58, 35–41 (1962).

[55] Zoutendijk, G. "Maximizing a Function in a Convex Region," *J. Roy. Statist. Soc.*, *Ser. B*, Vol. 21, 338–355 (1959).

[56] Zoutendijk, G. *Methods of Feasibles Directions*. Amsterdam: Elsevier, 1960.

CHAPTER **5**

Dynamic Programming

5.1　Introduction

This chapter and Chapter 6 are concerned with optimization of systems in which each variable can be represented as a function of one parameter. In many cases this parameter is time. In these cases the optimization problem is a dynamic one and the problem is one of determining the optimal trajectory. These techniques are very useful in inventory problems, optimal control problems, and the design of multistage processing systems, among others.

To illustrate the basic difference between dynamic and static systems consider the following example. Suppose we are given the problem of determining the optimal inventory policy for two systems that differ only in the properties of the demand for inventory. In the first case, the rate of demand, r, is constant; that is, it is not a function of time. The rate of demand in the second system is a time-varying function (see Figure 5.1). Since the rate of demand in the first case is constant, we need only specify the optimal

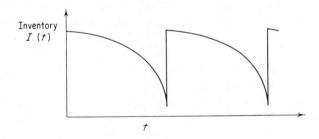

Figure 5.1.

inventory policy for one period. Because nothing changes from period to period this policy will be optimal for all future intervals of time.

The second system is more complicated (see Figure 5.1) in that the rate of demand varies with time. The optimal policy must be determined for each period, because, in general, it will change from period to period. This inventory system is dynamic because its properties vary with time.

In previous chapters we have discussed optimization techniques that are usually applied to static systems. Chapter 2 contained a development of classical optimization theory. The theory of linear programming was discussed in Chapter 3 and various techniques for nonlinear optimization problems were presented in Chapter 4. We now turn to dynamic systems.

There are three techniques for solving what we shall call dynamic optimization problems. They are the calculus of variations, the maximum principle, and dynamic programming. The latter is the most general, because a larger class of problems may be formulated and solved by dynamic programming than either of the other approaches.

Dynamic, or multistage, optimization problems arise in many different contexts. The examples that follow will serve to illustrate the necessity for optimization in dynamic systems. Many other examples may be found in the literature.

The first example we shall consider is a problem in optimal control. Suppose we have a rocket on the launch pad and the desired objective is to have this rocket hit a moving target in a given time interval. The target will take evasive action to attempt to avoid being hit. If we assume that the rocket can generate enough speed to overtake the target, the problem is to generate a set of commands to the missile that will enable it to hit the target in the given interval. This is a multistage decision problem. We observe the target and from its actions generate, periodically, a new direction and speed for our interceptor.

A second example is the design of a sequence of processing units that will accept raw material and produce a finished product of acceptable quality. Since the output of one element in the sequence is the input to the next element, the design of one depends on the design of the element preceding it. The desired objective is to minimize the cost of the sequence of processing units while maintaining acceptable quality. The decisions that can be made are the design specifications of the individual components of the system. This is a multistage decision problem.

The final example of multistage decision making is a reliability problem. Suppose we desire to maximize reliability of a system while not exceeding a given amount of money available for construction. The system is a sequence of components arranged serially into stages so that if one stage fails the entire system fails. A stage is defined as a group of identical components arranged so that only one is operating and the others are on stand-by. In the event that the original component fails, one of the other components immediately becomes operable. The decision at each stage is the number of redundant components to install. Additional redundant components at each stage improve the system reliability but also increase the cost.

All multistage decision processes have certain similarities [1]. Consider the single-stage decision process represented in Figure 5.2. All decision processes have certain parameters, represented as inputs to our box. These parameters,

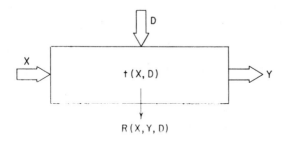

Figure 5.2.

X, give all relevant information about inputs to the box and are called *state variables*. The next component of a decision process is the set of independent variables, which are represented by the vector $\mathbf{D}$[1] and are called decision variables. Associated with each decision $\mathbf{D}$ and each state variable $\mathbf{X}$ is an output from the box which is the result of making a decision. These outputs, **Y**, are called the *output state variables* and they completely characterize the outputs from the box. The outputs are related to the inputs through a stage transformation function that is represented by

$$\mathbf{Y} = \mathbf{t}(\mathbf{X}, \mathbf{D}) \tag{5.1}$$

Finally, there is a return or objective function that measures the effectiveness of the decisions that are made and the outputs that arise from these decisions. Since the decisions we make may change with changes in the state of the system, the return function is represented as

$$R = \mathrm{r}(\mathbf{X}, \mathbf{D}, \mathbf{Y}) \tag{5.2}$$

Since **Y** is completely specified by **X** and **D** through the stage transformation function we may eliminate **Y** from the return function,

$$R = \mathrm{r}[\mathbf{X}, \mathbf{D}, \mathbf{t}(\mathbf{X}, \mathbf{D})] = \mathrm{r}(\mathbf{X}, \mathbf{D}) \tag{5.3}$$

In many problems it is useful to express the return in terms of the input and output state variables. If we can invert the stage transformation function

---

[1] The reader should note the change in notation compared to the previous chapters. Practically speaking, these conflicts also exist in the literature and are unavoidable.

and express **D** in terms of **X** and **Y**, then **D** may be eliminated from the return function. Thus

$$\mathbf{D} = \mathbf{t}^{-1}(\mathbf{X}, \mathbf{Y}) \tag{5.4}$$

$$R = r[\mathbf{X}, \mathbf{t}^{-1}(\mathbf{X}, \mathbf{Y}), \mathbf{Y}] = r(\mathbf{X}, \mathbf{Y}) \tag{5.5}$$

Finally, it may be useful to express the return as a function of the output rather than the input stage variable. If the inverse function exists,

$$\mathbf{X} = \bar{\mathbf{t}}(\mathbf{Y}, \mathbf{D}) \tag{5.6}$$

then

$$R = r(\mathbf{X}, \mathbf{D}, \mathbf{Y}) = r[\bar{\mathbf{t}}(\mathbf{Y}, \mathbf{D})\mathbf{D}, \mathbf{Y}] = r(\mathbf{Y}, \mathbf{D}) \tag{5.7}$$

The implicit function theorem gives us necessary and sufficient conditions for the existence of the inverses discussed above when the functions $t(\cdot)$ are differentiable (see Chapter 2).

A *serial multistage decision process* is one where a number of single-stage processes are connected in series so that the output of one stage is the input to the succeeding stage. Figure 5.3 is a representation of a serial multistage decision process.

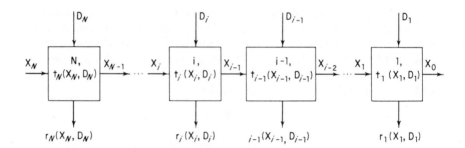

Figure 5.3.

It is clear from Figure 5.3 that the decisions at each stage cannot be made independently of one another. The input to stage i, $\mathbf{X}_i$, is a function of the input to stage $i + 1$, $\mathbf{X}_{i+1}$, and the decision $\mathbf{D}_{i+1}$. Since in general the decision at state i depends on the state of the system $\mathbf{X}_i$, the dependence of the optimal $\mathbf{D}_i$ on $\mathbf{D}_{i+1}$ is established.

Each stage in a multistage decision problem has a return function associated with it. The objective of this multistage problem is to optimize some function of the individual stage returns, $g[r_1(\cdot), \ldots, r_N(\cdot)]$. The *composition* of the N-stage return function determines whether a given problem can be solved by dynamic programming.

Dynamic programming is a *decomposition* technique for solving multistage decision problems. The problem of finding an optimal set of decisions for a given set of input parameters (state variables) to an N-stage problem can be approached in two ways. The first involves applications of classical optimization theory, when appropriate, to the problem of determining values of the independent variables (decisions) that optimize the composite return function. The dynamic programming approach is to decompose the N-decision variable problem into N one-decision variable problems. In many cases these N subproblems are easier to solve than the original problem. The decomposition is effected in a manner so that the optimal solution to the N-variable problem is obtained from the optimal solutions to the N one-dimensional problems.

5.2   Composition and the Principle of Optimality

Dynamic programming is based on the principle of optimality, which says: "An optimal policy (set of decisions) has the property that whatever the initial state and decisions are, the remaining decisions must constitute an optimal policy with regard to the state resulting from the first decision" [2].

We will consider the implication of this principle as a multistage decision problem. Suppose the desired objective is to maximize the N-stage objective function which is given by the sum of the individual stages returns,

$$\max_{\mathbf{D}_N, \ldots, \mathbf{D}_1} [r_N(\mathbf{X}_N, \mathbf{D}_N) + r_{N-1}(\mathbf{X}_{N-1}, \mathbf{D}_{N-1}) + \cdots + r_1(\mathbf{X}_1, \mathbf{D}_1)]$$

subject to

$$\mathbf{X}_{j-1} = \mathbf{t}_j(\mathbf{X}_j, \mathbf{D}_j) \qquad j = 1, \ldots, N$$

Then defining

$$f_N(\mathbf{X}_N) = \max_{\mathbf{D}_N, \ldots, \mathbf{D}_1} [r_N(\mathbf{X}_N, \mathbf{D}_N) + \cdots + r_1(\mathbf{X}_1, \mathbf{D}_1)] \qquad (5.8)$$

subject to

$$\mathbf{X}_{j-1} = \mathbf{t}_j(\mathbf{X}_j, \mathbf{D}_j) \qquad j = 1, \ldots, N$$

we have

$$f_N(\mathbf{X}_N) = \left\{ \max_{\mathbf{D}_N} \max_{\mathbf{D}_{N-1}, \ldots, \mathbf{D}_1} [r_N(\mathbf{X}_N, \mathbf{D}_N) + \cdots + r_1(\mathbf{X}_1, \mathbf{D}_1)] \right\} \qquad (5.9)$$

subject to

$$\mathbf{X}_{j-1} = \mathbf{t}_j(\mathbf{X}_j, \mathbf{D}_j)$$

But $r_N(\mathbf{X}_N, \mathbf{D}_N)$ does not depend on $\mathbf{D}_{N-1}, \ldots, \mathbf{D}_1$. Therefore, the maximization with respect to these variables may be accomplished as shown below:

$$f_N(\mathbf{X}_N) = \max_{\mathbf{D}_N} \left\{ r_N(\mathbf{X}_N, \mathbf{D}_N) + \right.$$

$$\left. \max_{\mathbf{D}_{N-1}, \ldots, \mathbf{D}_1} [r_{N-1}(\mathbf{X}_{N-1}, \mathbf{D}_{N-1}) + \cdots + r_1(\mathbf{X}_1, \mathbf{D}_1)] \right\}$$

subject to

$$\mathbf{X}_{j-1} = \mathbf{t}_j(\mathbf{X}_j, \mathbf{D}_j) \qquad j = 1, \ldots, N \tag{5.10}$$

Using equation (5.8) we may now rewrite (5.10) as

$$f_N(\mathbf{X}_N) = \max_{\mathbf{D}_N} [r_N(\mathbf{X}_N, \mathbf{D}_N) + f_{N-1}(\mathbf{X}_{N-1})]$$

where

$$\mathbf{X}_{n-1} = \mathbf{t}_n(\mathbf{X}_n, \mathbf{D}_n) \qquad n = 1, \ldots, N$$

We pointed out above that the objective in dynamic programming is to choose a set of decisions to optimize some function of the individual stage returns. To deal with a certain class of functions, Mitten introduced the notion of composition of individual stage returns [3]. The function of the individual stage returns can be written

$$g[r_N(\cdot), \ldots, r_1(\cdot)] = r_N(\cdot) \oplus r_{N-1}(\cdot) \oplus r_{N-2}(\cdot) \cdots \oplus r_1(\cdot) \tag{5.11}$$

where $\oplus$ is called the composition operator. The meaning of the composition operator depends on the particular problem under consideration. In the second example, discussed in Section 5.1, the objective was to minimize the total cost of the processing system, where the total cost may be represented as the sum of the costs of each individual stage in the system. In this case the composition operators will all be $+$:

$$g[r_N(\cdot), \ldots, r_1(\cdot)] = r_N(\cdot) + r_{N-1}(\cdot) + \cdots + r_1(\cdot) \tag{5.12}$$

In the last example we want to maximize the system reliability. Thus the general objective function of equation (5.8) may be written

$$g[r_N(\cdot), \ldots, r_1(\cdot)] = r_N(\cdot) \cdot r_{N-1}(\cdot) \cdots r_1(\cdot) \tag{5.13}$$

For this problem the composition operation for stage returns is the product of individual stage returns.

The composition operator may vary from stage to stage. For example,

$$g[r_3(\cdot), r_2(\cdot), r_1(\cdot)] = r_3(\cdot) \oplus r_2(\cdot) \oplus r_1(\cdot)$$
$$= r_3(\cdot) \cdot r_2(\cdot) + r_1(\cdot)$$

Thus the composition operator between stages 2 and 3 is $\cdot$ and $+$ between stages 2 and 1.

Unfortunately, not all multistage decision problems can be approached by dynamic programming. We must require separability of the objective function. That is, we must be able to represent the objective function as the composition of the individual stage returns,

$$g[r_N(\mathbf{X}_N, \mathbf{D}_N), \ldots, r_1(\mathbf{X}_1, \mathbf{D}_1)]$$
$$= r_N(\mathbf{X}_N, \mathbf{D}_N) \oplus r_{N-1}(\mathbf{X}_{N-1}, \mathbf{D}_{N-1}) \oplus \cdots \oplus r_1(\mathbf{X}_1, \mathbf{D}_1)$$

One can easily construct examples of functions that do not satisfy this requirement. For example, the following return function is not separable:

$$g[r_4(\mathbf{X}_4, \mathbf{D}_4), r_3(\mathbf{X}_3, \mathbf{D}_3), r_2(\mathbf{X}_2, \mathbf{D}_2), r_1(\mathbf{X}_1, \mathbf{D}_1)]$$
$$= [r_4(\mathbf{X}_4, \mathbf{D}_4) + r_2(\mathbf{X}_2, \mathbf{D}_2)] \cdot [r_3(\mathbf{X}_3, \mathbf{D}_3) + r_1(\mathbf{X}_1, \mathbf{D}_1)]$$

Fortunately, there are many applied problems that satisfy the separability condition.[2]

Theorem: *A sufficient condition for decomposition by dynamic programming of an objective to function with separable returns is that the N-stage objective function, $g[r_N(\cdot), \ldots, r_1(\cdot)]$, be a monotonically nondecreasing function of $r_{N-1}(\cdot), \ldots, r_1(\cdot)$.*

Proof of the theorem may be found in [3]. Problems in which the composition operator is + satisfy this condition [3]. An example of an objective function that does not satisfy this monotonicity requirement is given below. Consider

$$g[r_3(\mathbf{X}_3, \mathbf{D}_3), r_2(\mathbf{X}_2, \mathbf{D}_2), r_1(\mathbf{X}_1, \mathbf{D}_1)] = r_3(\mathbf{X}_3, \mathbf{D}_3) \cdot r_2(\mathbf{X}_2, \mathbf{D}_2) \cdot r_1(\mathbf{X}_1, \mathbf{D}_1)$$

where the range of r_i may be both positive and negative. Thus when $r_3(\mathbf{X}_3, \mathbf{D}_3)$ < 0 and $r_2(\mathbf{X}_2, \mathbf{D}_2) > 0$, $g[\cdot]$ is monotonically decreasing as $r_1(\cdot)$ increases and this example fails the test. However, this condition is not necessary and it may still be possible to decompose problems by dynamic programming when they fail the test presented above.

5.3   Finite-Stage Processes

We now turn our attention to systems with a finite number of stages. Several different types of examples will be considered—problems where the variables are discrete, examples when the variables are continuous, and processes where some of the variables of interest are random variables. Comparisons will be drawn between the various types of problems regarding ease of solution and generalizations of the structure of the solution.

In the previous two sections, the functions discussed were functions of an arbitrary, but finite, number of variables. For example, the stage transformation was expressed as

$$\mathbf{X}_{n-1} = \mathbf{t}_n(\mathbf{X}_n, \mathbf{D}_n)$$

where each variable was a vector variable. In this section the difficulties of obtaining solutions for problems where the state-vector variable has a

---

[2] Notice that we implicitly assumed that $r_N(\cdot)$ was a function of the input stage variable, $\mathbf{X}_N$, and the decision, $\mathbf{D}_N$, only. Thus to apply dynamic programming we must have the problem under consideration expressible in these terms.

larger number of components will become evident. The discussion of ways to help circumvent this computational difficulty will be deferred to Section 5.5.

In our discussion of dynamic programming we shall avoid, for the most part, discussions of how the various problem formulations are obtained and concentrate primarily on obtaining the solution to the problem as stated. The challenging and more difficult problem of constructing the mathematical model will not be considered.

The first example will now be considered. Suppose we desire to

$$\max_{d_i \geq 0} \sum_{i=1}^{3} d_i^2$$

subject to

$$
\begin{aligned}
x_{i-1} &= x_i - d_i & i &= 1, 2, 3 \\
x_i &= 0, 1, 2, \ldots, 5 & i &= 0, 1, 2 \\
x_3 &= 5
\end{aligned}
$$

Using the results of Section 5.2 we have

$$f_1(x_1) = \max d_1^2$$

Investigating the limits on d_i we find that d_i is bounded from below by 0. Also notice that because each x_{i-1} is required to be nonnegative, d_i is bounded from above by x_i. Finally, since the x_i are required to be integers, the only values of d_i that will satisfy this requirement are the nonnegative integers,

$$d_i = 0, 1, 2, \ldots, x_i$$

Thus

$$f_1(x_1) = \max d_i^2 \qquad d_i = 0, 1, \ldots, x_i$$

The maximum clearly is obtained when $d_1 = x_1$. Therefore, $f_1(x_1) = x_1^2$.

We now proceed to the second stage:

$$
\begin{aligned}
f_2(x_2) &= \max [d_2^2 + f_1(x_1)] & d_2 &= 0, 1, \ldots, x_2 \\
&= \max [d_2^2 + x_1^2] & d_2 &= 0, 1, \ldots, x_2
\end{aligned}
$$

But from the stage transformation function we have $x_1 = x_2 - d_2$. It follows that

$$f_2(x_2) = \max [d_2^2 + (x_2 - d_2)^2] \qquad d_2 = 0, 1, \ldots, x_2$$

The optimum value of d_2 is not as obvious as it was in the previous stage. Notice that the possible values of x_2 are 0, 1, 2, 3, 4, and 5. The optimal value of d_2 must be determined for each of the values of x_2. This is most conveniently displayed in tabular form as illustrated in Table 5.1. $f_2(x_2)$ is tabulated in the table along with the optimal values of d_2, d_2^*, for each x_2.

TABLE 5.1[3]

x_2	d_2	$x_1 (= x_2 - d_2)$	d_2^2	$f_1(x_1)$	$q_2(x_2, d_2)$	$f_2(x_2)$
0	0	0	0	0	0	0
1	0*	1	0	1	1	1
	1*	0	1	0	1	1
2	0*	2	0	4	4	4
	1	1	1	1	2	
	2*	0	4	0	4	4
3	0*	3	0	9	9	9
	1	2	1	4	5	
	2	1	4	1	5	
	3*	0	9	0	9	9
4	0*	4	0	16	16	16
	1	3	1	9	10	
	2	2	4	4	8	
	3	1	9	1	10	
	4*	0	16	0	16	16
5	0*	5	0	25	25	25
	1	4	1	16	17	
	2	3	4	9	13	
	3	2	9	4	13	
	4	1	16	1	17	
	5*	0	25	0	25	25

Notice that there are alternative optima for each x_2; that is, when x_2 is 4, d_2^* may either be 0 or 4. Now that we have $f_2(x_2)$ determined, we continue to $f_3(x_3)$ (Table 5.2), where it is given by

$$f_3(x_3) = \max_{d_3 = 0, 1, \ldots, x_3} [d_3^2 + f_2(x_2)]$$
$$\text{subject to } x_2 = x_3 - d_3$$
$$= \max_{d_3 = 0, 1, \ldots, x_3} [d_3^2 + f_2(x_3 - d_3)^2]$$

TABLE 5.2

x_3	d_3	$x_2 (= x_3 - d_3)$	d_3^2	$f_2(x_2)$	$q_3(x_3, d_3)$	$f_3(x_3 = 5)$
5	0*	5	0	25	25	25
	1	4	1	16	17	
	2	3	4	9	13	
	3	2	9	4	13	
	4	1	16	1	17	
	5*	0	25	0	25	25

---

[3] The * denotes the optimal value of d. $q_2(x_2, d_2)$ is the sum of d_2^2 and f_1x_1.

However, we have only one value of x_3, $x_3 = 5$. Thus

$$f_3(x_3 = 5) = \max_{d_3 = 0, 1, 2, 3, 4, 5} [d_3^2 + f_2(x_3 - d_3)^2]$$

We have obtained the optimal solution to a three-variable problem by solving three one-variable problems. This is decomposition by dynamic programming. The solution to the three one-variable problems was obtained with much less effort than solving one problem in three variables. The savings could be even greater if the number of stages and/or the number of possible values of x_i were increased.

Notice that the problem solved above is similar to the one given below.

$$\max \sum_{i=1}^{3} d_i^2$$

subject to

$$\sum_{i=1}^{3} d_i = 5 \qquad d_i = 0, 1, 2, 3, 4, 5$$

since if

$$x_{i-1} = x_i - d_i$$
$$d_i = x_i - x_{i-1}$$

then

$$\sum_{i=1}^{3} d_i = \sum_{i=1}^{3} (x_i - x_{i-1}) = x_3 - x_0$$

This implies that $x_0 = 0$ because $x_3 = 5 = \sum_{i=1}^{3} d_i$. We see that the two problems are identical.

The next example we consider is a two-state-variable, one-decision-variable problem.

$$\max_{d_i = 0, 1, \ldots} \sum_{i=1}^{3} c_i d_i$$

subject to

$$\sum_{i=1}^{3} k_i d_i \leq 10$$

$$\sum_{i=1}^{3} l_i d_i \leq 15$$

where the parameters are given in the following table.

i	c_i	k_i	l_i
1	1	2	3
2	3	3	5
3	5	4	7

We must obtain the stage transformation functions for this problem. In general, when the constraints are linear, the stage transformation function will be of the form

$$x_{i-1} = x_i - a_i d_i \tag{5.14}$$

The rationale behind this is seen by considering a problem with the following constraint on the decision variables:

$$\sum_{i=1}^{N} a_i d_i \leq b \tag{5.15}$$

Define x_i as the amount of b unused at the preceding $(N - i)$ stages,

$$x_i = b - \sum_{j=i+1}^{N} a_j d_j$$

Then

$$x_{i-1} = b - \sum_{j=i}^{N} a_j d_j$$

Subtracting yields

$$x_i - x_{i-1} = a_i d_i$$

Rearranging we obtain

$$x_{i-1} = x_i - a_i d_i$$

We have obtained a general stage transformation function when the decisions are restricted by linear constraints. For the example we find

$$x_{i-1} = x_i - k_i d_i$$
$$y_{i-1} = y_i - l_i d_i$$

Recall that, by definition, we have

$$f_1(x_1, y_1) = \max_{d_1} c_1 d_1$$

where

$$d_1 = 0, 1, \ldots \leq \min\left(\frac{x_1}{k_1}, \frac{y_1}{l_1}\right)$$

The results are most conveniently displayed in Table 5.3.

TABLE 5.3

x_1	y_1	d	$r_1(x_1, y_1)$	$f_1(x_1, y_1)$
0	0	0*	0	0
	⋮			
	⋮			
	15			
1	0	0*	0	0
	⋮			
	⋮			
	15			
2	0			
	1	0*	0	0
	2			
	3	0		
	⋮	1*	1	1
	⋮			
	15			
3	0			
	1	0*	0	0
	2			
	3			
	⋮	0	0	
	⋮			
	⋮			
	15	1*	1	1
4	0			
	1	0*	0	0
	2			
	3	0	0	
	4			
	5	1*	1	1
	6			
	⋮	0	0	
	⋮	1	1	2
	⋮	2*	2	
	15			
5	0			
	1	0*	0	0
	2			
	3	0	0	
	4			
	5	1*	1	1
	6			
	⋮	0	0	
	⋮	1	1	
	⋮			
	15	2*	2	2

(continued)

TABLE 5.3 (Continued)

x_1	y_1	d	$r_1(x_1, y_1)$	$f_1(x_1, y_1)$
6	0			
	1	0*	0	0
	2			
	3	0	0	
	4			
	5	1*	1	1
	6	0	0	
	7	1	1	
	8	2*	2	2
	9	0	0	
	⋮	1	1	
		2	2	
	⋮			
	15	3*	3	3
7	0	0*	0	0
	1			
	2			
	3	0	0	
	4	1*	1	1
	5			
	6	0	0	
	7	1	1	
	8	2*	2	2
	9	0	0	
	⋮	1	1	
	⋮	2	2	
		3*	3	3
	15			
8	0			
	1	0*	0	0
	2			
	3	0	0	
	4			
	5	1*	1	1
	6	0	0	
	7	1	1	2
	8	2*	2	
	9	0	0	
	10	1	1	
	11	2	2	3
		3*	3	
	12	0	0	
	⋮	1	1	
	⋮	2	2	4
	⋮	3	3	
	15	4*	4	

(*continued*)

TABLE 5.3 (Continued)

x_1	y_1	d	$r_1(x_1, y_1)$	$f_1(x_1, y_1)$
9	0			
	1	0*	0	0
	2			
	3	0	0	
	4			
	5	1*	1	1
	6	0	0	
	7	1	1	
	8	2*	2	2
	9	0	0	
	10	1	1	3
		2	2	
	11	3*	3	
	12	0	0	
	⋮	1	1	
	⋮	2	2	
	⋮	3	3	4
	15	4*	4	
10	0			
	1	0*	0	0
	2			
	3	0	0	
	4			
	5	1*	1	1
	6	0	0	
	7	1	1	2
	8	2*	2	
		0	0	
	9	1	2	3
	10	2	2	
	11	3*	3	
	12	0	0	
		1	1	
	13	2	2	
		3	3	4
	14	4*	4	
	15	0	0	
		1	1	
		2	2	
		3	3	5
		4	4	
		5*	5	

We now have $f_1(x_1, y_1)$ for all possible combinations of x_1 and y_1. Let us turn to the computations of $f_2(x_2, y_2)$, which are displayed in Table 5.4.

TABLE 5.4

x_2	y_2	d_2	x_1	y_1	$r_2(x_2, y_2, d_2)$	$f_1(x_1, y_1)$	$q_2(x_2, y_2)$	$f_2(x_2, y_2)$
0	0	0*	0	0	0	0	0	0
	⋮			⋮				
	15			15				
1	0			0				
	⋮			⋮				
	15	0*	1	15	0	0	0	0
2	0			0		0	0	0
	⋮			⋮				
	15	0	2	15	0	1	1	1
3	0	0*	3	0	0	0	0	0
	1	0*	3	1	0	0	0	0
	2	0*	3	∠	0	0	0	1
	3	0*	3	3	0	1	1	0
	4	0*	3	4	0	1	1	0
	5	0	3	5	0	1	1	3
		1*	0	0	3	0	3	
	6	0	3	6	0	1	1	3
		1*	0	1	3	0	3	
	7	0	3	7	0	1	1	3
		1*	0	2	3	0	3	
	8	0	3	8	0	1	1	3
		1*	0	3	3	0	3	
	9	0	3	9	0	1	1	3
		1*	0	4	3	0	3	
	10	0	3	10	0	1	1	3
		1*	0	5	3	0	3	
	11	0	3	11	0	1	1	3
		1*	0	6	3	0	3	
	12	0	3	12	0	1	1	3
		1*	0	7	3	0	3	
	13	0	3	13	0	1	1	3
		1*	0	8	3	0	3	
	14	0	3	14	0	1	1	3
		1*	0	9	3	0	3	
	15	0	3	15	0	1	1	3
		1*	0	10	3	0	3	

(*continued*)

TABLE 5.4 (Continued)

x_2	y_2	d_2	x_1	y_1	$r_2(x_2, y_2, d_2)$	$f_1(x_1, y_1)$	$q_2(x_2, y_2)$	$f_2(x_2, y_2)$
4	0	0*	4	0	0	0	0	0
	1	0*	4	1	0	0	0	0
	2	0*	4	3	0	0	0	0
	3	0*	4	3	0	1	1	1
	4	0*	4	4	0	1	1	1
	5	0	4	5	0	1	1	
		1*	1	0	3	0	3	3
	6	0	4	6	0	2	2	
		1*	1	1	3	0	3	3
	7	0	4	7	0	2	2	
		1*	1	2	3	0	3	3
	8	0	4	8	0	2	2	
		1*	1	3	3	0	3	3
	9	0	4	9	0	2	2	
		1*	1	4	3	0	3	3
	10	0	4	10	0	2	2	
		1*	1	5	3	0	3	3
	11	0	4	11	0	2	2	
		1*	1	6	3	0	3	3
	12	0	4	12	0	2	2	
		1*	1	7	3	0	3	3
	13	0	4	13	0	2	2	
		1*	1	8	3	0	3	3
	14	0	4	14	0	2	2	
		1*	1	9	3	0	3	3
	15	0	4	15	0	2	2	
		1*	1	10	3	0	3	3
5	0	0*	5	0	0	0	0	0
	1	0*	5	1	0	0	0	0
	2	0*	5	2	0	0	0	0
	3	0*	5	3	0	1	1	1
	4	0*	5	4	0	1	1	1
	5	0	5	5	0	1	1	
		1*	2	0	3	0	3	3
	6	0	5	6	0	2	2	
		1*	2	1	3	0	3	3
	7	0	5	7	0	2	2	
		1*	2	2	3	0	3	3
	8	0	5	8	0	2	2	
		1*	2	3	3	1	4	4
	9	0	5	9	0	2	2	
		1*	2	4	3	1	4	4
	10	0	5	10	0	2	2	
		1*	2	5	3	1	4	4
	11	0	5	11	0	2	2	
		1*	2	6	3	1	4	4
	12	0	5	12	0	2	2	
		1*	2	7	3	1	4	4

(continued)

TABLE 5.4 (Continued)

x_2	y_2	d_2	x_1	y_1	$r_2(x_2, y_2, d_2)$	$f_1(x_1, y_1)$	$q_2(x_2, y_2)$	$f_2(x_2, y_2)$
	13	0	5	13	0	2	2	
		1*	2	8	3	1	4	4
	14	0	5	14	0	2	2	
		1*	2	9	3	1	4	4
	15	0	5	15	0	2	2	
		1*	2	10	3	1	4	4
6	0	0*	6	0	0	0	0	0
	1	0*	6	1	0	0	0	0
	2	0*	6	2	0	0	0	0
	3	0*	6	3	0	1	1	1
	4	0*	6	4	0	1	1	1
	5	0	6	5	0	1	1	
		1*	3	0	3	0	3	3
	6	0	6	6	0	2	2	
		1*	3	1	3	0	3	3
	7	0	6	7	0	2	2	
		1*	3	2	3	0	4	3
	8	0	6	8	0	2	3	
		1*	3	3	3	1	4	4
	9	0	6	9	0	3	3	
		1*	3	4	3	1	4	4
	10	0	6	10	0	3	3	
		1	3	5	3	1	4	6
		2*	0	0	6	0	6	
	11	0	6	11	0	3	3	
		1	3	6	3	1	4	6
		2*	0	1	6	0	6	
	12	0	6	12	0	3	3	
		1	3	7	3	1	4	6
		2*	0	2	6	0	6	
	13	0	6	13	0	3	3	
		1	3	8	3	1	4	6
		2*	0	3	6	0	6	
	14	0	6	14	0	3	3	
		1	3	9	3	1	4	6
		2*	0	4	6	0	6	
	15	0	6	15	0	3	3	
		1	3	10	3	1	4	6
		2*	0	5	6	0	6	
7	0	0*	7	0	0	0	0	0
	1	0*	7	1	0	0	0	0
	2	0*	7	2	0	0	0	0
	3	0*	7	3	0	1	1	1
	4	0*	7	4	0	1	1	1
	5	0	7	5	0	1	1	
		1*	4	0	3	0	3	3
	6	0	7	6	0	2	2	
		1*	4	1	3	0	3	3

(*continued*)

TABLE 5.4 (Continued)

x_2	y_2	d_2	x_1	y_1	$r_2(x_2, y_2, d_2)$	$f_1(x_1, y_1)$	$q_2(x_2, y_2)$	$f_2(x_2, y_2)$
	7	0	7	7	0	2	2	
		1*	4	2	3	0	3	3
	8	0	7	8	0	2	2	
		1*	4	3	3	1	4	4
	9	0	7	9	0	3	3	
		1*	4	4	3	1	4	4
7	10	0	7	10	0	3	3	
		1	4	5	3	1	4	6
		2*	1	0	6	0	6	
	11	0	7	11	0	3	3	
		1	4	6	3	2	5	6
		2*	1	1	6	0	6	
	12	0	7	12	0	3	3	
		1	4	7	3	2	5	6
		2*	1	2	6	0	6	
	13	0	7	13	0	3	3	
		1	4	8	3	2	5	6
		2*	1	3	6	0	6	
	14	0	7	14	0	3	3	
		1	4	9	3	2	5	6
		2*	1	4	6	0	6	
	15	0	7	15	0	3	3	
		1	4	10	3	2	5	6
		2*	1	5	6	0	6	
8	0	0*	8	0	0	0	0	0
	1	0*	8	1	0	0	0	0
	2	0*	8	2	0	1	1	1
	3	0*	8	3	0	1	1	1
	4	0*	8	4	0	1	1	1
	5	0	8	5	0	1	1	
		1*	5	0	3	0	3	3
	6	0	8	6	0	2	2	
		1*	5	1	3	0	3	3
	7	0	8	7	0	2	2	
		1*	5	2	3	0	3	3
	8	0	8	8	0	2	2	
		1*	5	3	3	1	4	4
	9	0	8	9	0	3	3	
		1*	5	4	3	1	4	4
	10	0	8	10	0	3	3	
		1	5	5	3	1	4	6
		2*	2	0	6	0	6	
	11	0	8	11	0	3	3	
		1	5	6	3	2	5	6
		2*	2	1	6	0	6	
	12	0	8	12	0	4	4	
		1	5	7	3	2	5	6
		2*	2	2	6	0	6	
	13	0	8	13	0	4	4	

(*continued*)

TABLE 5.4 (Continued)

x_2	y_2	d_2	x_1	y_1	$r_2(x_2, y_2, d_2)$	$f_1(x_1, y_1)$	$q_2(x_2, y_2)$	$f_2(x_2, y_2)$
	13	1	5	8	3	2	5	7
		2*	2	3	6	1	7	
	14	0	8	14	0	4	4	
		1	5	9	3	2	5	7
		2*	2	4	6	1	7	
	15	0	8	15	0	4	4	
		1	5	10	3	2	5	7
		2*	2	5	6	1	7	
9	0	0*	9	0	0	0	0	0
	1	0*	9	1	0	0	0	0
	2	0*	9	2	0	0	0	0
	3	0*	9	3	0	1	1	1
	4	0*	9	4	0	1	1	1
	5	0	9	5	0	1	1	
		1*	6	0	3	0	3	3
	6	0	9	6	0	2	2	
		1*	6	1	3	0	3	3
	7	0	9	7	0	2	2	
		1*	6	2	3	0	3	3
	8	0	9	8	0	2	2	
		1*	6	3	3	1	4	4
	9	0	9	9	0	3	3	
		1*	6	4	3	1	4	4
	10	0	9	10	0	3	3	
		1	6	5	3	1	4	6
		2*	3	0	6	0	6	
	11	0	9	11	0	3	3	
		1	6	6	3	2	5	6
		2*	3	1	6	0	6	
	12	0	9	12	0	4	4	
		1	6	7	3	2	5	7
		2*	3	2	6	0	6	
	13	0	9	13	0	4	4	
		1	6	8	3	2	5	7
		2*	3	3	6	1	7	
	14	0	9	14	0	4	4	
		1	6	9	3	3	6	7
		2*	3	4	6	1	7	
	15	0	9	15	0	4	4	
		1	6	10	3	3	6	7
		2*	3	5	6	1	7	
10	0		10	0	0	0	0	0
	1	0*	10	1	0	0	0	0
	2	0*	10	2	0	0	0	0
	3	0*	10	3	0	1	1	1
	4	0*	10	4	0	1	1	1
	5	0*	10	5	0	1	1	
		1*	7	0	3	0	3	3

(*continued*)

TABLE 5.4 (Continued)

x_2	y_2	d_2	x_1	y_1	$r_2(x_2, y_2, d_2)$	$f_1(x_1, y_1)$	$q_2(x_2, y_2)$	$f_2(x_2, y_2)$
	6	0	10	6	0	2	2	
		1*	7	1	3	0	3	3
	7	0	10	7	0	2	2	
		1*	7	2	3	0	3	3
	8	0	10	8	0	2	2	
		1*	7	3	3	1	4	4
	9	0	10	9	0	3	3	
		1*	7	4	3	1	4	4
	10	0	10	10	0	3	3	
		1	7	5	3	1	4	6
		2*	4	0	6	0	6	
	11	0	10	11	0	3	3	
		1	7	6	3	2	5	6
		2*	4	1	6	0	6	
	12	0	10	12	0	4	4	
		1	7	7	3	2	5	6
		2*	4	2	6	0	6	
	13	0	10	13	0	4	4	
		1	7	8	3	2	5	7
		2*	4	3	6	1	7	
	14	0	10	14	0	4	4	
		1	7	9	3	3	5	7
		2*	4	4	6	1	7	
	15	0	10	15	0	5	5	
		1	7	10	3	3	6	9
		2	4	5	6	1	7	
		3*	1	0	9	0	9	

Finally we obtain $f_3(x_3, y_3)$. It is clear that $\sum_i c_i d_i$ will be maximum when $x_3 = 10$ and $y_3 = 15$. We need to consider only these two values for input state variables. The result is shown in Table 5.5.

TABLE 5.5

x_3	y_3	d_3	x_2	y_2	$r_3(x_3, y_3, d_3)$	$f_2(x_2, y_2)$	$q_3(x_3, y_3)$	$f_3(x_3, d_3)$
10	15	0	10	15	0	9	9	
		1	6	8	5	3	8	10
		2	2	1	10	0	10	

The example given above serves to illustrate the difficulties encountered when the number of state variables is increased. The increase in the number of computations was only annoying in the example given. However, when the number of combinations of state variables that must be considered exceeds 50,000, the amount of storage required reaches the limits of most current computers.[4] The computation time also increases rapidly with increases in the number of state variables. Time limitations on a given problem would be determined by the increased value derived from the optimal solution.

Let us turn to the case where the functions are differentiable. Suppose in the first example the variables are continuous. Specifically,

$$\max_{d_i \geq 0} \sum_{i=1}^{3} d_i^2$$

subject to

$$x_{i-1} = x_i - d_i \qquad i = 1, 2, 3$$
$$x_3 = 5$$
$$x_i \geq 0 \qquad\qquad i = 0, 1, 2$$

Thus

$$f_1(x_1) = \max d_1^2 \qquad 0 \leq d_1 \leq x_1$$

Employing the Lagrange multiplier method of Chapter 2 we have

$$F(d_1, \lambda_1, \lambda_2, u_1, u_2) = d_1^2 + \lambda_1(d_1 - x_1 + u_1^2) + \lambda_2(-d_1 + u_2^2)$$

$$\frac{\partial F}{\partial d_1} = 0 = 2d_1 + \lambda_1 - \lambda_2 = 0$$

$$\frac{\partial F}{\partial \lambda_1} = 0 = d_1 - x_1 + u_1^2$$

$$\frac{\partial F}{\partial \lambda_2} = 0 = -d_1 + u_2^2$$

$$\frac{\partial F}{\partial u_1} = 0 = 2\lambda_1 u_1$$

$$\frac{\partial F}{\partial u_2} = 0 = 2\lambda_2 u_2$$

$$\lambda_1, \lambda_2 \leq 0$$

Assume $\lambda_1, u_2 \neq 0$. This implies $u_1 = \lambda_2 = 0$. Thus

$$d_1 = -\frac{\lambda_1}{2} = x_1$$

Since $x_1 \geq 0$, $\lambda_1 \leq 0$ and the necessary conditions are satisfied. The other solution occurs when $\lambda_1 = u_2 = d_1 = 0$. This is not the maximum because $\lambda_2 \geq 0$. Therefore, $f_1(x_1) = x_1^2$.

---

[4] This limiting figure was derived from the core memory available in most large-scale computers. If one desires to use other types of memory devices, this limit can be increased.

We now turn to the determination of $f_2(x_2)$:

$$f_2(x_2) = \max_{0 \le d_2 \le x_2} [d_2^2 + f_1(x_1)]$$

subject to $x_1 = x_2 - d_2$

$$f_2(x_2) = \max_{0 \le d_2 \le x_2} [d_2^2 + (x_2 - d_2)^2]$$

Upon solving this constrained problem we find

$$f_2(x_2) = x_2^2$$
$$d_2^* = x_2$$

Note that in this case there are alternative optima with $d_2^* = 0$ and $f_2(x_2) = x_2^2$. Finally,

$$f_3(x_3 = 5) = \max_{0 \le d_3 \le x_3} [d_3^2 + f_2(x_2)]$$

subject to $x_2 = x_3 - d_3$

$$f_3(x_3) = \max_{0 \le d_3 \le x_3} [d_3^2 + (x_3 - d_3)^2]$$

The solution again yields alternative optima—$d_3^* = (x_3$ or $0)$ and $f_3(x_3) = x_3^2 = 25$. The decision rule is thus

$$d_3 = 5 \qquad d_2 = d_1 = 0$$

or

$$d_3 = 0 \qquad d_2 = 5 \qquad d_1 = 0$$

and, finally,

$$d_3 = d_2 = 0 \qquad d_1 = 5$$

The results of this example can be extended to an arbitrary, but finite, number of stages. The problem becomes

$$\max_{d_i \ge 0} \sum_{i=1}^{N} d_i^2$$

$$x_{i-1} = x_i - d_i \qquad i = 1, \ldots, N$$
$$x_i \ge 0 \qquad i = 1, \ldots, N$$
$$x_N = c$$

We have shown $f_1(x_1) = x_1^2$, $f_2(x_2) = x_2^2$, and $f_3(x_3) = x_3^2$. Using an induction proof we assume

$$f_{n-1}(x_{n-1}) = x_{n-1}^2$$

Then

$$f_n(x_n) = \max_{0 \le d_n \le x_n} [d_n^2 + f_{n-1}(x_{n-1})]$$

subject to

$$x_{n-1} = x_n - d_n$$

Incorporating the stage transformation function yields

$$f_n(x_n) = \max_{0 \le d_n \le x_n} [d_n^2 + (x_n - d_n)^2] = \max_{0 \le d_n \le x_n} q_n(x_n, d_n)$$

The Lagrangian and associated Kuhn-Tucker conditions are

$$F(x_n, \lambda_1, \lambda_2, u_1, u_2) = q_n(x_n, d_n) + \lambda_1(d_n - x_n - u_1^2) + \lambda_2(-d_n + u_2^2)$$

$$\frac{\partial F}{\partial d_n} = 0 = 2d_n - 2(x_n - d_n) + \lambda_1 - \lambda_2 = 0$$

$$\frac{\partial F}{\partial \lambda_1} = 0 = d_n - x_n + u_1^2$$

$$\frac{\partial F}{\partial \lambda_2} = 0 = -d_n + u_2^2$$

$$\frac{\partial F}{\partial u_1} = 0 = 2\lambda_1 u_1$$

$$\frac{\partial F}{\partial u_2} = 0 = 2\lambda_2 u_2$$

$$\lambda_1, \lambda_2 \le 0$$

There are three feasible solutions: $d_n = x_n$, $d_n = 0$, and $d_n = x_n/2$. Evaluating these possibilities we find $d_n = (0, x_n)$ and

$$f_n(x_n) = x_n^2$$

Thus

$$f_N(x_N) = c^2$$
$$d_i = c\delta_{ik} \qquad i = 1, \ldots, N$$

where

$$\delta_{ik} = \begin{cases} 0 & i \ne k \\ 1 & i = k \end{cases}$$

This result holds for any $k = 1, \ldots, N$.

Let us turn our attention to another example with an arbitrary, but finite, number of stages. Suppose we wish to

$$\min_{d_n \ge 0} \sum_{n=1}^{N} d_n^2$$

subject to

$$\sum_{n=1}^{N} n d_n = c$$

Previously we have established that when the constraints were linear the stage transformation functions have the form

$$x_{n-1} = x_n - a_n d_n$$

For the problem at hand $a_n = n$, and

$$x_{n-1} = x_n - n d_n$$

Following the dynamic programming decomposition approach we have

$$f_1(x_1) = \min_{d_1 = x_1} d_1^2$$

More elaboration of this result is in order. Recall that we may view x_1 as the amount of c that was not allocated in stages $2, \ldots, N$. Since our constraint is an equality constraint, we must require that any portion of c unused in the previous stages be allocated at stage 1. Therefore, $d_1 = x_1$ and we are free to choose only $N - 1$ of the d_n independently. Notice that this result may be generalized to arbitrary equality constraints; that is, whenever we encounter an equality constraint, one degree of freedom in the choice of the d is lost. Thus

$$f_1(x_1) = x_1^2$$

Let us compute the optimal two-stage return for an input x_2:

$$f_2(x_2) = \min_{0 \le d_2 \le x_2/2} [d_2^2 + f_1(x_1)]$$

subject to $x_1 = x_2 - 2d_2$.
    Thus

$$f_2(x_2) = \min_{0 \le d_2 \le x_2/2} [d_2^2 + x_1^2] = \min_{0 \le d_2 \le x_2/2} [d_2^2 + (x_2 - 2d_2)^2]$$

$$= \min_{0 \le d_2 \le x_2/2} q_2(x_2, d_2)$$

Forming the Lagrange function we obtain

$$F_2(d_2, \lambda_1, \lambda_2) = d_2^2 + (x_2 - 2d_2)^2 + \lambda_1\left(d_2 - \frac{x_2}{2} + u_1^2\right) + \lambda_2(-d_2 + u_2^2)$$

The Kuhn-Tucker conditions are

(1) $$\frac{\partial F(\cdot)}{\partial d_2} = 2d_2 - 4(x_2 - 2d_2) + \lambda_1 - \lambda_2 = 0$$

(2) $$\lambda_1\left(d_2 - \frac{x_2}{2}\right) = 0$$

(3) $$\lambda_2 d_2 = 0$$

(4) $$\lambda_1, \lambda_2 \ge 0$$

The solution to these equations is

$$d_2 = \frac{2x_2}{5} \qquad \lambda_1 = \lambda_2 = 0$$

This is the optimum solution because $q_2(x_2, d_2)$ is strictly convex in d_2 and the constraints are convex.

Substituting this result for d_2 into the definition of $f_2(x_2)$ we find

$$f_2(x_2) = \frac{x_2^2}{5}$$

A pattern appears to be developing in that both $f_1(x_1)$ and $f_2(x_2)$ were linear functions of x_1^2 and x_2^2, respectively. However, to be sure this is the correct pattern, let us determine $f_3(x_3)$:

$$f_3(x_3) = \min_{0 \le d_3 \le x_3/3} [d_3^2 + f_2(x_2)]$$

subject to $x_2 = x_3 - 3d_3$. Therefore,

$$f_3(x_3) = \min_{0 \le d_3 \le x_3/3} [d_3^2 + \tfrac{1}{5}(x_3 - 3d_3)^2]$$

Again we have a convex function defined on a convex set so that there is a unique solution to the necessary conditions, and further these conditions are sufficient for a minimum. The Kuhn-Tucker conditions are

(1) $\qquad\qquad 2d_3 - \tfrac{6}{5}(x_3 - 3d_3) + \lambda_1 - \lambda_2 = 0$

(2) $\qquad\qquad \lambda_1\left(d_3 - \dfrac{x_3}{3}\right) = 0$

(3) $\qquad\qquad \lambda_2 d_3 = 0$

(4) $\qquad\qquad \lambda_1, \lambda_2 \ge 0$

The solution is $d_3^* = \tfrac{3}{14}x_3$, $\lambda_1 = \lambda_2 = 0$. Using this result we compute $f_3(x_3)$:

$$f_3(x_3) = [(\tfrac{3}{14})^2 x_3^2 + (\tfrac{1}{5})(\tfrac{5}{14})^2 x_3^2] = \frac{x_3^2}{14}$$

It appears certain that a pattern has been established. Let us either prove or disprove our intuition by assuming

$$f_{n-1}(x_{n-1}) = K_{n-1} x_{n-1}^2$$

Then if $f_n(x_n) = K_n x_n^2$ our reasoned guess will have been justified. Recall that

$$f_n(x_n) = \min_{0 \le d_n \le x_n/n} [d_n^2 + f_{n-1}(x_{n-1})]$$

$$x_{n-1} = x_n - nd_n$$

Using the assumed form of $f_{n-1}(\cdot)$ and eliminating x_{n-1} by using the stage transformation function we obtain

$$f_n(x_n) = \min_{0 \le d_n \le x_n/n} [d_n^2 + K_{n-1}(x_n - nd_n)^2]$$

Again we find that the term in brackets is strictly convex and the constraints are convex. Thus the solution to the equations shown below yields the desired value of d_n.

(1) $$2d_n - 2nK_{n-1}(x_n - nd_n) + \lambda_1 - \lambda_2 = 0$$

(2) $$\lambda_1\left(d_n - \frac{x_n}{n}\right) = 0$$

(3) $$\lambda_2 d_n = 0$$

(4) $$\lambda_1, \lambda_2 \ge 0$$

The solution is

$$d_n^* = \frac{nK_{n-1}x_n}{1 + n^2k_{n-1}} \qquad \lambda_1 = \lambda_2 = 0$$

Evaluating $f_n(x_n)$ we find

$$f_n(x_n) = \frac{n^2 K_{n-1}^2 x_n^2}{[1 + n^2 K_{n-1}]^2} + \frac{K_{n-1}x_n^2}{[1 + n^2 K_{n-1}]^2} = \frac{K_{n-1}x_n^2}{1 + n^2 K_{n-1}} = K_n x_n^2$$

where

$$K_n = \frac{K_{n-1}}{1 + n^2 K_{n-1}}$$

Thus our hypothesis was correct and for any stage j we have

$$f_j(x_j) = K_j x_j^2$$

$$K_j = \frac{K_{j-1}}{1 + j^2 K_{j-1}}$$

$$K_1 = 1$$

The optimal decision at any stage j, $j = 1, \ldots, N$ is given by

$$d_j = jK_j x_j$$

with $x_N = c$.

Random Variables

The final result we shall obtain in this section is the extension of dynamic programming to certain systems where the variables are random. Consider the following problem, which has its origin in optimal control theory:

$$\min \sum_{i=0}^{N-1} (x_i^2 + d_{i+1}^2)$$

subject to $x_{i-1} = x_i - d_i + u_i$, where u_i is a random variable whose probability density function is known and given by

$$g_i(\mu_i, \sigma_i^2) \qquad -\infty < \mu_i, \sigma_i^2 < \infty$$

The first result will be obtained for the case when the random variables u_i and u_j, $i \neq j$, are independent.

It would now appear that all the necessary information for solving the problem is at hand. However, on closer inspection we find that the variables of interest are random variables. Thus we really have only limited control over the realization of the x_i. We shall use in such circumstances the expected value of the objective function as a measure of effectiveness.

Under the expected value criterion the problem becomes

$$\min_{d_i\ u_i} E\left(\sum_{i=0}^{N-1} x_i^2 + d_{i+1}^2\right)$$

subject to

$$x_{i-1} = x_i - d_i + u_i$$

We now calculate $f_1(x_1)$:

$$\bar{f}_1(x_1) = \min_{d_1} (x_0^2 + d_1^2)$$

$$= \min_{d_1\ u_1} E[(x_1 - d_1 + u_1)^2 + d_1^2]$$

$$= \min_{d_1\ u_1} E[q_1(x_1, u_1, d_1)]$$

$$\frac{\partial E[q_1(x_1, u_1, d_1)]}{\partial d_1} = E[-2(x_1 - d_1 + u_1)] + 2d_1 = 0$$

Solving this equation we obtain

$$d_1 = \frac{x_1 + r_i}{2}$$

Using this result and the definition of $f_1(x_1)$ yields

$$\bar{f}_1(x_1) = E\left[x_1 + u_1 - \frac{x_1 + \mu_1}{2}\right]^2 + \tfrac{1}{4}(x_1 + \mu_1)^2$$

$$= \frac{x_1^2 + \mu_1^2}{2} + \sigma_1^2 + x_1\mu_1$$

$$\bar{f}_2(x_2) = \min_{d_2\ u_2} E[x_1^2 + d_2^2 + f_1(x_1)]$$

$$= \min_{d_2\ u_2} E\left[(x_2 - d_2 + u_2)^2 + d_2^2\right.$$

$$\left. + \frac{(x_2 - d_2 + u_2)^2}{2} + \frac{\mu_1^2}{2} + \sigma_1^2 + \mu_1(x_2 - d_2 + u_2)\right]$$

$$= \min_{d_2\ u_2} E\left[\tfrac{3}{2}(x_2 - d_2 + u_2)^2 + d_2^2 + \frac{\mu_1^2}{2} + \sigma_1^2 + \mu_1(x_2 - d_2 + u_2)\right]$$

$$\frac{\partial E[q_2(\cdot)]}{\partial d_2} = -3(x_2 - d_2 + u_2) + 2d_2 - \mu_1 = 0$$

Solving yields

$$d_2 = \frac{3x_2 + 3\mu_2 + \mu_1}{5}$$

Thus

$$\bar{f}_2(x_2) = 0.6x_2^2 + 1.1\sigma_2^2 + 0.6\mu_2^2 + 0.6\mu_1^2 + 1.2\mu_2 x_2 + \sigma_1^2 + 0.4x_2\mu_1$$

Assume that the general form of the solution is given by

$$\bar{f}_{n-1}(x_{n-1}) = a_{n-1}x_{n-1}^2 + \sum_{i=1}^{n-1} b_{n-1}(i)\sigma_i^2 + \sum_{i=1}^{n-1} c_{n-1}(i)\mu_i^2$$

$$+ \sum_{i=1}^{n-1} \mu_i x_{n-1} h_{n-1}(i)$$

Then

$$\bar{f}_n(x_n) = \min_{d_n \, u_n} E[x_{n-1}^2 + d_n^2 + \bar{f}_{n-1}(x_{n-1})]$$

subject to

$$x_{n-1} = x_n - d_n + u_n$$

This yields

$$\bar{f}_n(x_n) = \min_{d_n \, u_n} E[(x_n - d_n + u_n)^2 + d_n^2 + a_{n-1}(x_n - d_n + u_n)^2$$

$$+ \sum_{i=1}^{n-1} b_{n-1}(i)\sigma_i^2 + \sum_{i=1}^{n-1} c_{n-1}(i)\mu_i^2$$

$$+ \sum_{i=1}^{n-1} [h_{n-1}(i)\mu_i(x_n - d_n + u_n)]$$

$$\bar{f}_n(x_n) = \min_{d_n \, u_n} E[q_n(x_n, d_n, u_n)]$$

$$\frac{\partial E[q_n(\cdot)]}{\partial d_n} = 0 = E_{u_n}\left[-2(x_n - d_n + u_n)(1 + a_{n-1}) + 2d_n - \sum_{i=1}^{N} h_{n-1}^{(i)}\mu_i \right]$$

$$d_n = \frac{(1 + a_{n-1})(x_n + \mu_n)}{2 + a_{n-1}} + \sum_{i=1}^{n-1} \frac{h_{n-1}(i)\mu_i}{2(2 + a_{n-1})}$$

Substituting this value of d_n into $q_n(\cdot)$ yields

$$\bar{f}_n(x_n) = a_n x_n + \sum_{i=1}^{n} b_n(i)\sigma_i^2 + \sum_{i=1}^{n} c_n(i)\mu_i + x_n \sum_{i=1}^{n} h_n(i)\mu_i$$

The coefficients of terms in the objective function are given by nonlinear difference equations. For example,

$$a_n = \frac{1 + a_{n-1}}{2 + a_{n-1}}$$

The determination of the remaining terms is left as an exercise for the reader.

We have seen, then, that the introduction of randomness into this particular problem causes only algebraic difficulty.[5] No conceptual hurdles are introduced. However, this is only true when the random variables are uncorrelated. When they are correlated, additional complications occur. In fact, when the random variables are correlated, additional state variables must be introduced—one for each degree of dependence of the density of $F(u_i)$ on $u_{i-1}, u_{i-2}, \ldots$.

The rationale behind the above statement is as follows. At stage 1, we took the expectation with respect to u_1. However, if u_1 is correlated with u_2, the probability density function of u_1 depends on the *observation* of u_2. Consequently, we must determine $E(\cdot)$ for all values of u_2, because at this stage u_2 is unknown. Thus u_2 becomes a state variable. Similarly, if the probability density function of u_1 depends on $u_2, \ldots, u_i$, each of these must be carried as a state variable at stage 1 since the $E_{u_1}(\cdot)$ depends on the actual observations of these random variables. When the solution may be obtained analytically, the algebra becomes clumsy but is still tractable. When solutions must be obtained computationally, the introduction of random variables that are correlated from stage to stage raises doubts as to the computational feasibility of obtaining the solution.

One other factor becomes important in obtaining the decision rule when correlation exists between the random variables at succeeding stages. The decision is a random variable because at each stage the optimal decision is a function of conditioned means. Thus until the observations of the random variables are available, the means cannot be calculated and the decision rule cannot be implemented.[6] The procedure for obtaining the decision rule at stage i is as follows: (1) obtain actual observations of random variables in stages $i + 1, \ldots, N$; (2) calculate the current mean, u_i, based on these observations; and (3) calculate the decision rule.

5.4   Infinite-Stage Problems

Infinite-stage problems may arise in two different ways. One example where infinite-stage decision problems may arise is in planning problems. In such problems the decisions are made at discrete points of time, but the planning organization, for obvious reasons, does not want to put a time limit on its effectiveness. Large industrial firms operate on the assumption that they will continue to function indefinitely and do their planning on this

---

[5] This statement should be qualified and is only true in general for linear transformation functions.

[6] Dreyfus [4] has a striking example of the usefulness of dynamic programming in stochastic situations.

basis—called an infinite planning horizon. The other way in which we may obtain an infinite number of stages can be illustrated by a missile control program. The manned space missions terminate after a fixed interval of time, but the time between stages—in the dynamic programming sense—becomes small. In effect, decisions are made continuously. Thus an infinite number of decisions are made in a finite time interval. Since we defined a stage as a point where decisions are made, an infinite-stage problem is obtained.

Problems arise with the infinite-stage problem that we did not encounter in the finite-stage formulation. For example, in a finite-stage resource allocation problem, the return function is defined as the sum of individual stage returns. In attempting to extend this type of measure of effectiveness to an infinite-stage problem, we encounter difficulties with the existence of an optimal solution. The measure of effectiveness has become an infinite sum of terms. To have an optimal solution exist, this sum must converge. A necessary (but not sufficient) condition for convergence is that

$$\lim_{n \to \infty} r_n(x_n, d_n) = 0 \qquad \cdot$$

However, we may not be satisfied with a return that decreases from stage to stage. More pragmatically, an operations researcher who prescribed such a decision rule for his employer would find it difficult to arrive at a convincing argument explaining why the profits must decrease.

Various schemes have been developed for arriving at a satisfactory solution to this dilemma. One method involves time averaging. The return function, $g[\cdot]$, is divided by N, the number of stages. Then to get the optimal solution we solve the infinite-stage problem by a limiting process,

$$\lim_{N \to \infty} \max \frac{g[\cdot]}{N} = \lim_{N \to \infty} \max \frac{1}{N} \sum_{n=1}^{N} r_n(x_n, d_n)$$

Another approach involves discounting the future returns to obtain present worth. A discount factor, α, between 0 and 1 is raised to the power n and multiplied by $r_n(\cdot)$. The overall return then becomes

$$\sum_{n=1}^{\infty} \alpha^n r_n(x_n, d_n)$$

One must beware of the subtle problems associated with the existence of solutions. What may seem to be the obvious measure of effectiveness for a finite-stage problem may have no meaning when extended to the infinite-stage concept. One may wonder why we are interested in obtaining solutions to problems of this nature. Would not it be just as effective to make N very large, but finite, and disregard existence problems? One reason is that, in many cases, the structure of the solution may be obtained from the study of infinite-stage problems. The knowledge of the structure may give increased insight into the problem at hand. Another reason is that in cases where the problem is one where the stages are continuous, the infinite-stage approach is the only one that has physical significance.

An example of the approach to continuous problems is illustrated below. In this problem the objective function becomes an integral instead of an infinite sum, and the difference equation representing the stage transformation function is replaced by a differential equation. The problem becomes

$$\max \int_t^T h(x, d, t)\, dt$$

subject to

$$\frac{dx}{dt} = g(x, d, t)$$

The variable t plays the role similar to n in the discrete-stage problem.

The classical method of approach to this problem is by the calculus of variations. However, analytical solutions cannot be obtained except for very simple problems. The variational approach results in a second-order partial differential equation that may be difficult to solve numerically.

Dynamic programming leads to a very efficient numerical approximation procedure. Define

$$f[x(t), t] = \max_{d(t)} \int_t^T h(x, d, t)\, dt$$

where the interval of integration is $[t, T]$. But

$$\int_t^T h(x, d, t)\, dt = \int_{t+\Delta t}^T h(x, d, t)\, dt + \int_t^{t+\Delta t} h(x, d, t)\, dt$$

Substituting this identity into the definition of $f[x(t), t]$ yields

$$f[x(t), t] = \max_{\substack{d(t) \\ [t,T]}} \left[\int_t^{t+\Delta t} h(x, d, t)\, dt + \int_{t+\Delta t}^T h(x, d, t)\, dt \right]$$

subject to

$$\frac{dx}{dt} = g(x, d, t)$$

$$f[x(t), t] = \max_{\substack{d(t) \\ [t,t+\Delta t]}} \ \max_{\substack{d(t) \\ [t+\Delta t, T]}} \left[\int_t^{t+\Delta t} h(x, d, t)\, dt + \int_{t+\Delta t}^T h(x, d, t)\, dt \right]$$

subject to

$$\frac{dx}{dt} = g(x, d, t)$$

But the first term in brackets depends only on $d(t)$ in the interval $[t, t + \Delta t]$. Thus the inner maximization may be moved inside this term to yield

$$f[x(t), t] = \max_{\substack{d(t) \\ [t,t+\Delta t]}} \left[\int_t^{t+\Delta t} h(x, d, t) \, dt + \max_{\substack{d(t) \\ [t+\Delta t, T]}} \int_{t+\Delta t}^{T} h(x, d, t) \, dt \right]$$

subject to

$$\frac{dx}{dt} = g(x, d, t)$$

But by definition

$$\max_{\substack{d(t) \\ [t+\Delta t, T]}} \int_{t+\Delta t}^{T} h(x, d, t) \, dt = f[x(t + \Delta t), t + \Delta t]$$

Therefore,

$$f[x(t), t] = \max_{\substack{d(t) \\ [t,t+\Delta t]}} \left[\int_t^{t+\Delta t} h(x, d, t) \, dt + f[x(t + \Delta t), t + \Delta t] \right]$$

where

$$x(t + \Delta t) = x(t) + \int_t^{t+\Delta t} g(x, d, t) \, dt$$

To implement the numerical approximation procedure recall that we may approximate

$$\int_t^{t+\Delta t} h(x, d, t) \, dt$$

by $h(x, d, t) \, \Delta t$ for small values of Δt. Using this approximation yields

$$f[x(t), t] = \max_{\substack{d(t) \\ [t,t+\Delta t]}} \left[h(x, d, t) \, \Delta t + f[x(t + \Delta t), t + \Delta t] \right]$$

subject to

$$x(t + \Delta t) = x(t) + g(x, d, t) \, \Delta t$$

If we went through a suitable limiting process, the maximum principle of Pontryagin [5] and the Euler equation could be obtained. This procedure will be discussed in Chapter 6.

5.5   Computational Aspects

In the preceding sections, the theory of dynamic programming was presented. In this section we turn to a discussion of computational problems associated with solving dynamic programs.

The iterative procedure pursued in solving problems by dynamic programming lends itself to adaptation to digital computers. In fact, the development of dynamic programming has gone hand in hand with the development of digital computers. In solving problems on the digital computer, it is useful to construct flow charts that illustrate the progress of the computations. To construct an easily legible chart some additional notation will be used. Recall that the functional equation of dynamic programming has the form[7]

$$f_n(\mathbf{x}_n) = \underset{\mathbf{D}_n}{\text{opt.}} \ [r_n(\mathbf{x}_n, \mathbf{D}_n) + f_{n-1}(\mathbf{x}_{n-1})]$$

subject to

$$\mathbf{x}_{n-1} = \mathbf{t}_n(\mathbf{x}_n, \mathbf{D}_n)$$

We define

$$f_0(\mathbf{x}_0) = 0 \qquad q_n(\mathbf{x}_n, \mathbf{D}_n) = r_n(\mathbf{x}_n, \mathbf{D}_n) + f_{n-1}(\mathbf{x}_{n-1})$$

Then

$$f_n(\mathbf{x}_n) = \underset{\mathbf{D}_n}{\text{opt.}} \ [q_n(\mathbf{x}_n, \mathbf{D}_n)]$$

where $\mathbf{x}_{n-1}$ has been eliminated using

$$\mathbf{x}_{n-1} = \mathbf{t}_n(\mathbf{x}_n, \mathbf{D}_n)$$

The flow chart is given in Figure 5.4. A brief explanation of some of the terms is in order. The fourth box specifies the calculation of $x_n(m)$. When solving problems on the digital computer we must specify a grid for the state and decision variables at each stage. In discrete problems the grid arises naturally. In continuous problems we must impose a grid as an approximation to the continuous functions. Naturally we desire a fine grid—however, the finer the grid, the larger the number of combinations of state variables for which $f_n(x_n)$ must be calculated. A tradeoff between accuracy and computer costs must be effected. This problem is not unique to the solution of dynamic programming problems. Similar difficulties are encountered in obtaining numerical solutions to differential equations. The values of $x_n(m)$, $m = 1, 2, \ldots, p(m)$, are simply the grid for x_n and $p(n)$ specifies the number of values of x_n (size of the grid). Notice that we allow the grid size to change from stage to stage. Such flexibility may be useful in certain types of problems.

We have mentioned several times in preceding sections the problems that arise when the number of combinations of state variables at each stage becomes large (that is, approximately one half of the rapid access storage capability). This problem, the curse of dimensionality, has led to several attempts to reduce the number of combinations of state variables that must be examined.

In previous chapters we have discussed various methods for transforming a constrained problem into an unconstrained problem. These concepts can be used, in certain cases, to reduce the number of state variables in a dynamic programming problem.

---

[7] When the composition operator, $\oplus$, is $+$.

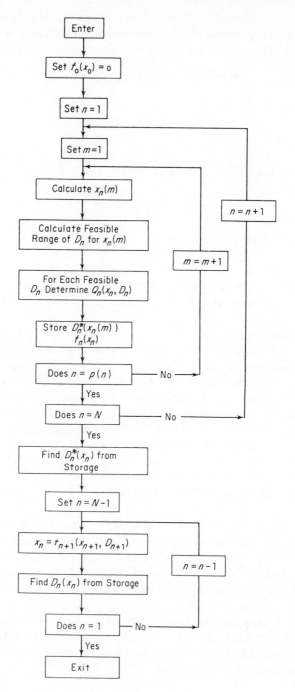

Figure 5.4.

Consider the problem of

$$\max_{d_n} \sum_{n=1}^{N} r_n(d_n)$$

subject to

$$\sum_{n=1}^{N} a_n d_n \le K_1$$

$$\sum_{n=1}^{N} b_n d_n \le K_2$$

We showed previously that these two constraints give rise to a two-state-variable dynamic programming problem:

$$f_n(x_n, z_n) = \max_{d_n} [r_n(d_n) + f_{n-1}(x_{n-1}, y_{n-1})]$$

subject to

$$x_{n-1} = x_n - a_n d_n$$
$$y_{n-1} = y_n - b_n d_n \qquad n = 1, \ldots, N$$

Another formulation that leads to only one state variable is obtained through the use of the Lagrange multiplier approach. Suppose we choose to eliminate the second constraint by incorporating it into the objective function by forming a Lagrange function,

$$F(\lambda, d_1, \ldots, d_N) = \sum_{n=1}^{N} r_n(d_n) + \lambda \left(\sum_{n=1}^{N} b_n d_n - K_2 + u_1^2 \right)$$

subject to

$$x_{n-1} = x_n - a_n d_n$$

Rearranging and recalling that $\lambda_1 u_1^2 = 0$ yields

$$F(d_1, \ldots, d_N, \lambda) = \max \sum_{n=1}^{N} [r_n(d_n) + \lambda b_n d_n] - \lambda K_2$$

subject to

$$x_{n-1} = x_n - a_n d_n$$

From Chapter 4 we recall that $F(\cdot)$ has a saddle point—maximum with respect to $d_1, \ldots, d_n$ and minimum with respect to λ. Thus we may treat the maximization problem by dynamic programming,

$$f_0(x_0, \lambda) = 0$$
$$f_n(x_n, \lambda) = \max_{d_n} [r_n(d_n) + \lambda a_n d_n + f_{n-1}(x_{n-1})]^{[8]}$$

---

[8] The term λK_2 has been omitted since for a fixed value of λ it is a constant and does not affect the optimal decision policy.

subject to

$$x_{n-1} = x_n - a_n d_n$$

The computational procedure is as follows. Choose a value for $\lambda = \lambda^0 \neq 0$ and solve the problem. For a given λ^0 this generates the optimal decision rule $d_1^0, \ldots, d_N^0$. Since we choose $\lambda^0 \neq 0$, the constraint must hold as a strict equality for some value of K_2, say K_2^0. However, except in the most fortuitous situation K_2^0 will not be the desired value K_2. Therefore, we choose another value of λ, say λ^1, and resolve the problem. This may seem to be a hit-and-miss procedure. However, recall that K_2 will be a monotonically increasing function of λ.[9] Thus we can guide the successive choices of λ to converge to the desired K_2. This technique is guaranteed to converge to the desired value of K_2 if the constraints form a convex set. In other cases there may not exist a value of λ that yields the desired value of K_2.

Another approach that serves to reduce the number of combinations of the state variables for which $f_n(x_n)$ must be calculated and stored is called the *one-at-a-time method*. Suppose we consider a problem with two decision variables at each stage,

$$\max \sum_{n=1}^{N} r_n(d_n^{(1)}, d_n^{(2)})$$

Further suppose that we have only two constraints and they are separable. Each constraint is a function of either d_n^1 or d_n^2 but not both:

$$\sum_{n=1}^{N} a_n d_n^{(1)} \leq K_1$$

$$\sum_{n=1}^{N} b_n d_n^{(2)} \leq K_2$$

In the case where the constraints form a convex set, the approximation procedure may be applied. When the objective function is concave[10] we may apply a procedure akin to the search techniques discussed in Chapter 4. We proceed as follows: Choose a set of d_n^i, $i =$ either 1 or 2, which satisfy the constraints. To be more explicit we can choose $d_n^2 = 0$, $n = 1, \ldots, N$. Now solve the problem

$$\max \sum_{n=1}^{N} r_n(d_n^{(1)}, d_n^{(2)} = 0)$$

---

[9] See Chapter 4.
[10] These two assumptions assure that any local maximum is global.

subject to

$$\sum_{n=1}^{N} a_n d_n^{(1)} \leq K_1$$

by the standard dynamic programming approach. This leads to a solution for $d_n^{(1)} = d_n^{(1)} (K_2 = 0)$. Now holding $d_n^{(1)}$ fixed at this solution, solve the following problem:

$$\max \sum_{n=1}^{N} r_n[d_n^1 (K_2 = 0), d_n^2]$$

subject to

$$\sum_{n=1}^{N} b_n d_n^{(2)} \leq \Delta > 0$$

This leads to a new set of values for $d_n^{(2)}$ that satisfy the constraint shown above. Holding the new values of $d_n^{(2)}$ constant we solve the problem

$$\max \sum_{n=1}^{N} r_n[d_n^{(1)}, d_n^{(2)}(\Delta)]$$

subject to

$$\sum_{n=1}^{N} a_n d_n^{(1)} \leq K_1$$

This iterative procedure is continued alternately, solving for values of $d_n^{(1)}$ and $d_n^{(2)}$. At each iteration, Δ is added to the right side of the constraint. In particular at the $(p + 1)st$ iteration we have

$$\sum_{n=1}^{N} b_n d_n \leq p\Delta$$

When the variables d_n^i are continuous, the iterative procedure converges to the optimal solution to the original problem [1].

We have discussed two procedures for reducing the storage problem caused by problems in which there is a large number of combinations of values of state variables to investigate. Another technique is to approximate the function $f_{n-1}(x_{n-1})$ by a low-order polynomial [6]. If a suitable approximation can be constructed, the only storage required would be for the coefficients in the polynomial. This approach does not reduce the computational problems introduced by dimensionality problems, but it has alleviated the storage problem associated with the curse of dimensionality [6].

The final procedure we shall discuss is called the coarse grid technique. Instead of defining a fine grid, we use a relatively small number of grid points and solve the problem for this reduced set of state variables. Once a solution to this problem is obtained, a finer grid is constructed around the grid points for those values of the state variables that yielded the optimal decision rule to the original approximation. This scheme is continued until a suitably accurate solution is obtained. It should be realized, however, that where alternative local optima exist, the final solution may yield any one of these local optima. Further, the local optima obtained may not be the global optimum.

Some conjectures about the future are now in order. In the past few years, great strides in problem solving have been made. These improvements are largely due to or as a result of the increased capability of digital computers. There is little cause to suspect that further advances will not be forthcoming. These improvements will further enlarge the scope of problems amenable to solution. Hopefully these advances will be accompanied by breakthroughs in the theory to alleviate the curse of dimensionality.

Problems

1. Determine the transformation function for dynamic programming problems having the following constraints:

   (a) $d_1^2 + d_2^2 + d_3^2 = K;$ $K \geq 0, d_i \geq 0.$
   (b) $d_1 + 2d_2 + 3d_3 \leq K.$

2. Solve the following problem by dynamic programming:

$$\max \sum_{i=1}^{N} \sin \frac{\theta_i}{2}$$

   subject to

$$\sum_{i=1}^{N} \theta_i \leq \alpha$$

$$\theta_i \geq 0$$

3. Use dynamic programming to solve

$$\max z = (x_1 - 1)^2 + 5x_2x_3$$

   subject to

$$x_1 + x_2 + x_3 \leq 6$$
$$x_i \geq 0 \qquad i = 1, 2, 3$$

4. Solve the following problem using dynamic programming:

$$\max z = w(x - 1)^2 + (y - 2)^3 + (z - 3)^4$$

   subject to

$$w + x + y + z \leq 5$$
$$w, x, y, z = 0, 1, 2, 3, \ldots$$

5. Suppose you are the owner of new car dealership. The manufacturer has added three new models, A, B, and C. You wish to invest no more than

$20,000 in these new models. Model A costs $2000 and sells for $2700. Model B costs $4000 and sells for $4800. Model C costs $3000 and sells for $3500. Assuming you wish to have at least one of each model, what should be your buying procedure?

6. Suppose we wish to

$$\max 3d_3 + 2d_2 + d_1$$

subject to

$$\sum_{i=1}^{3} d_i \leq m$$

But the system has a random element in the output of each stage,

$$x_{i-1} = x_i - d_i + k_i \qquad i = 1, 2, 3$$

when k_i is a random variable with the following density:

$$\left. \begin{array}{l} P(k_i = 0) = \frac{1}{2} \\ P(k_i = 1) = \frac{1}{2} \end{array} \right\} \ i = 1, 2, 3$$

Solve this problem by dynamic programming.

7. Suppose you wish to buy stock in one or all of three different corporations. Stock A is presently worth $30 per share and your broker tells you that by the time it is purchased it may be worth $28, $29, $30, or $31 per share, each with equally likely probability. Stock B is worth $28 per share and is rising. It may be worth $29 or $30 per share with equal probability by the time it is purchased. Stock C is worth $29 per share and is not expected to change by the time it is purchased. What is the optimal buying policy to maximize your expected holdings after the purchase? Your purchases will be in blocks of 100 and your total purchase will be for no more than 500 shares.

8. Consider the following "diverging branch" problem shown. Show mathematically that this problem can be solved using dynamic programming. [*Hint:* For stages 11 through m_1 and stages 1 through $k - 1$ the normal algorithm holds. At stage k, $f_{k+m1} = r_k \circ f_{x-1} \circ f_{m1}$, where "$\circ$" denotes the composition operator. For stages $k + 1$ through N, the normal algorithm holds.]

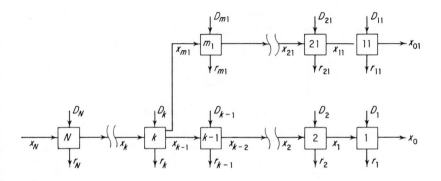

9. For the "converging branch" problem illustrated, show how dynamic programming can be used to obtain the sequence of optimal decisions. Consider two cases: (1) x_{m1} can be chosen at will; (2) x_{m1} unknown. [*Hint:* For case 1, solve for D_1 through D_{j-1} using procedures developed in the text. Solve the upper branch using state inversion and find $f_{m1}(x_{01})$.] Compute

$$f_{j+m1} = \underset{x_{01}}{\text{opt.}} \; D_j[r_j(x_{01}, x_j, D_j) \circ f_{j-1}(x_{01}, x_j, D_j) \circ f_{m1}(x_{01})]$$

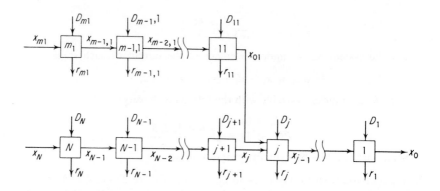

Solve for D_{j+1} through x_N in usual manner. For case 2, solve the upper branch for $f_{m1}(x_{m1}, x_{01})$. At stage j compute

$$f_{j+m1}(x_j, x_{m1}) = \underset{x_{01}}{\text{opt.}} \; D_j[r_j(x_{01}, x_j, D_j) \circ f_{j-1}[t_j(x_{01}, x_j, D_j)] \circ f_{m1}(x_{m1}, x_{01})]$$

Show that

$$f_{n+m1}(x_n, x_{m1}) = \underset{D_n}{\text{opt.}} \; [r_n(x_n, D_n) \circ f_{n-1+m1}[t_n(x_n, D_n), x_{m1}]$$

$$n = j+1, \ldots, N$$

10. In the "feed-forward system" shown, develop the recursive equations. Can you optimize with respect to x_{01} at stage j? Why or why not?

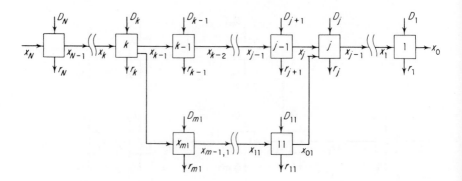

11. Develop the recursive equations for the "feedback system" shown.

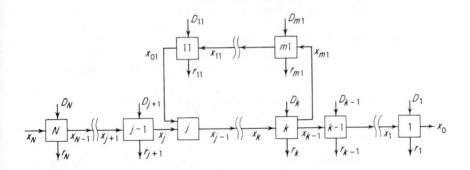

12. Consider the topologically complex network shown. Derive the recursive relationships for

(a) The converging branch.
(b) The first feed-forward loop.
(c) The second feed-forward loop.
(d) Stage 1.
(e) Stage 2.

(f) Stage 3.
(g) Stages 4 and 5.
(h) Stage 6.
(i) Stage 7.

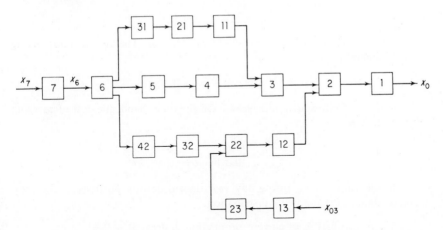

13. Consider the problem of maximizing the reliability of a system by introducing redundancies in components of the system. Specifically, suppose the system is composed of seven components in series. The reliability of the system is defined to be the probability that the system works if the probability of components i working is $p_i > 0$. Further assume that the probability that component i falls is statistically independent from that of component j, $i \neq j$; all i, j. The cost of component i is c_i and the total cost cannot exceed a. It is desired to maximize system reliability by adding redundant components. Formulate this as a dynamic programming problem.

14. (a) In Problem 13 suppose we desire to minimize cost with the restriction that the system reliability must be no less than 0.9.
    (b) Formulate this as a dynamic programming problem.

15. Solve Problems 13 and 14 using the following data: $p_1 = 0.9$, $p_2 = 0.95$, $p_3 = 0.7$, $p_4 = 0.75$, $p_5 = 0.99$, $p_6 = 0.82$, $p_7 = 0.6$; $c_1 = \$25$, $c_2 = \$75$, $c_3 = \$10$, $c_4 = \$15$, $c_5 = \$100$, $c_6 = \$20$, and $c_7 = \$15$; $a = 600$, $b = 0.6$.

16. Suppose the data in Problem 15 were changed as follows:

    (a) $a = 750$, $b = 0.90$.
    (b) $a = 1000$, $b = 0.99$.

    Solve both problems using the appropriate data. Does the entire problem need to be resolved?

17. The citrus industry has the problem of scheduling orange production. Unfortunately trees planted in year i do not produce oranges until the $(i + 7)$th year. Thus the industry must perform some long-term planning. The problem is eased considerably by employing some excellent statisticians to provide market forecasts for the future demand. However, the problem is not deterministic because hurricanes may destroy part of the crop. The demand in year j is given by

$$a_j = 5(1.1)^j + 0.8_j$$

where a_j = demand (1000 barrels) in the jth year. The cost of not meeting the demand is given by

$$c_j = |d_j - a_j| \, 900$$

where d_j is the production in year j. On the other hand, the cost of carrying inventory is

$$e_j = \begin{cases} 75l_j & l_j \geq 0 \\ 0 & l_j < 0 \end{cases}$$

If a hurricane comes during any year, it will destroy portions of the crop according to the following distribution.

prob(10% of current production destroyed) = 0.90
prob(20% of current production destroyed) = 0.80
prob(30% of current production destroyed) = 0.75
prob(40% of current production destroyed) = 0.50
prob(50% of current production destroyed) = 0.25
prob(60% of current production destroyed) = 0.10
prob(70% of current production destroyed) = 0.01

The probability of a hurricane in year j is 0.2. Determine the optimum production schedule to minimize the sum of the costs over a 5-year period assuming no initial inventory.

References Cited and Bibliography

[1] Nemhauser, G. L. *Introduction to Dynamic Programming*. New York: Wiley, 1966.

[2] Bellman, R. E. *Dynamic Programming*. Princeton, N.J.: Princeton University Press, 1957.

[3] Mitten, L. G. "Composition Principles for Synthesis of Optimal Multistage Processes," *Operations Res.*, Vol. 12 (1964).

[4] Dreyfus, S. E. *Dynamic Programming and the Calculus of Variations*. New York: Academic Press, 1966.

[5] Kopp, R. E. "Pontryagin Maximum Principle," *Optimization Techniques*. New York: Academic Press, 1962.

[6] Bellman, R. E., and S. E. Dreyfus. *Applied Dynamic Programming*. Princeton, N.J.: Princeton University Press, 1962.

CHAPTER 6

The Maximum Principle

6.1 Introduction

In this chapter we shall present another approach to optimization for systems where the variables are functions of one parameter; for example, time. The examples contained in the introduction to Chapter 5 are equally useful ones for applications of the material to be covered in this chapter.

The first topic to be covered is the calculus of variations—a well-known tool in classical mathematics, mechanics, and so on. Although the variational approach has been known for many years—it was developed independently by Euler and Lagrange—its usefulness in optimization has been limited.

After a brief discussion of the calculus of variations, we shall proceed to the maximum principles—continuous and discrete—and finally to a discussion and comparison of these techniques with dynamic programming.

6.2 Calculus of Variations

The types of problems that may be approached by variational methods are usually given in the form [1]

$$\min_{y(x)} J = \int_a^b F[x, y(x), y'(x)] \, dx \tag{6.1}$$

where $y'(x) = dy(x)/dx$. This problem is known as the "simplest" problem in the calculus of variations. The method of attack for problems in the above format is similar to that discussed in Chapter 2. The optimal curve, $y^0(x)$, is found by showing that certain necessary conditions must be satisfied for every x in the interval $[a, b]$. This is just the opposite from the dynamic programming approach, where one develops the optimal curve in a stagewise manner.

To proceed with the derivation of the necessary conditions mentioned above, the concept of a variation must be developed. Suppose we define $y^0(x)$ as the function that yields the extremal point of J. Notice that in the problem under consideration we are attempting to find a *function*, $y(x)$, that minimizes J. In this context J is called a functional. This problem is analogous to the one of finding the point x^0 that minimizes some function $f(x)$. Instead of a point x^0 we must specify the entire function $y^0(x)$ to define the optimal solution.

When we were concerned with functions, the approach was to make an arbitrary perturbation in the independent variables and by showing from these arguments that the first derivative must vanish we obtained the necessary conditions for a minimum. In the calculus of variations we shall make an arbitrary perturbation in the function $y(x)$ about the optimum curve, $y^0(x)$, and from this derive necessary conditions for the functional, J, to be a minimum. This perturbation, δ, is called a variation. $\delta y(x) = y(x) - y^0(x)$,

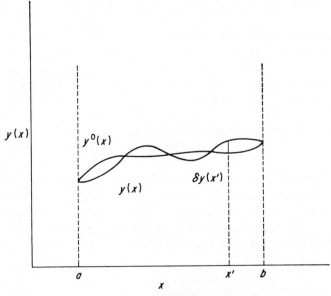

Figure 6.1.

$a \le x \le b$. Notice that we are defining, for every x in $[a, b]$, a new *function*, $y(x)$, which is at most infinitesimally different from $y^0(x)$ for every x on $[a, b]$ (see Figure 6.1). The difference between $y(x)$ and $y^0(x)$ will be represented by $\epsilon\phi(x)$:

$$\delta y(x) = y(x) - y^0(x) = \epsilon\phi(x) \qquad (6.2)$$

where $\phi(x)$ is an arbitrary differentiable function of x and ϵ is a small positive number. It is important to notice that the operator δ implies a perturbation of a function $y(\cdot)$ for every value of the independent variable x.

The variation has certain important properties that will be required in the following developments. For example, the operator commutes with both the differentiation and integration operator:

$$\frac{d}{dx}[\delta y(x)] = \frac{d}{dx}[y(x) - y^0(x)] = \frac{\epsilon \, d\phi(x)}{dx} \tag{6.3}$$

$$\frac{\delta \, d[y(x)]}{dx} = \frac{dy(x)}{dx} - \frac{dy^0(x)}{dx} = \frac{d}{dx}[y(x) - y^0(x)]$$

$$= \frac{d}{dx}\,\epsilon\phi(x) = \epsilon\,\frac{d}{dx}\,\phi(x) \tag{6.4}$$

Thus

$$\frac{d}{dx}[\delta y(x)] = \delta\,\frac{d}{dx}[y(x)] \tag{6.5}$$

Other properties of the variation operator will be left to the reader to establish.

Now that the required tools are at hand, we turn to the problem of deriving necessary conditions for an extremal point of the functional J. Suppose we are interested in finding the function $y(x)$ that yields a minimum of J. By analogy to the theory of minima of functions, we require that the variation of J vanish for the $y(x)$ that minimizes J.

Theorem: *A necessary condition for a minimum of J is*

$$\delta J = 0 \tag{6.6}$$

PROOF. Suppose there exists an optimal curve, $y^0(x)$, for which the variation δJ did not vanish. Then by changing $y^0(x)$ slightly we could decrease J, and by contradiction the hypothetical optimal curve, $y^0(x)$, does not yield a minimum of J. A similar heuristic argument can be developed for curves, $y(x)$, that maximize J. Thus a necessary condition for J to have an extrema is that the variation of J vanish.

The variation of J may be expressed as

$$\delta J = \delta \int_a^b F(x, y, y') \, dx \tag{6.7}$$

Since the variation commutes, equation (6.7) reduces to

$$\delta J = \int_a^b \delta F(x, y, y') \, dx \tag{6.8}$$

From the definition of $\delta F(\cdot)$ we have

$$\delta F(x, y, y') = F(x, y, y') - F(x, y^0, y'^0)$$
$$= F[x, y^0 + \epsilon\phi(x), y'^0 + \epsilon\phi'(x)] - F(x, y^0, y'^0) \qquad (6.9)$$

Expanding this result in a Taylor's series about y^0, y'^0 and neglecting terms of order ϵ^2 and greater yields

$$\delta F(\cdot) = F(x, y^0, y'^0) + \epsilon\phi(x) \frac{\partial F(\cdot)}{\partial y}\Big|_{y'=y'^0} + \epsilon\phi'(x) \frac{\partial F(\cdot)}{\partial y'}\Big|_{y=y^0}$$

$$(6.10)$$

$$-F(x, y^0, y'^0) = \epsilon\left[\frac{\phi(x) \partial F(\cdot)}{\partial y} + \frac{\phi'(x) \partial F(\cdot)}{\partial y'}\right]$$

Thus

$$\delta J = \epsilon \int_a^b \left[\frac{\phi(x) \partial F(\cdot)}{\partial y} + \frac{\phi'(x) \partial F(\cdot)}{\partial y'}\right] dx \qquad (6.11)$$

to terms of order ϵ. If we integrate the second term in the above equation by parts we obtain

$$\int_a^b \frac{\phi'(x) \partial F(\cdot)}{\partial y'} dx = \phi(x) \frac{\partial F}{\partial y'}\Big|_a^b - \int_a^b \phi(x) \frac{d}{dx} \frac{\partial F(\cdot)}{\partial y'} dx$$

Thus

$$\frac{\delta J}{\epsilon} = \int_a^b \phi(x)\left[\frac{\partial F(\cdot)}{\partial y} - \frac{d}{dx}\frac{\partial F(\cdot)}{\partial y'}\right] dx + \frac{\phi(x) \partial F}{\partial y'}\Big|_a^b \qquad (6.12)$$

Since the variation must vanish at a stationary point we require

$$\phi(x)\frac{\partial F}{\partial y'}\Big|_a^b + \int_a^b \phi(x)\left[\frac{\partial F(\cdot)}{\partial y} - \frac{d}{dx}\frac{\partial F(\cdot)}{\partial y'}\right] dx = 0 \qquad (6.13)$$

There are several special cases of the above equation. Each of these will be illustrated by example. The first is one where the end points are fixed; that is, $y(b)$ and $y(a)$ are given. One type of problem where this might arise is in inventory control of a batch product such as penicillin. As an idealized example suppose a customer orders a large supply of the drug. He knows the total demand over the period under consideration and has some initial demand. The question that the drug supplier must answer is how to set his production so as to (1) have an initial amount $y(a)$ at the start of the contract, (2) meet the demands during the life of the contract, and (3) have $y(b)$ in stock for contingencies at the end of the contract period. Thus the initial and final inventories are fixed and the only decision that is to be made is to set the production schedule to minimize cost. In this example, where the end points are fixed, we can allow no variation in $y(x)$ at these points. Thus the arbitrary function $\phi(x)$ must vanish identically at the end points,

$$\phi(a) = \phi(b) = 0$$

since $\phi(x) = y(x) - y^*(x)$. Thus equation (6.13) becomes

$$\int_a^b \phi(x) \left[\frac{\partial F(\cdot)}{\partial y} - \frac{d}{dx} \frac{\partial F(\cdot)}{\partial y'} \right] dx = 0$$

Since $\phi(x)$ is any arbitrary continuous function the quantity shown above in brackets must vanish if the integral is to vanish. We are then left with

$$\frac{\partial F(\cdot)}{\partial y} - \frac{d}{dx} \frac{\partial F(\cdot)}{\partial y'} = 0 \qquad (6.14)$$

which is the well-known Euler-Lagrange equation.

Other variations of equation (6.13) may be obtained depending on the boundary conditions imposed on the problem under consideration. For example, if the initial condition, $y(a)$, is given but the final condition is free, then we require that

$$\left. \frac{\partial F}{\partial y'} \right|_{x=b} = 0$$

in addition to the Euler-Lagrange equation. This situation is analogous to the case where the supplier is going out of the penicillin business after completing the current contract because he has discovered a more suitable antibiotic that yields a larger profit.

We now turn to a discussion of variational problems under constraints. The approach will be similar to the approach we followed in dealing with constrained functions. Now we shall discuss constrained optimization of functionals. Let us consider the problem posed at the beginning of the chapter:

$$\max_{y(x)} \left[J = \int_a^b F[x, y(x), y'(x)] \, dx \right]$$

subject to the additional requirement that

$$\int_a^b G[x, y(x), y'(x)] \, dx = 0 \qquad (6.15)$$

We again resort to the Lagrange multiplier approach to develop necessary conditions. Form the analogous Lagrange function,

$$L[x, y(x), y'(x), \lambda] = \int_a^b F[y(x), y'(x), x] \, dx + \lambda \int_a^b G[y(x), y'(x), x] \, dx$$

$$= \int_a^b \left(F[y(x), y'(x), x] + \lambda G[y(x), y'(x), x] \right) dx \qquad (6.16)$$

Theorem: *A necessary condition for the original function $F(\cdot)$ to be a maximum is that the variation of the Lagrange function vanish in addition to the derivative with respect to λ:*

$$\frac{dL(\cdot)}{d\lambda} = 0 = \int_a^b G[y(x), y(x), x] \, dx \qquad (6.17)$$

and $\delta L = 0$, which implies

$$\frac{\partial F}{\partial y} + \lambda \frac{\partial G}{\partial y} - \frac{d}{dx}\left(\frac{\partial F}{\partial y'} + \lambda \frac{\partial G}{\partial y'}\right) = 0 \tag{6.18}$$

Again, as in the case when we were dealing with equality-constrained functions, no restrictions are placed on λ.

We now turn to an example before proceeding to a discussion of the maximum principle. Suppose we are faced with the problem of determining the optimal quarterly production schedule for a petroleum refinery that produces, among other things, oil. The cost associated with a given production is composed of three components: (1) production schedule, $y(t)$; (2) change in the production, $y'(t)$; and (3) the time, t, at which the production occurs. The rationale behind this formulation is:

1. The cost component due to the production is related to the operating cost per unit and the raw material cost per unit.
2. Changes in the production also influence the cost (may be viewed as an analog to a setup cost). However, decreases may be viewed as just as undesirable as increases; thus we square these changes.
3. The time at which production occurs also adds to the cost, because raw material costs will increase with time due to factors such as inflation and the fact that raw material prices increase during the production run due to supply and demand.

From the considerations mentioned above we may construct an objective function for our hypothetical refinery. The total cost for a particular production schedule, $y(t)$, is defined to be $J[y(t)]$, where

$$J[y(t)] = \int_0^3 [ay(t) + by'^2(t) + ct]\,dt$$

In addition, we are constrained to meet the demand during the period,

$$G[y(t)] = \int_0^3 y(t)\,dt = d$$

where d is the total quarterly demand. Forming the "Lagrange function" yields

$$L[y(t), y'(t), t, \lambda] = \int_0^3 [ay(t) + by'^2(t) + ct]\,dt + \lambda\left[\int_0^3 y(t)\,dt - d\right]$$

$$\frac{dL(\cdot)}{d\lambda} = \int_0^3 y(t)\,dt - d = 0 \Rightarrow \int_0^3 y(t)\,dt = d$$

$$\delta L = 0 = \frac{\partial F}{\partial y} + \lambda \frac{\partial G}{\partial y} - \frac{d}{dt}\left(\frac{\partial F}{\partial y'} + \lambda \frac{\partial G}{\partial y'}\right) = 0$$

This condition yields

$$a + \lambda - \frac{d}{dt}[2by'(t)] = 0$$

Rearranging yields

$$y''(t) = \frac{a + \lambda}{2b} \qquad \text{or} \qquad y(t) = \left(\frac{a + \lambda}{4b}\right)t^2 + k_1 t + k_2$$

where k_1 and k_2 are constants and must be determined from the boundary conditions. The conditions for this problem would normally be that the production rate at the beginning and end of the quarter be specified. For example, if the quarter begins January 1, we might have the production schedule at the start of the period fixed to be the same as December 31. The production schedule at the end of the period might be zero due to the fact that the winter is over and the demand for heating oil will drop correspondingly. Suppose we require that the total production, d, be 10^6 barrels and the instantaneous production at the beginning of the period is 450,000 barrels/month. Thus $y(0) = 450,000$, $y(3) = 0$, $d = 1,000,000$ barrels. We know the form of the optimal solution,

$$y(t) = \left(\frac{a + \lambda}{4b}\right)t^2 + k_1 t + k_2$$

Now the parameters k_1 and k_2 may be determined:

$$y(0) = 450,000 = \frac{a + \lambda}{4b}(0)^2 + k_1(0) + k_2$$

Therefore, $k_2 = 450,000$. We also know $y(3) = 0$. Thus

$$y(3) = \frac{a + \lambda}{4b} + (3)^2 k_1(3) + 450,000 = 0$$

or

$$k_1 = -\frac{3(a + \lambda)}{4b} - 150,000$$

Finally, we require that the total demand be met. Hence

$$\int_0^3 y(t)\, dt = 10^6$$

Thus

$$\int_0^3 \left[\left(\frac{a + \lambda}{4b}\right)t^2 - \frac{3(a + \lambda)}{4b}t - 150,000t + 450,000\right] dt = 10^6$$

or

$$\left[\left(\frac{a + \lambda}{12b}\right)t^3 - \frac{3}{4b}\frac{(a + \lambda)t^2}{2} - 75,000t^2 + 450,000t\right]\Big|_0^3 = 10^6$$

Evaluating the limits yields

$$\frac{(a + \lambda)9}{4b} - \frac{13.5(a + \lambda)}{4b} - 75{,}000(9) + 450{,}000(3) = 10^6$$

Rearranging we obtain

$$\frac{a + \lambda}{b} = -\frac{325{,}000(4)}{4.5}$$

From our knowledge of the parameters of the objective function (a and b) we can obtain a numerical value for λ and thus completely specify $y(t)$. For example, if $a = 2$ and $b = 0.01$, we find

$$a + \lambda = -2888.9$$
$$\lambda = -2890.9$$

The necessary conditions for a functional to be stationary are easily extended to the case when $y(x)$ and $y'(x)$ are vector functions:

$$\mathbf{y}(x) = \begin{bmatrix} y_1(x) \\ y_2(x) \\ \vdots \\ y_N(x) \end{bmatrix} \qquad \mathbf{y}'(x) = \frac{d}{dx}\mathbf{y}(x) = \begin{bmatrix} y'_1(x) \\ y'_2(x) \\ \vdots \\ y'_N(x) \end{bmatrix}$$

In this case the Euler-Lagrange conditions become

$$F_{y_i} - \frac{d}{dx}F_{y'_i} = 0 \qquad i = 1, \ldots, N \tag{6.19}$$

The derivation of these conditions is left as an exercise for the reader.

The question of sufficient conditions for a variational problem will not be covered in depth in this discussion. However, it can be shown that sufficiency is related to the second variation [2]. If one can show that the function $y(x)$ which satisfies the Euler-Lagrange equation makes the second variation positive for all nontrivial [$\phi(x) \neq 0$] variations, then a local minimum has been obtained.

6.3   Continuous Maximum Principle

In Section 6.2 we demonstrated the procedure involved when confronted with integral constraints in a variational problem. Suppose instead of constraints in the form of integrals we are faced with differential equation constraints

$$\min_{y(x)} \left(J = \int_a^b F[x, y(x), z(x)]\, dx \right)$$

subject to

$$\frac{dz}{dx} = q[x, y(x), z(x)] \tag{6.20}$$

This problem is different from those previously considered since the differential equation constraint must be satisfied for all x in $[a, b]$. The integral constraint mentioned previously is a point constraint. Thus

$$\int_a^b g[x, y(x), y'(x)] \, dx = 0$$

simply means that

$$g[b, y(b), y'(b)] - g[a, y(a), y'(a)] = 0$$

This basic difference leads to a different formulation of the problem. Since the differential equation must be satisfied for all x in $[a, b]$ we must have the Lagrange multiplier, λ, associated with this constraint be a function of x. We can view this as a problem with a very large number of constraints—one for each value of x in $[a, b]$. For each of these constraints we need a Lagrange multiplier. Since in reality there are an infinite number of values of x in $[a, b]$ we require an infinite number of values of λ—one for each x. Thus λ becomes a function of x. The problem from this point on is identical to the one considered previously. Introducing the variable Lagrange multiplier we have

$$J = \int_a^b \left\{ F[y(x), z(x), x] + \lambda(x) \left(\frac{dz}{dx} - q[x, y(x), z(x)] \right) \right\} dx \tag{6.21}$$

The Euler-Lagrange conditions for this problem become

$$\frac{\partial F(\cdot)}{\partial y} - \lambda(x) \frac{\partial q(\cdot)}{\partial y} = 0 \tag{6.22}$$

This equation was derived by taking the variation with respect to $y(x)$. This process introduces a variation in $z(x)$ due to the fact that $z'(x)$ is a function of $y(x)$. Thus, in addition to the equation shown above, we also require

$$(\delta J)_z = 0 \tag{6.23}$$

This leads to the second necessary condition,

$$\frac{\partial F(\cdot)}{\partial z} - \lambda(x) \frac{\partial q(\cdot)}{\partial z} - \frac{d\lambda(x)}{dx} = 0 \tag{6.24}$$

Finally, we have

$$\frac{dz(x)}{dx} = q[x, y(x), z(x)] \tag{6.25}$$

These three equations form the necessary conditions for a minima (or maxima) of J. We have two first-order differential equations. Therefore, two boundary conditions must be supplied. Normally $z(a)$ is given. The other boundary condition arises from conditions on the variation at $x = b$. In the case where $\delta y(x = b)$ is arbitrary we require that $\lambda(x = b)$ vanish. Thus we are confronted with solving the following two-point boundary-value problem while maintaining optimality, i.e.,

$$\frac{\partial F(\cdot)}{\partial y} - \lambda(x) \frac{\partial q(\cdot)}{\partial y} = 0$$

Notice that we will have a Lagrange multiplier associated with each differential equation constraint imposed on the problem. Thus if we extend these results to the case where we have a vector decision function $\mathbf{y}(x)$ and a system of differential equation constraints,

$$\frac{d\mathbf{z}(x)}{dx} = \mathbf{g}[\mathbf{z}(x), \mathbf{y}(x), x] = \begin{bmatrix} g_1(\cdot) \\ g_2(\cdot) \\ \vdots \\ g_N(\cdot) \end{bmatrix}$$

the necessary conditions become

$$\frac{\partial F(\cdot)}{\partial y_i} - \sum_{j=1}^{N} \lambda_j \frac{\partial g_j(\cdot)}{\partial y_i} = 0 \qquad i = 1, \ldots, M \qquad (6.26)$$

$$\frac{\partial F(\cdot)}{\partial z_j} - \sum_{i=1}^{N} \lambda_i(x) \frac{\partial g_i(\cdot)}{\partial z_j} - \frac{d\lambda_j(x)}{dx} = 0 \qquad j = 1, \ldots, N \qquad (6.27)$$

$$\frac{dz_j(x)}{dx} = g_j[\mathbf{z}(x), \mathbf{y}(x), x] \qquad (6.28)$$

where

$$\mathbf{z}(a) = \mathbf{c} \qquad \boldsymbol{\lambda}(b) = \mathbf{0} \qquad (6.29)$$

We would like to have an easy recipe for generating these conditions for a given problem. In the case of constrained maximization of functions we introduced the Lagrange function. This function was so constructed that when we partially differentiated this function with respect to each of the variables, the necessary conditions were generated. A similar set of rules can be developed for variational problems. Recall that the original problem was stated as

$$\min_{\mathbf{y}(x)} J = \int_{a}^{b} F[\mathbf{z}(x), \mathbf{y}(x), x] \, dx$$

subject to

$$\frac{dz_j(x)}{dx} = g_j[\mathbf{z}(x), \mathbf{y}(x), x] \qquad j = 1, \ldots, N$$

Suppose for convenience we define another differential equation

$$\frac{dz_0(x)}{dx} = F[\mathbf{z}(x), \mathbf{y}(x), x] \qquad (6.30)$$

Then

$$\int_a^b \frac{dz_0(x)}{dx}\, dx = \int_a^b F[\mathbf{z}(x), \mathbf{y}(x), x]\, dx$$

or

$$z_0(b) - z_0(a) = \int_a^b F[\mathbf{z}(x), \mathbf{y}(x), x]\, dx$$

If we define $z_0(a) = 0$ we find that

$$z_0(b) = \int_a^b F[\mathbf{z}(x), \mathbf{y}(x), x]\, dx = J \qquad (6.31)$$

The problem now becomes

$$\min_{\mathbf{y}(x)} z_0(b)$$

subject to

$$\frac{dz_0}{dx} = F[\mathbf{z}(x), \mathbf{y}(x), x] \equiv g_0[\mathbf{z}(x), \mathbf{y}(x), x]$$

$$\frac{dz_j}{dx} = g_j[\mathbf{z}(x), \mathbf{y}(x), x] \qquad j = 1, \ldots, N$$

We now have $N + 1$ differential equations. Associated with each is a Lagrange multiplier $\lambda_0(x), \lambda_1(x), \ldots, \lambda_N(x)$. We form a Hamiltonian function $H(\cdot)$ by multiplying the right side of each differential equation by its associated Lagrange multiplier and summing these products,

$$H[\mathbf{y}(x), \mathbf{z}(x), \boldsymbol{\lambda}(x), x] = \sum_{j=0}^N \lambda_j(x) g_j[\mathbf{z}(x), \mathbf{y}(x), x] \qquad (6.32)$$

Theorem: *The necessary conditions for a minimum are:*

(a) $\dfrac{\partial H}{\partial y_i} = 0 = \sum_{j=0}^N \lambda_j(x) \dfrac{\partial g_j(\cdot)}{\partial y_i} \qquad i = 1, \ldots, M \qquad (6.33)$

(b) $\dfrac{\partial H}{\partial z_i} = \dfrac{d\lambda_i(x)}{dx} = \sum_{j=0}^N \lambda_j(x) \dfrac{\partial g_j(\cdot)}{\partial z_i} \qquad i = 1, \ldots, N \qquad (6.34)$

(c) $\dfrac{\partial H}{\partial \lambda_j} = \dfrac{dz_j}{dx} = g_j(\cdot) \qquad j = 0, \ldots, N \qquad (6.35)$

with the boundary conditions

$$z_j(a) = c_j \qquad j = 1, \ldots, N$$

$$\lambda_j(b) = 0 \qquad j = 1, \ldots, N \qquad (6.36)$$

and

$$z_0(a) = 0 \qquad \lambda_0(b) = -1$$

It can be shown easily that these equations correspond to those presented previously. At first glance it might appear that a sign error had occurred. However, the defining equation for λ_0, together with the boundary condition that $\lambda_0(b) = -1$, compensate for the apparent inconsistency. For example,

$$\frac{d\lambda_0(x)}{dx} = \sum_{j=0}^{N} \lambda_j(x) \frac{\partial g_j(\cdot)}{dz_0}$$

But the $g_j(\cdot)$ are functions of x, $z_1(x), \ldots, z_N(x)$, $y_1(x), \ldots, y_M(x)$ only. Thus

$$\frac{\partial g_j(\cdot)}{\partial z_0} = 0$$

This result yields

$$\frac{d\lambda_0(x)}{dx} = 0$$

Solving this differential equation we find

$$\lambda_0(x) = K \text{ (constant)}$$

where $\lambda_0(b) = -1$. This means that $\lambda_0(x) = -1$. Upon substituting this result back into (a), (b), and (c), we obtain equations identical to those presented previously.

The results given above have been well known for many years. Recently the more difficult problem of

$$\min J = \int_a^b F[\mathbf{z}(x), \mathbf{y}(x), x] \, dx$$

subject to

$$\frac{d\mathbf{z}(x)}{dx} = \mathbf{g}[\mathbf{z}(x), \mathbf{y}(x), x]$$

$$h_j[y(x), \ldots, y_m(x)] \le 0 \qquad j = 1, \ldots, r \le M$$

has been solved, and a set of necessary conditions for $\mathbf{y}(x)$ to yield a minimum of J has been derived. This derivation is attributed to the eminent Russian mathematician L. S. Pontryagin and his co-workers, and the conditions are commonly referred to as the maximum principle. These conditions are very similar to those given above and in fact are identical in the case when the optimal $\mathbf{y}(x)$ is contained in the interior of the set defined above. When the optimal solution is not in the interior of this set, condition (a) is replaced by

$$\min_{\mathbf{y}(x)} H[\mathbf{z}(x), \mathbf{y}(x), x]$$

The other conditions, (b) and (c), remain the same. A proof of the statement given above is beyond the scope of this book. The details of the derivation are contained in *The Mathematical Theory of Optimal Processes* [3].

We shall now give several examples of the details of setting up and solving problems of the variational type. Suppose we wish to maximize

$$J = \int_a^b [\gamma z_1^2(x) + \omega y^2(x)]\, dx$$

subject to

$$\frac{dz_1}{dx} = -\alpha z_1 + \beta y = g_1(\cdot)$$

where $z_1(a) = 0$. Following the approach described earlier we define

$$\frac{dz_0(x)}{dx} = \gamma z_1^2(x) + \omega y^2(x) = g_0(\cdot) \qquad z_0(a) = 0$$

Forming the Hamiltonian we write

$$H[z_1(x), y(x), x] = \sum_{j=0}^{1} \lambda_j(x) g_j(\cdot)$$
$$= \lambda_0(x)[\gamma z_1^2(x) + \omega y^2(x)] + \lambda_1(x)[-\alpha z_1 + \beta y]$$

The necessary conditions are

$$\frac{\partial H}{\partial y} = 0 = 2\lambda_0(x)\omega y(x) + \lambda_1(x)\beta = 0$$

$$\frac{\partial H}{\partial z_0} = \frac{d\lambda_0}{dx} = 0$$

$$\frac{\partial H}{\partial z_1} = \frac{d\lambda_1}{dx} = \lambda_0(x)2\gamma z_1(x) - \lambda_1(x)\alpha$$

$$\frac{\partial H}{\partial \lambda_0} = \frac{dz_0}{dx} = \gamma z_1^2(x) + \omega y^2(x)$$

$$\frac{\partial H}{\partial \lambda_1} = \frac{dz_1}{dx} = -\alpha z_1 + \beta y$$

with $z_0(a) = 0$, $z_1(a) = 0$, $\lambda_0(b) = -1$, and $\lambda_1(a) = 0$.

As was pointed out earlier, the function $\lambda_0(x) = -1$ for all x. Upon substituting this result into the remaining equations we find

$$\frac{\partial H}{\partial y} = -2\omega y(x) + \beta \lambda_1(x) = 0$$

$$\frac{d\lambda_1}{dx} = -2\gamma z_1(x) - \lambda_1(x)\alpha$$

$$\frac{dz_0}{dx} = \gamma^2(x) + \omega y^2(x)$$

$$\frac{dz_1}{dx} = -\alpha z_1 + \beta y$$

The function $y(x)$ can be eliminated using the first equation. Thus

$$y(x) = \frac{\beta}{2\omega}[\lambda_1(x)] = q\lambda_1(x)$$

$$\frac{d\lambda_1}{dx} = -2\gamma z_1(x) - \lambda_1(x)\alpha$$

$$\frac{dz_0}{dx} = \gamma z_1^2(x) + \omega q^2 \lambda_1^2(x)$$

$$\frac{dz_1}{dx} = -\alpha z_1(x) + \beta q \lambda_1(x)$$

Solving the first and third equations simultaneously we find

$$z_1(x) = \frac{\lambda_1(a)\beta q \exp\left[-\frac{1}{2}(\alpha + 2\delta)x\right]\sin px}{P}$$

$$\lambda_1(x) = \lambda_1(a) \exp\left[-\frac{1}{2}(\alpha + 2\delta)x\right]\left(\cos px + \frac{2\delta - \alpha}{2p}\sin px\right)$$

where

$$p = \left[\delta(\alpha + 2\beta q - \delta) - \frac{\alpha^2}{4}\right]^{1/2}$$

The optimal trajectory for the decision function is given by

$$y(x) = q\lambda_1(x)$$

These results can be substituted into z_0' and the minimum value of J may be computed by integrating $z_0'(x)$. Two special cases can be considered for different values of the system parameters. For example, when $z_1(a) = 0$, $\beta = 25$, $q = \frac{1}{8}$, $\alpha = 2$, $\delta = 4$, and $\lambda(b) = \frac{1}{2}$, we have

$$z_1(x) = -47.6e^{-5x}\sin 4x$$
$$\lambda_1(x) = -61.0e^{-5x}(\cos 4x + \tfrac{3}{4}\sin 4t)$$

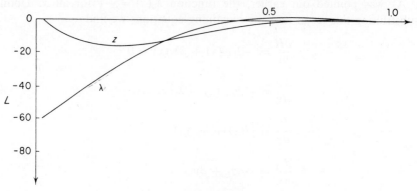

Figure 6.2.

A graph of the optimal trajectory for $z(x)$ and $y(x)$ is shown in Figure 6.2. The second set of parameters for which $z(x)$ and $y(x)$ are calculated are $\beta = 1$, $q = 5$, $\alpha = 4$, $\delta = 1$, $\lambda_1(2) = 0.25$, and $z(a) = 0$. For these values we obtain

$$z_1(x) = 160e^{-3x} \sin 3x$$
$$\lambda_1(x) = 96e^{-3x}(\cos 3x - \tfrac{1}{3} \sin 3x)$$

The graphs for these parameters are contained in Figure 6.3.

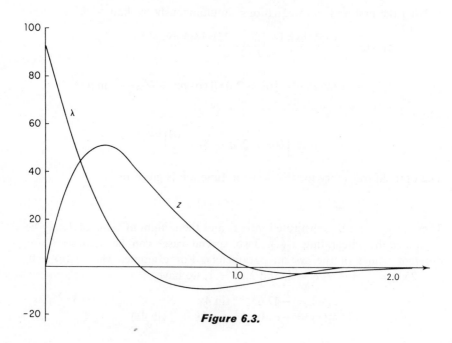

Figure 6.3.

Let us turn our attention to a production scheduling and inventory problem. Suppose the inventory balance equation can be represented as

$$\frac{dI}{dt} = -a \cos wt - bt + P(t)$$

$P(t)$ is the instantaneous production and $a \cos wt + bt$ is the corresponding instantaneous demand function. The desired objective is to choose the production schedule $P(t)$ to minimize

$$J = \int_0^T [I^2(t) + cP(t) + dP'^2(t)] \, dt$$

The rationale behind the instantaneous cost is:

1. The inventory cost is symmetrical about zero; that is, the cost of a unit shortage is the same as the unit cost of carrying a unit inventory.
2. The production contributes a term to the instantaneous cost that is proportional to the production rate.
3. A component of the instantaneous cost is a term that is proportional to the square of the change in the production rate. This is analogous to a setup cost.

The problem as stated is not in the form presented previously and thus the rules for deriving the necessary conditions cannot be applied to the existing problem. However, the problem can be transformed into one for which the rules may be applied. Suppose we define

$$z_1(\cdot) = I(\cdot)$$
$$y(\cdot) = P'(\cdot)$$
$$z_2(\cdot) = P(\cdot)$$

With these definitions we may express the problem in the form

$$\min J = \int_0^T [z_1^2(t) + cz_2(t) + dy^2(t)] \, dt$$

subject to

$$\frac{dz_1}{dt} = -a \cos wt - bt + z_2(t)$$

$$\frac{dz_2}{dt} = y(\cdot)$$

By introducing the artificial variable that represents the instantaneous cost we have

$$\frac{dz_0}{dt} = z_1^2 + cz_2 + dy^2$$

The initial conditions are specified as follows

$$z_0(0) = 0$$
$$z_1(0) = I(0) \qquad \text{(which for this problem we assume is 0 units)}$$
$$z_2(0) = P(0) \qquad \text{(we shall assume the initial production rate is 0 units)}$$

Introducing the Lagrange multipliers and forming the Hamiltonian we obtain

$$H[y(t), \mathbf{z}(t), (t), t] = \sum_{j=0}^{2} \lambda_j(t) z_j(t)$$
$$= \lambda_0(t)(z_1^2 + cz_2 + dy^2)$$
$$+ \lambda_1(t)(-a \cos wt - bt + z_2) + \lambda_2(t) y(t)$$

The necessary conditions are

(1) $$\frac{\partial H}{\partial y} = 0 = 2d\lambda_0 y + \lambda_2$$

(2a) $$\frac{\partial H}{\partial z_0} = \frac{d\lambda_0}{dt} = 0$$

(2b) $$\frac{\partial H}{\partial z_1} = \frac{d\lambda_1}{dt} = 2\lambda_0 z_1$$

(2c) $$\frac{\partial H}{\partial z_2} = \frac{d\lambda_2}{dt} = c\lambda_0 + \lambda_1$$

(3a) $$\frac{\partial H}{\partial \lambda_0} = \frac{dz_0}{dt} = z_1^2 + cz_2 + d_y{}^2$$

(3b) $$\frac{\partial H}{\partial \lambda_1} = \frac{dz_1}{dt} = -a \cos wt - bt + z_2(t)$$

(3c) $$\frac{\partial H}{\partial \lambda_2} = \frac{dz_2}{dt} = y(t)$$

with initial conditions as specified previously.
   Solving equation (1) we find

$$y = -\frac{\lambda_2}{2d\lambda_0}$$

The solution to equation (2a) yields $\lambda_0(t) = K_1$ (constant). Since we have $\lambda_0(T) = -1$, this means that $K_1 = -1$ and $\lambda_0(t) = -1$. Using this result and the solution for $y(t)$ the necessary conditions may be simplified.

(2b) $$\frac{d\lambda_1}{dt} = -2z_1$$

(2c) $$\frac{d\lambda_2}{dt} = -c + \lambda_1$$

(3a)
$$\frac{dz_0}{dt} = z_1^2 + cz_2 + \frac{\lambda_2^2}{4d}$$

(3b)
$$\frac{dz_1}{dt} = -a \cos wt - bt + z_2$$

(3c)
$$\frac{dz_2}{dt} = +\frac{\lambda_2}{2d}$$

subject to

$$\lambda_1(T) = 0 = \lambda_2(T)$$
$$z_1(0) = z_2(0) = 2$$

Solving these equations simultaneously we find

$$I(t) = z_1(t) = A \sinh dt + B \cosh dt + E \cos dt + F \sin dt + G \sin wt$$
$$P(t) = z_2(t) = Ad \cosh dt + Bd \sinh dt - Ed \sin dt + a \cos wt + bt$$

where A, B, d, E, F, G, W, a, and b are constants of the problem.

The solutions to these two examples were obtained analytically because the equations were linear in the variables involved. Thus the two-point boundary-value problems caused little more than algebraic difficulty. Unfortunately when the system equations (3) are nonlinear, one must resort to a numerical iterative procedure. One numerical procedure involves (1) guessing the initial conditions for those equations whose boundary conditions are specified as final conditions, (2) solving (integrating) the differential equations and checking to see if the final conditions are satisfied, and (3) if the final conditions are not matched, we choose another set of initial conditions and repeat steps (2) and (3). As in most other areas of nonlinear mathematics, the development of theory has not kept pace with the increased need for solution procedures. Problems have been encountered where convergence cannot be obtained. This difficulty is magnified as the size of the system of differential equations to be solved increases. However, some promising results are reported in [4].

The conditions just developed are only necessary. To derive sufficient conditions one must again turn to the second variation and consider the sign of second-order terms. This is, in general, a most difficult task. This difficulty is compounded when point constraints are placed on the decision variables. To keep the above remarks in perspective one must realize that problems of this nature—that is, nonlinear differential equation constraints, together with the two-point boundary-value problem—are inherently difficult problems. We would not expect to arrive at a simple solution procedure for such complex problems.

The brief introduction to the concepts of variational calculus given above is not meant to be complete but to stimulate the reader to pursue this interesting subject in more detail. Several excellent references are available. For the mathematically inclined, we recommend the book by Pontryagin and co-workers [3]. For a text with a slant more toward applications, especially in the chemical process industries, we suggest *The Continuous Maximum Principle* by Fan [5].

6.4   Discrete Maximum Principle

In Section 6.3 we discussed the continuous maximum principle. In this section we turn to a discrete analog of this problem. In Section 6.3 the constraints were differential equations; in this section we consider problems where the constraints are difference equations. In the continuous maximum principle the objective was to minimize an integral functional; in this section we deal with the discrete analog to that problem—one where the functional is a summation. We shall again restrict our attention to developing necessary conditions. Our derivation is based on the Lagrange multiplier technique presented in Chapter 2. For an alternative approach we suggest the derivation presented in *The Discrete Maximum Principle* by Fan and Wang [6]. Their derivation, which is based on the work of Katz [7], follows a variational argument.

Consider the problem

$$\min_{z_n, y_n} J = \sum_{n=1}^{N} g_n(z_{n-1}, y_n)$$

subject to

$$z_n = T_n(z_{n-1}, y_n) \qquad n = 1, \ldots, N$$

with $z_0 = K$ (a constant). Forming the Lagrange function we have

$$F(z_1, \ldots, z_N, y_1, \ldots, y_N, \lambda_1, \ldots, \lambda_N)$$
$$= \sum_{n=1}^{N} g_n(z_{n-1}, y_n) + \lambda_n(T_n(z_{n-1}, y_n) - z_n) \qquad (6.37)$$

The necessary conditions (see Chapter 2) are

(1) $\quad \dfrac{\partial F}{\partial y_j} = \dfrac{\partial g_j(z_{j-1}, y_j)}{\partial y_j} + \lambda_j \dfrac{\partial T_j(z_{j-1}, y_j)}{\partial y_j} = 0 \qquad j = 1, \ldots, N \qquad (6.38)$

(2) $\quad \dfrac{\partial F}{\partial \lambda_j} = 0 \Rightarrow z_j = T_j(z_{j-1}, y_j) \qquad (6.39)$

(3) $\quad \dfrac{\partial F}{\partial z_j} = 0 = -\lambda_j + \dfrac{\partial g_{j+1}(z_j, y_{j+1})}{\partial z_j} + \lambda_{j+1} \dfrac{\partial T_{j+1}(z_j, y_{j+1})}{\partial z_j}$

$$j = 1, \ldots, N - 1 \qquad (6.40)$$

(3a) $\quad \dfrac{\partial F}{\partial z_N} = -\lambda_N = 0 \qquad (6.41)$

or

$$\lambda_j = \frac{\partial g_{j+1}}{\partial z_j} + \lambda_{j+1} \frac{\partial T_{j+1}}{\partial z_j} \qquad j = 1, \ldots, N-1$$

The three conditions presented above are necessary for $\sum_{n=1}^{N} g_n(z_{n-1}, y_n)$ to be an extremum subject to the difference equations constraints. Recall that these conditions are also sufficient in the case that $g_n(\cdot)$ is convex, the constraints form a convex set, and $\lambda \geq 0$.

These necessary conditions were derived from the Lagrange multiplier approach developed in Chapter 2. Another approach is to introduce a discrete-stage Hamiltonian. Before doing this it is convenient to define a new state variable z_j^0, where

$$z_0^0 = 0$$
$$z_{i+1}^0 = z_i^0 + g_i(z_i, y_i) = T_i^0$$

From this definition it is clear that

$$z_N^0 = \sum_{n=1}^{N} g_n(z_n, y_n)$$

Thus we now have two state variables, z_i^0 and z_i. Introducing a Lagrange multiplier λ_i^0 for the new state variable, we form the Hamiltonian as follows for each stage. Thus

$$H_n = \lambda_n^0 T_n^0 + \lambda_n T_n \qquad n = 1, \ldots, N \tag{6.42}$$

Then defining

$$\frac{\partial H_n}{\partial z_{n-1}} = \lambda_{n-1} \qquad n = 1, \ldots, N \tag{6.43}$$

$$\frac{\partial H_n}{\partial z_{n-1}^0} = \lambda_{n-1}^0 \qquad n = 1, \ldots, N \tag{6.44}$$

If we choose y_n to make the nth-stage Hamiltonian stationary,

$$\frac{\partial H_n}{\partial y_n} = 0 \qquad n = 1, \ldots, N \tag{6.45}$$

we obtain the same condition as if we partially differentiated the Lagrange function with respect to y_n and set the result to zero.

Since we have defined the

$$\frac{\partial H_n}{\partial z_{n-1}} = \lambda_{n-1} \qquad n = 1, \ldots, N$$

with $\lambda_N = 0$, we obtain the identical condition to that found if we took $\partial F/\partial z_{n-1} = 0$. We consider only feasible solutions, so we require

$$z_n = T_n(z_{n-1}, y_n) \qquad n = 1, \ldots, N$$

Finally by virtue of the way λ_i^0 is defined we obtain $\lambda_N^0 = 1$.

Thus we have a different way of looking at deterministic sequential decision problems. This is identical to the type of problem we considered in Chapter 5; however, in this case we find we must solve two difference equations,

$$z_n = T_n(z_{n-1}, y_n) \qquad n = 1, \ldots, N$$

with $z_0 = K_1$, and

$$\lambda_{n-1} = \lambda_n^0 \frac{\partial g_n}{\partial z_{n-1}} + \lambda_n \frac{\partial T_n}{\partial z_{n-1}} \qquad n = 1, \ldots, N$$

where $\lambda_N = 0$ and $\lambda_N^0 = 1$, while requiring that $\partial H_n / \partial y_n$ vanish at each stage.

We again find ourselves confronted with a two-point boundary-value problem. The difficulties with such problems were discussed in Section 6.3. The reader may desire to refer back to the discussion presented there.

The generalization of the arguments presented above for the case of one-state variable to systems where

$$\mathbf{z}_i = \begin{bmatrix} z_i^1 \\ z_i^2 \\ \vdots \\ z_i^p \end{bmatrix} \qquad \mathbf{y}_i = \begin{bmatrix} y_i^1 \\ \vdots \\ y_i^s \end{bmatrix}$$

are algebraically messy but conceptually no more difficult. The reader may want to derive the results for the vector-variable case. For completeness we include the statement of these conditions. Suppose we are given a function $\sum_{n=1}^{N} g_n(\mathbf{z}_{n+1}, \mathbf{y}_n)$ to minimize subject to system constraints

$$\mathbf{z}_n = T_n(\mathbf{z}_{n-1}, \mathbf{y}_n)$$

where $\mathbf{z}_0 = \mathbf{K}$, and the state variables $\mathbf{z}_n$ and $\mathbf{z}_{n-1}$ are P-dimensional, $\mathbf{y}_n$ is an s-dimensional vector decision variable, and $\mathbf{T}_n(\cdot)$ is a p-dimensional vector transformation whose first partial derivatives are continuous. The necessary conditions may be obtained as follows:

Lagrange multiplier approach	Variational approach
1. Form the Lagrangian	Form the Hamiltonian
$F(\mathbf{z}_1, \ldots, \mathbf{z}_N, \mathbf{y}_1, \ldots, \mathbf{y}_N, \lambda_1, \ldots, \lambda_N)$ $= \sum_{n=1}^{N} [(g_n(\mathbf{z}_{n-1}, \mathbf{y}_n) + \lambda_n^t(T_n(\cdot) - \mathbf{z}_n)]$ where $\lambda_n^t = (\lambda_n^1, \lambda_n^2, \ldots, \lambda_n^p)$	$H_n = \lambda_n \mathbf{T}_n(\cdot)$ where $T_n^0 = g_n + z_n^0$ and $\lambda_n = (\lambda_n^0, \lambda_n^1, \ldots, \lambda_n^p)$
2. Set the partial of $F(\cdot)$ with respect to each of its arguments equal to 0:	Set the partials of H_{j+1} with respect to z_j^i equal to λ_j^i

$$\frac{\partial F}{\partial z_j^i} = \frac{\partial g_{j+1}}{\partial z_j^i}(\cdot) - \lambda_j^i + \sum_{k=1}^{p} \lambda_{j+1}^k \frac{\partial T_{j+1}(\mathbf{z}_j, \mathbf{y}_{j+1})}{\partial z_j^i} \tag{6.46}$$
$$= 0$$

$$i = 1, \ldots, p_j \qquad j = 1, \ldots, N-1$$

$$\frac{\partial F}{\partial z_N^i} = -\lambda_N^i = 0$$

> Set the partial of H_n with respect to y_n equal to zero

$$\frac{\partial F}{\partial y_j^i} = T_j^i(\mathbf{z}_{j-1}, \mathbf{y}_j) - z_j^i = 0 \tag{6.47}$$

$$i = 1, \ldots, P \qquad j = 1, \ldots, N$$

$$\frac{\partial F}{\partial y_j^i} = \frac{\partial g_j(\mathbf{z}_{j-1}, \mathbf{y}_j)}{\partial y_j^i} + \sum_{k=1}^{P} \lambda_j^k \frac{\partial T_j^k(\mathbf{z}_{j-1}, \mathbf{y}_j)}{\partial y_j^i} = 0 \tag{6.48}$$

> Boundary conditions:
> $\lambda_N^0 = 1 \cdot \lambda_n^i = 0$
> $i = 1, \ldots, N$

Dynamic Programming and the Maximum Principle

At this point it is suitable to compare the two techniques that have been presented as alternative approaches to solving sequential decision problems. One should suspect at this point that the variational approach is not unrelated to that taken by dynamic programming. To illustrate this relationship let us derive the Euler-Lagrange equations from the dynamic programming point of view.[1] Recall that the problem we face is

$$\min \int_a^b F[y(x), y'(x), x] \, dx$$

subject to

$$\frac{dy}{dx} = g[y(x), y'(x), x]$$

Since the integral has the additive property,

$$\int_a^b F(\cdot) \, dx = \int_a^c F(\cdot) \, dx + \int_c^b F(\cdot) \, dx \qquad a \le c \le b \tag{6.49}$$

it satisfies Mitten's sufficiency condition. Defining,

$$f[y(a), a] = \min_y \left[\int_a^{a+\Delta} F(\cdot) \, dx + \int_{a+\Delta}^b F(\cdot) \, dx \right]$$

$$= \min_{y[a, a+\Delta], y[a+\Delta, b]} \left[\int_a^{a+\Delta} F(\cdot) \, dx + \int_{a+\Delta}^b F(\cdot) \, dx \right]$$

---

[1] This argument was first advanced by Bellman (see, for example, reference [8]).

Following the standard dynamic programming argument we note that the first integral does not depend on $y(\cdot)$ in the interval $[a + \Delta, b]$. Thus we can write

$$f[y(a), a] = \min_{y[a, a+\Delta]} \left[\int_a^{a+\Delta} F(\cdot)\, dx + \min_{y[a+\Delta, b]} \int_{a+\Delta}^b F(\cdot)\, dx \right] \quad (6.50)$$

$$f[y(a), a] = \min_{y[a, a+\Delta]} \left(\int_a^{a+\Delta} F(\cdot)\, dx + f[y(a + \Delta), a + \Delta] \right) \quad (6.51)$$

For small Δ we note that (1) choosing $y[a, a + \Delta]$ is equivalent to choosing $y'(a)$.

(2)
$$\int_a^{a+\Delta} F(\cdot)\, dx = F[y(a), y'(a), a]\, \Delta + 0(\Delta^2) \quad (6.52)$$

and (3)

$$y(a + \Delta) = \int_a^{a+\Delta} g(\cdot)\, dx + y(a)$$

$$= g[y(a), y'(a), a]\, \Delta + y(a) = \Delta y'(a) + y(a) \quad (6.53)$$

Thus

$$f[y(a), a] = \min_{y'} \left[F(y, y', a)\, \Delta + f[y(a) + y'(a)\, \Delta, a + \Delta] + 0(\Delta^2) \right] \quad (6.54)$$

Expand the last term shown above in a Taylor's series about $x = a$ and $y(x = a)$. We have

$$f[y(a) + y'(a)\, \Delta, a + \Delta] = f[y(a), a] + \frac{\partial f(\cdot)}{\partial y}\, y'\, \Delta + \frac{\partial f(\cdot)}{\partial x}\, \Delta + 0(\Delta^2)$$

Substituting this result into the expression for $f[y(a), a]$ we find

$$f[y(a), a] = \min_{y'} \left[F(y, y', a)\, \Delta + \frac{\partial f(\cdot)}{\partial x}\, \Delta + \frac{\partial f(\cdot)}{\partial y}\, y'\, \Delta + 0(\Delta^2) + f[y(a), a] \right]$$

Since $f[y(a), a]$ does not depend on y we may remove it from the brackets. We are left with

$$0 = \min_{y'} \left[F(y, y', a) + \frac{\partial f(\cdot)}{\partial x} + \frac{\partial f(\cdot)}{\partial y}\, y' + \frac{0(\Delta^2)}{\Delta} \right] \Delta \quad (6.55)$$

Dividing by Δ and taking $\lim_{\Delta \to 0}$ we have

$$\min_{y'} \left[F(y, y', a) + \frac{\partial f(\cdot)}{\partial x} + \frac{\partial f(\cdot)}{\partial y}\, y' \right] = 0 \quad (6.56)$$

Thus a necessary condition is that along the optimal decision trajectory

$$F(y, y', a) + \frac{\partial f(\cdot)}{\partial x} + \frac{\partial f}{\partial y}\, y' = 0 \quad (6.57)$$

We also have as a necessary condition that the partial derivative of the quantity in brackets with respect to y' must vanish (necessary for a minimum):

$$\frac{\partial F}{\partial y'} + \frac{\partial f}{\partial y} = 0 \Rightarrow \frac{\partial f}{\partial y} = -\frac{\partial F}{\partial y'} \tag{6.58}$$

We want to eliminate terms in $f(\cdot)$ to get the Euler-Lagrange equation. To eliminate $f(\cdot)$ we differentiate the above expression with respect to x,

$$\frac{d}{dx}\left(\frac{\partial F}{\partial y'} + \frac{\partial f}{\partial y}\right) = \frac{d}{dx}\frac{\partial F}{\partial y'} + \frac{d}{dx}\frac{\partial f}{\partial y} = \frac{d}{dx}\frac{\partial F}{\partial y'} + \frac{\partial^2 f}{\partial y\,\partial x} + \frac{\partial^2 f}{\partial y^2}\frac{dy}{dx} = 0$$

Rearranging yields

$$\frac{\partial^2 f(\cdot)}{\partial y\,\partial x} + \frac{\partial^2 f}{\partial y^2}\frac{dy}{dx} = -\frac{d}{dx}\frac{\partial F}{\partial y'} \tag{6.59}$$

We have one other condition that can be used,

$$F(\cdot) + \frac{\partial f(\cdot)}{\partial x} + \frac{\partial f}{\partial y}\frac{dy}{dx} = 0 \Rightarrow \frac{\partial f(\cdot)}{\partial x} + \frac{\partial f(\cdot)}{\partial y}\frac{dy}{dx} = -F(\cdot) \tag{6.60}$$

If we partially differentiate this with respect to y we obtain

$$\frac{\partial^2 f}{\partial x\,\partial y} + \frac{\partial^2 f}{\partial y^2}\frac{dy}{dx} + \frac{\partial f}{\partial y}\frac{\partial y'}{\partial y} = -\frac{\partial F}{\partial y} - \frac{\partial F}{\partial y'}\frac{\partial y'}{\partial y}$$

Rearranging yields

$$\frac{\partial^2 f}{\partial x\,\partial y} + \frac{\partial^2 f}{\partial y^2}y' = -\frac{\partial F}{\partial y} - \frac{\partial f}{\partial y}\frac{dy}{dy'} - \frac{\partial F}{\partial y'}\frac{\partial y'}{\partial y} \tag{6.61}$$

But we have shown that the left side of the above equation also equals

$$-\frac{d}{dx}\frac{\partial F}{\partial y'}$$

Setting these two expressions equal yields

$$\frac{\partial F}{\partial y'}\frac{\partial y'}{\partial y} + \frac{\partial F}{\partial y} + \frac{\partial f}{\partial y}\frac{dy'}{dy} = \frac{d}{dx}\frac{\partial F}{\partial y'} \tag{6.62}$$

Finally we recall that $\partial f/\partial y = -\,\partial F/\partial y'$. Using this fact we obtain the desired result:

$$\frac{\partial F}{\partial y} = \frac{d}{dx}\frac{\partial F}{\partial y'}$$

By the laborious argument presented above we have demonstrated how the Euler-Lagrange condition may be obtained via dynamic programming. One may also obtain the maximum principle by the same or similar argument [9]. However, from an applications point of view the equivalence of the results of the two approaches is only reassuring. It does not answer the question of which to use in any given situation. We shall now address ourselves to this question.

Unfortunately there are few cases where any clear-cut guidelines can be established. One such example is when the variables of interest are not continuous; that is, only integer-valued decision variables are admissible. In the derivation of the variational equations we assumed that all functions have at least continuous first partial derivatives. When the decision variables are defined on some discrete set this assumption is invalid. Consequently in such situations we have no variational methods available to choose from, and to obtain a solution we must resort to dynamic programming. For problems where the number of combinations of state variables that must be considered is larger than the rapid-access memory capacity, real difficulties may be encountered. This is because all the state-variable reduction procedures for which convergence can be established depend on continuity. In problems where some or all of the variables are discrete, continuity is not maintained. However, since dynamic programming is the only alternative to total enumeration of the set of feasible solutions, we would recommend dynamic programming. There are many examples of problems in which some of the variables of interest are discrete. As one example consider the problem of deciding whether, and if so when, W.T.H. Rent-A-Car should expand their fleet. Here the decision variable—number of cars to buy—is discrete. The decision would depend on several variables. Among those would be the number of cars, age of each car currently in the fleet, the mileage of each fleet car, its condition, and so on. Some of these would be continuous variable (for example, mileage), whereas others are discrete.

Another example where the choice is already made, owing to limitations of the variational approach, is systems where the stage transformation function has a random component contained in the relationship. As we discussed in Chapter 5, such problems are amenable to solution by dynamic programming. The difference between the results obtained by dynamic programming and those of the variational approach is illustrated when we encounter processes that are affected by random variables.

Dynamic programming yields a decision rule that depends on the state of the system—it yields a feedback law. Using the variational approach one obtains a feed-forward law—the solution is obtained as a function of the initial conditions only. This difference in the form of the decision rule is of little consequence in deterministic systems, because once the decision rule and initial conditions are specified the optimal system trajectory is completely determined. However, when the system is probabilistic, one would desire a rule that adapts to the unknown fluctuations due to the random variables. Under such circumstances dynamic programming offers a decided advantage.[2] Many such systems are encountered in practice. Demand in inventory

---

[2] A particularly striking example is presented by Dreyfus [9].

systems, reliability problems and traffic control systems are but a few examples of systems that are probabilistic in nature.

Problems that have the desired differentiability and deterministic structure offer a choice of the optimization scheme. In such situations either the variational or dynamic programming approach is applicable, and one must decide for each problem which approach will prove the most feasible from a computational point of view. Before discussing the merits of each, we shall illustrate how one would computationally approach a general example formulated as a variational problem from a dynamic programming point of view. Recall that from the dynamic programming derivation of the Euler-Lagrange condition we had

$$f[y(a), a] = \min_{y'} \left[F(y, y', z) \Delta + f[y(a + \Delta), a + \Delta] \right] + 0(\Delta^2)$$

This defines a recursive relationship equivalent to the one we had in dynamic programming. If we make Δ small and neglect terms of order Δ^2 and higher we get an approximation to the optimal solution. The "goodness" of this solution—how close the solution is to the optimal solution—depends on the choice of Δ. The size of Δ determines the number of stages in the dynamic programming calculations. Since computation time is only linearly related to the number of stages and since on-line storage requirements are independent of the number of stages, one can get a reasonable approximation to the optimal solution by making Δ small.

Another difficulty we wish to emphasize is the increase in computation time due to size of the vector-state variable. When the number of combinations of values of state variables increases, the computation time also increases, as do the storage requirements. Thus a problem with three state variables, each of which takes on 100 values, yields 10^6 combinations to be considered. Even with multiprocessing computers, where one has essentially unlimited rapid-access memory capacity, computation time becomes a problem. On the other hand, a problem with three state variables yields six simultaneous differential (or difference) equations to be solved. In addition, three of the boundary conditions are initial conditions, whereas the remaining three are final conditions. For nonlinear systems[3] one encounters convergence problems that have already been mentioned. Very little experience has been reported comparing the two approaches computationally.

Finally, we must note that the equations obtained by applications of the maximum principle yield only necessary conditions for extrema. One may spend considerable computation time obtaining solutions to these equations only to find that the solution yields a maximum when a minimum is desired. In addition, inequality constraints on the state variables are exceedingly difficult to handle from the variational approach.

---

[3] Linear problems may be solved analytically using either approach.

It may have appeared from the above discussion that problems with more than two or three state variables are unfeasible to solve from a computational point of view. We emphasize the difficulties involved to make the point that complex problems are difficult to solve. This area is a fertile research area and much is being done to develop efficient algorithms, new hardware, and, more important, new approaches to dynamic optimization problems. We hope this discussion will stimulate the reader to contribute to the solution of these complex problems.

Problems

1. Minimize

$$F = \tfrac{1}{2} \int_0^1 (y^2 + z)\, dx$$

subject to

$$z' = y \qquad \begin{matrix} z(0) = 2 \\ z(1) = 3 \end{matrix}$$

using direct substitution.

2. Solve Problem 1 with the following boundary conditions:

$$z(0) = 2$$
$$z(1) = \text{unspecified}$$

3. Minimize

$$J = \int_0^{0.707} (z_1^2 + y^2)\, dx$$

subject to

$$\begin{matrix} z_1' = z_1 + y \\ z_2' = z_1 \end{matrix} \qquad \begin{matrix} z_1(2) = 1 \\ z_1(0) = 0 \\ z_2(0) = 0 \end{matrix}$$

4. Find necessary conditions for the following:

$$\min J = \tfrac{1}{2} \int_0^1 [(z_1 + z_2 + z_3)^2 + y^2]\, dx$$

subject to

$$\begin{matrix} z_1' = z_2 \\ z_2' = z_3 \\ z_3' = y \end{matrix} \qquad \begin{matrix} z_1(0) = 1 \\ z_2(1) = 0 \\ z_3(0) = 0 \end{matrix}$$

5. Refer to Problem 4.

   (a) Show what changes in boundary conditions result if

   $$\mathbf{z}(0) = \mathbf{z}_0 \qquad \mathbf{z}(1) = \mathbf{z}_f$$

   (b) Is the new control (y) more or less difficult to implement?

6. Derive necessary conditions for

$$\min J = \theta[z(t_f), t_f] + \int_0^{t_f} \phi[z(t_f), z'(t_f), t_f] \, dt$$

$$z(0) = z_0$$

7. (a) Prove that the shortest distance between two points is a straight line, that is, a minimum distance between $(0, 0)$ and (x_f, t_f), where a differential area ds is given by $ds^2 = dx^2 + dt^2$.
   (b) Show that the necessary conditions yield a minimum and not a maximum.

8. Given the following problem:

$$\min J = \int_{t_0}^{t_f} \phi[z(t), z'(t), z'', \ldots, z^N(t)] \, dt$$

with

$$\begin{array}{ll} z(t_0) = z_0 & z(t_0) = c_1, \ldots, z^{(n-1)}(t_0) = c_{n-1} \\ z(t_f) = z_f & z(t_f) = D_1, \ldots, z^{(n-1)}(t_f) = D_{n-1} \end{array}$$

prove that the necessary conditions are

$$0 = \phi_z - \frac{d}{dt} \phi_z + \frac{d^2}{dt^2}(\phi_z) + \cdots + (-1)^N \frac{d^N}{dt^N} \phi_{z^N}$$

(*Hint:* Integrate by parts N times.)

9. Use the results of Problem 8 to find necessary conditions for the following:

$$\min \tfrac{1}{2} \int_2^1 (z_1^2 + z_2^2 + z_3^2 + y^2) \, dt$$

subject to

$$\begin{array}{lll} z_1' = z_2 & z_1(0) = 1 & z_1(1) = 0 \\ z_2' = z_3 & z_2(0) = 1 & z_2(1) = 0 \\ z_3' = y & z_3(0) = 2 & z_3(1) = 1 \end{array}$$

10. Derive necessary conditions for

$$\min J = \int_{t_0}^{t_f} \phi(z, z', x) \, dx$$

where t_f is unspecified.

11. Solve the following problem using direct substitution and the Lagrange function, and show equivalence between Lagrange multiplier and higher-order derivatives of x_1,

$$\min \int_0^1 \tfrac{1}{2} y^2 \, dx$$

subject to

$$\begin{array}{lll} z_1' = z_2 & z_1(0) = 2 & z_1(1) = 0 \\ z_2' = y & z_2(0) = 1 & z_2(1) = 0 \end{array}$$

References Cited and Bibliography

[1] Bliss, G. A. *Lectures on the Calculus of Variations*. Chicago: University of Chicago Press, 1946.

[2] Elsgoic, L. E. *Calculus of Variations*. London: Pergamon Press, 1962.

[3] Pontryagin, L. S., V. G. Boltyanskii, R. V. Gamkrelidze, and E. F. Mischenko. *The Mathematical Theory of Optimal Processes*. New York: Wiley-Interscience, 1962.

[4] Roberts, S. M., and J. Shipman. "The Kantarovich Theorem and Two Point Boundary Value Problems," *IBM Journal*, pp. 402–406, Sept. 1966.

[5] Fan, L. T. *The Continuous Maximum Principle*. New York: Wiley, 1966.

[6] Fan, L. T., and C. S. Wang. *The Discrete Maximum Principle*. New York: Wiley, 1965.

[7] Katz, S. "A Discrete Version of Pontryagin's Maximum Principle," *J. Electron Control*, Vol. 13 (1962).

[8] Bellman, R. E. *Dynamic Programming*. Princeton, N.J.: Princeton University Press, 1957.

[9] Dreyfus, S. E. *Dynamic Programming and the Calculus of Variations*. New York: Academic Press, 1964.

CHAPTER 7

Theory of Queues

7.1   Introduction

In developing a conceptual framework for decision models in Chapter 1, it became apparent that random variation frequently plays an important role in the formulation of an objective function and the subsequent search for an optimal course of action. Frequently a random variable appears in an objective function or constraint. On many occasions knowledge of the random properties of a system is required before detailed problem formulation can begin. In other situations, knowledge of these stochastic properties is sufficient to allow "ballpark" predictions of the effect of alternative courses of action.

In this chapter our primary goal is to develop methods for the analysis of the stochastic properties of service systems. Such a system is pictured in Figure 7.1. We shall be concerned with a stream of customers requiring service, being served, and departing from the service system. Although we

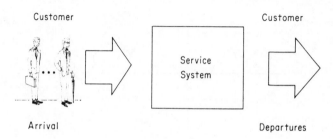

Figure 7.1.

shall speak in terms of customers at a service facility, these customers can
have many forms, including patients arriving at a doctor's office, cars
arriving at toll booths, and parts arriving at a warehouse. We shall not
concern ourselves with applications but will concentrate on the mathematics
required to analyze these systems. The reader who wishes to read further on
applications is referred to Morse [1], Cox and Smith [2], or Saaty [3]. We
shall make an attempt to demonstrate the range of applications by means of
the problems at the end of the chapter.

7.2   Stochastic Processes

A *stochastic process*, $\mathbf{X}(t)$, is a collection, or ensemble, of random variables
defined at a time $t \in T$.

T is called the *index set* of the stochastic process. T can be a set of integer
values: $T = 1, 2, \ldots$, in which case we have a *discrete-time stochastic process*,
or it can be a set of continuous values: $T = (-\infty < t < \infty)$ in which case
we have a *continuous-time stochastic process*. The particular value of $\mathbf{X}(t)$
at time t is called the *state* of process. Note that we can have discrete- and
continuous-state stochastic processes.

An example of continuous-time, continuous-state stochastic process might
be the quantity of fuel oil found in our home furnace fuel tank. The quantity
of water in a reservoir is another example. Our studies of operations research
in this text will be primarily concerned with discrete-state stochastic processes.
During the course of the text, we shall discuss both discrete- and continuous-
time cases.

A graph of a typical sample of a stochastic process $\mathbf{X}(t)$ is called a *realization*. Figure 7.2 is a realization of a random noise voltage: a continuous-state,
continuous-time stochastic process. Figure 7.3 is a realization of the quantity
of water found in a reservoir immediately before the water level is adjusted:

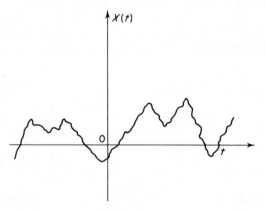

Figure 7.2.

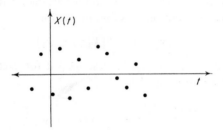

Figure 7.3.

a continuous-state, discrete-time stochastic process. Figure 7.4 is a sequence of tossed coins: a discrete state, discrete-time stochastic process. Figure 7.5 is a realization of the number of people at a supermarket checkout counter: a discrete-state, continuous-time stochastic process.

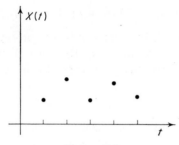

Figure 7.4.

Note that $\mathbf{X}(t)$ is, in general, an r-dimensional stochastic process. Consequently at some time t_1, $\mathbf{X}(t_1)$ is a vector of the form

$$\mathbf{X}(t_1) = [X^1(t_1), X^2(t_1), \ldots, X^r(t_1)] \tag{7.1}$$

In the analysis of this chapter $\mathbf{X}(t)$ will be a one-dimensional stochastic process $X(t)$. We shall consider only cases where $X(t)$ is real.

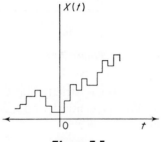

Figure 7.5.

Since at some time, t_1, $X(t_1)$ is a random variable, it has associated with it some probability distribution function of the form

$$F(x_1; t_1) = P[X(t_1) \leq x_1] \tag{7.2}$$

The stochastic process is completely described if for every $t_1, t_2, \ldots, t_k$ we know the joint distribution function

$$F(x_1, x_2, \ldots, x_k; t_1 \cdots t_k)$$
$$= P[X(t_1) \leq x_1, X(t_2) \leq x_2, \ldots, X(t_k) \leq x_k] \tag{7.3}$$

If the index set T is an infinite set, then $X(t)$ is completely described as $k \to \infty$. At first glance it seems that we shall never be able to completely describe $X(t)$. We shall see below that, for a certain general class of processes, a limited knowledge of the past history of the process is sufficient to describe $F(x_1, x_2, \ldots, x_k; t_1, t_2, \ldots, t_k)$.

A stochastic process is said to be *strictly stationary*, if for every $t_1, t_2, \ldots, t_k$, and any h in T, the k-dimensional vectors,

$$[X(t_1), X(t_2), \ldots, X(t_k)] \qquad [X(t_1 + h), X(t_2 + h), \ldots, X(t_k + h)] \tag{7.4}$$

are identically distributed. In other words, the process is strictly stationary if the ensemble remains invariant to an arbitrary shift in time, or equivalently if all probability measures remain invariant to this shift. In essence we are saying

$$F(x_1, x_2, \ldots, x_k; t_1, t_2, \ldots, t_k)$$
$$= F(x_1, x_2, \ldots, x_k; t_1 + h, t_2 + h, \ldots, t_k + h) \tag{7.5}$$

As an example, consider the realization shown in Figure 7.6.

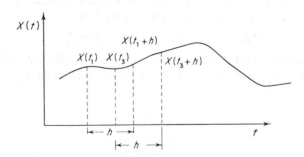

Figure 7.6.

If the stochastic process $X(t)$ is strictly stationary, then the bivariate distribution of $X(t_1)$ and $X(t_2)$ is identical with the bivariate distribution of $X(t_1 + h)$ and $X(t_2 + h)$:

$$F(x_1, x_2; t_1, t_2) = F(x_1, x_2; t_1 + h, t_2 + h) \tag{7.6}$$

A stochastic process $X(t)$ is *wide-sense stationary* if the covariance

$$\text{cov}\,[X(t), X(t + h)] = R(h) \tag{7.7}$$

for any t and h, where

$$\begin{aligned}\text{cov}\,[X(t), X(t + h)] \\ = E\{[X(t) - E\{X(t)\}][X(t + h) - E\{X(t + h)\}]\}\end{aligned} \tag{7.8}$$

In other words, the covariance is a function of the length of the time shift h, but not the time origin t. Wide-sense stationary stochastic processes are also called *weakly stationary*, *second-order stationary*, and *covariance stationary*. Implicit in both definitions of stationarity is an assumption that both t and $t + h$ are members of the index set T. Such a set is called a *linear index set*.

7.3   Markov Processes

A stochastic process $X(t)$, $t \geq 0$, is said to be a *Markov process*, if, for a set of points $t_1 < t_2 < \cdots < t_n$ in the index set of the process, the conditional distribution of $X(t_n)$, for given values of $X(t_1)$, $X(t_2)$, ..., $X(t_{n-1})$, depends only on $X(t_{n-1})$, the most recent known value. More precisely,

$$\begin{aligned}P[X(t_n) \leq x_n \mid X(t_1) = x_1, \ldots, X(t_{n-1}) = x_{n-1}] \\ = P[X(t_n) \leq x_n \mid X(t_{n-1}) = x_{n-1}]\end{aligned} \tag{7.9}$$

This definition, taken from Parzen [4], defines a first-order Markov process. A second-order process would have its conditional distribution depending on the two most recent known values: $X(t_{n-1})$ and $X(t_{n-2})$. A kth-order Markov process would also depend on the k most recent known values: $X(t_{n-1})$, $X(t_{n-2})$, ..., $X(t_{n-k})$. From this point on, our use of the term Markov process will be intended to mean a first-order Markov process. If the process has a finite number of possible states, it is called a finite Markov process. We should note that the cumulative distribution given in equation (7.9) is a function of *transition probabilities*. For an N-state process,

$$P[X(t_n) \leq x_n \mid X(t_{n-1}) = x_{n-1}] = \sum_{x_j=1}^{x_n} p(x_j, t_n \mid x_{n-1}, t_{n-1})$$

$p(x_j, t_n \mid x_{n-1}, t_{n-1})$ is the probability that the process is in state x_j at time t_n given that it was in state x_{n-1} at the time t_{n-1}. The process is *homogeneous* if the transition probabilities depend only on the time difference $t_n - t_{n-1}$ and not on the time origin t_{n-1}. Note that $p(x_j, t_j \mid x_i, t_i)$ is a shorthand notation for $p[X(t_j) = x_j \mid X(t_i) = x_i]$ for $t_j > t_i$. We shall usually simplify the notation further by writing $p(x_j, t_j \mid x_i, t_i) = p_{ij}$.

One can easily show, by using the definition of a Markov process given by equation (7.9), that the joint distribution function required for complete description of the process may be written as follows:

$$P[X(t_1) \le x_1, X(t_2) \le x_2, \ldots, X(t_k) \le x_k]$$

$$= P[X(t_1) \le x_1] \prod_{i=2}^{k} P[X(t_i) \le x_i \mid X(t_{i-1}) = x_{i-1}] \quad (7.10)$$

The equivalent joint probability distribution is

$$P[X(t_1) = x_1, X(t_2) = x_2, \ldots, X(t_k) = x_k]$$

$$= P[X(t_1) = x_1] \prod_{i=2}^{k} P[X(t_i) = x_i \mid X(t_{i-1}) = x_{i-1}] \quad (7.11)$$

Thus all that is needed to completely describe the process is the initial condition, $P[X(t_1) = x_1]$, and the transition probabilities.

Markov Chains

In this section we shall consider discrete-state, discrete-time Markov processes, or *Markov chains*. In these processes it is convenient to assume that the time between transitions is constant. This is done with no loss in generality. In our analysis we shall assume a unit time between transitions: $t_n - t_{n-1} = 1$. We shall assume that the index set, $T = 0, 1, 2, \ldots$, and our initial conditions are defined at $t = 0$.

The transition probabilities are most conveniently displayed in matrix form:

$$\pi = [p_{ij}] = \begin{bmatrix} p_{11} & p_{12} & p_{23} & \cdots \\ p_{21} & p_{22} & p_{23} & \cdots \\ p_{31} & p_{32} & p_{33} & \cdots \\ . & . & . & \cdots \\ . & . & . & \cdots \\ . & . & . & \cdots \end{bmatrix}$$

The matrix has dimension N for an N-state Markov process. Note that sums across the rows have the following property:

$$\sum_{j=1}^{N} p_{ij} = 1$$

Our primary motive in this section is to determine the state probability $p(j; t)$, the probability that the process is in state j at time t or after t transitions. This state probability distribution for a Markov chain may be expressed in the form of a *Chapman–Kolmogorov equation*[1]:

$$p(j; t + 1) = \sum_{i=1}^{N} p(i; t)p_{ij} \qquad j = 1, \ldots, N \qquad (7.12)$$

This equation has been written for a finite-state process. If the Markov process has an infinite number of states, the upper limit on the summation will be infinity. If we define a row vector

$$\mathbf{P}(t + 1) = [p(1; t + 1), p(2; t + 1), \ldots, p(N; t + 1)],$$

then we may express this equation in vector form

$$\mathbf{P}(t + 1) = \mathbf{P}(t)\boldsymbol{\pi} \qquad (7.13)$$

Assume that $\mathbf{P}(0) = [p(1; 0), p(2; 0), \ldots, p(N; 0)]$ gives the initial conditions of the process. Note that this is a system of linear, first-order, homogeneous difference equations. The solution of difference equations by use of the z transform is discussed in Appendix B. The reader who is not familiar with these concepts should read Appendix B before going further. We should note that it is possible to solve this vector equation for $\mathbf{P}(t)$ with the theory of finite matrices. The interested reader should see Feller [5]. The analysis for Markov chains with an infinite number of states is more difficult and will not be covered here.

We may take the z transform of a vector difference equation by taking the z transform of each member of the vector. We shall define the z transform of some function $f(t)$, $t = 0, 1, 2, \ldots$, as follows:

$$F(z) = \sum_{t=0}^{\infty} f(t)z^t$$

We shall define $\mathbf{P}(z)$ to be the vector z transform of $\mathbf{P}(t)$. Taking the z transform of equation (7.13) we find

$$z^{-1}[\mathbf{P}(z) - \mathbf{P}(0)] = \mathbf{P}(z)\boldsymbol{\pi}$$

With algebra we find

$$\mathbf{P}(z) = \mathbf{P}(0)(\mathbf{I} - z\boldsymbol{\pi})^{-1} \qquad (7.14)$$

where $\mathbf{I}$ is the identity matrix.

Suppose we let $\mathbf{H}(t)$ be the inverse transform of the matrix $(\mathbf{I} - z\boldsymbol{\pi})^{-1}$. Then the inverse transform of equation (7.14) has the form

$$\mathbf{P}(t) = \mathbf{P}(0)\mathbf{H}(t) \qquad (7.15)$$

---

[1] The reader should be cautioned that satisfaction of the Chapman-Kolmogorov equation is *not* sufficient for a stochastic process to be a Markov process.

In general, $H(t)$ will contain two parts: a steady-state portion S, not a function of t, and a transient part $T(t)$ that dies out as t grows large:

$$H(t) = S + T(t) \qquad (7.16)$$

Consider a Markov chain with an initial state vector $P(0) = (1, 0)$ and transition probability matrix

$$\pi = \begin{bmatrix} 0.4 & 0.6 \\ 0.3 & 0.7 \end{bmatrix}$$

In this case

$$(I - z\pi) = \begin{bmatrix} 1 - 0.4z & -0.6z \\ -0.3z & 1 - 0.7z \end{bmatrix}$$

Taking the inverse of this matrix we find

$$(I - z\pi)^{-1} = \begin{bmatrix} \dfrac{1 - 0.7z}{(1 - z)(1 - 0.1z)} & \dfrac{0.6z}{(1 - z)(1 - 0.1z)} \\ \dfrac{0.3z}{(1 - z)(1 - 0.1z)} & \dfrac{1 - 0.4z}{(1 - z)(1 - 0.1z)} \end{bmatrix}$$

Expanding each term in the matrix by a partial fraction expansion we find

$$(I - z\pi)^{-1} = \frac{1}{1 - z} \begin{bmatrix} \frac{1}{3} & \frac{2}{3} \\ \frac{1}{3} & \frac{2}{3} \end{bmatrix} + \frac{1}{1 - 0.1z} \begin{bmatrix} \frac{2}{3} & -\frac{2}{3} \\ -\frac{1}{3} & \frac{1}{3} \end{bmatrix}$$

This is the transform domain equivalent of $H(t)$:

$$H(z) = S(z) + T(z)$$

By using an inverse z transformation we find

$$H(t) = \begin{bmatrix} \frac{1}{3} & \frac{2}{3} \\ \frac{1}{3} & \frac{2}{3} \end{bmatrix} + (0.1)^t \begin{bmatrix} \frac{2}{3} & -\frac{2}{3} \\ -\frac{1}{3} & \frac{1}{3} \end{bmatrix}$$

The state probability distribution of the Markov chain is

$$P(t) = P(0)H(t)$$
$$= (1, 0) \begin{bmatrix} \frac{1}{3} & \frac{2}{3} \\ \frac{1}{3} & \frac{2}{3} \end{bmatrix} + (1, 0)(0.1)^t \begin{bmatrix} \frac{2}{3} & -\frac{2}{3} \\ -\frac{1}{3} & \frac{1}{3} \end{bmatrix}$$

With multiplication,

$$p(1; t) = \tfrac{1}{3} + \tfrac{2}{3}(0.1)^t$$
$$p(2; t) = \tfrac{2}{3} - \tfrac{2}{3}(0.1)^t$$

Steady-State Solutions

In many cases it is only desired to find S, the steady-state portion of $P(t)$. Note that

$$\lim_{t \to \infty} P(t) = S$$

It is frequently useful to use the final value theorem (see Appendix B) of the z transform to define the steady state:

$$\lim_{z \to 1} (1 - z)\mathbf{P}(z) = \lim_{t \to \infty} \mathbf{P}(t)$$

In terms of the preceding example,

$$\lim_{t \to \infty} \mathbf{P}(t) = (1, 0)\begin{bmatrix} \frac{1}{3} & \frac{2}{3} \\ \frac{1}{3} & \frac{2}{3} \end{bmatrix}$$

Note also that

$$\lim_{z \to 1} (1 - z)\mathbf{P}(z) = \lim_{z \to 1} (1 - z)\mathbf{P}(0)\mathbf{H}(z) = (1, 0)\begin{bmatrix} \frac{1}{3} & \frac{2}{3} \\ \frac{1}{3} & \frac{2}{3} \end{bmatrix}$$

Discontinuous Markov Processes

We now turn to *discontinuous,* or *discrete-state continuous-time, Markov processes.* In this process the index set T can have continuous values, $T = -\infty < t < \infty$. All initial conditions will be defined at $t = 0$.

We shall define a_{ij} as the transition rate from state i to state j for $i \neq j$. Assume that in this process the probability of a transition from state i to state j in a short time interval, Δt, is $a_{ij} \Delta t$, $i \neq j$. Our discussion will only concern those processes in which a_{ij} is not a function of time t. In the form of our previous notation,

$$p(x_j, t + \Delta t \mid x_i, t) = p_{ij} = a_{ij} \Delta t \qquad i \neq j \tag{7.17}$$

The state probability distribution for a discontinuous Markov process can also be expressed in the form of a Chapman-Kolmogorov equation,

$$p(j; t + \Delta t) = \sum_{i=1}^{N} p(i; t)p_{ij} \tag{7.18}$$

Substituting the definition for p_{ij},

$$p(j; t + \Delta t) = \sum_{\substack{i=1 \\ i \neq j}}^{N} p(i; t)a_{ij} \Delta t + p(j; t)\left[1 - \sum_{\substack{i=1 \\ i \neq j}}^{N} a_{ji} \Delta t\right] \tag{7.19}$$

If we define p_{jj} as the probability of no transition, in the previous expression

$$p_{jj} = 1 - \sum_{\substack{i=1 \\ i \neq j}}^{N} a_{ji} \Delta t$$

That is, p_{jj} is 1 minus the probability of making a transition in the time interval Δt.

If we let

$$a_{jj} = -\sum_{\substack{i=1 \\ i \neq j}}^{N} a_{ij} \qquad j = 1, \ldots, N$$

we may rewrite equation (7.19) as

$$p(j; t + \Delta t) = p(j; t)(1 + a_{jj} \Delta t) + \sum_{\substack{i=1 \\ i \neq j}}^{N} p(i; t)a_{ij} \Delta t$$

Rearranging,

$$p(j; t + \Delta t) - p(j; t) = \sum_{i=1}^{N} p(i; t)a_{ij} \Delta t$$

If we divide both sides by Δt and take the limit as $\Delta t \to 0$, we have

$$\frac{d}{dt} p(j; t) = \sum_{i=1}^{N} p(i; t)a_{ij} \qquad j = 1, \ldots, N \qquad (7.20)$$

This set of equations may be expressed as a matrix differential equation.

$$\frac{d}{dt} \mathbf{P}(t) = \mathbf{P}(t)\mathbf{A} \qquad (7.21)$$

where $\mathbf{P}(t)$ is a vector of state probabilities defined earlier. To solve for the state probabilities in either form, we must specify the initial state vector $\mathbf{P}(0)$.

There are several ways to tackle the solution of equation (7.21). It is easy to show [6] that the solution has the form

$$\mathbf{P}(t) = \mathbf{P}(0)e^{\mathbf{A}t} \qquad (7.22)$$

The exponential $e^{\mathbf{A}t}$ is an infinite series

$$e^{\mathbf{A}t} = \mathbf{I} + t\mathbf{A} + \frac{t^2}{2!} \mathbf{A}^2 + \frac{t^3 \mathbf{A}^3}{3!} + \cdots$$

Our discussion of Markov processes in the theory of queues will be concerned with a very simple class of Markov processes. The structure of these queueing problems makes the pursuit of a solution of the form shown in equation (7.22) unnecessary. In fact, we shall demonstrate it to be easier to solve the sets of simultaneous equations given by equation (7.20).

Before proceeding with the discussion it will be of value to discuss the properties of a Markov process. The theorem below will prove of value in later discussion.

Theorem: *A necessary condition for a discrete-state, continuous-time stochastic process to be a Markov process is that its probability density of time* *intervals between arrivals into state i and transition out of state i to state j have the form*

$$h_{ij}(t) = a_{ij}e^{-a_{ij}t} \qquad i \neq j; t \geq 0$$

where a_{ij} is the transition rate from state i to state j.[2]

PROOF. Assume we have a Markov process with transition rate matrix $\mathbf{A} = [a_{ij}]$. In this process, the probability of a transition from state i to state j, $i \neq j$, in a short time interval Δt is $a_{ij} \Delta t$.

Let $n_0(t)$ be the probability that the process has not yet gone from state i to state j at time t. Then

$$n_0(t + \Delta t) = n_0(t)(1 - a_{ij} \Delta t)$$

With algebra we find

$$\frac{n_0(t + \Delta t) - n_0(t)}{\Delta t} = -a_{ij}n_0(t)$$

Taking the limit as $\Delta t \to 0$,

$$\frac{dn_0(t)}{dt} = -a_{ij}n_0(t)$$

We can easily see that $n_0(0) = 1$. This is a simple linear differential equation with solution

$$n_0(t) = e^{-a_{ij}t}$$

Note that the probability of no transition from i to j in time t may be written

$$n_0(t) = 1 - \int_0^t h_{ij}(t)\, dt$$

Substituting,

$$e^{-a_{ij}t} = 1 - \int_0^t h_{ij}(t)\, dt$$

Taking the derivative of both sides,

$$h_{ij}(t) = a_{ij}e^{-a_{ij}t}$$

7.4   Poisson Process

In the study of stochastic service systems we frequently come upon systems subject to instantaneous changes due to random events, such as stock arrivals in a storeroom, airplanes at an airport, or patients at a hospital. The *Poisson*

---

[2] We assumed earlier that a_{ij} is not a function of time.

process is a particular type of Markov process that has received widespread use in describing the statistical properties of such systems.

Let $p(n; t)$ be the probability that exactly n random events occur during a time interval $(0; t)$. $p(0; t)$ is the probability of no events in time t and $1 - p(0; t)$ is the probability of one or more such chance events. We shall assume that for a small length of time Δt, the probability of one or more events is $1 - p(0; \Delta t) = \lambda \Delta t + o(\Delta t)$. The term $o(\Delta t)$ indicates a quantity that is of an order smaller than Δt. Thus we assume that whatever the number of events during the time interval $(0, t)$, the probability that during the interval $(t, t + \Delta t)$ an event occurs is $\lambda \Delta t$. The probability of more than one event is $o(\Delta t)$.

It is clear that the process just postulated is a Markov process, because

$$P[X(t + \Delta t) = x^* \mid X(t_1) = x_1, \ldots, X(t_n) = x_n]$$
$$= \lambda \Delta t + o(\Delta t)$$

when $x^* = x_1 + 1$ and is zero for all $x^* \neq x_1 + 1$.

Suppose we wish to find the state probability distribution $p(n; t)$. Since the process is a Markov process, we know we may express $p(n; t + \Delta t)$ using the Chapman-Kolmogorov equation:

$$p(n; t + \Delta t) = p(n; t)(1 - \lambda \Delta t) + p(n - 1; t)\lambda \Delta t + o(\Delta t) \qquad n \geq 1 \tag{7.23}$$

Note the greatly simplified form of the equation. This occurs since the transition rate $a_{ij} = \lambda$, $j = i + 1$, and $a_{ij} = 0$ for all other j, $i \neq j$. With algebra and dividing both sides of this equation by Δt we find

$$\frac{p(n; t + dt) - p(n; t)}{\Delta t} = -\lambda p(n; t) + \lambda p(n - 1; t) + \frac{o(\Delta t)}{\Delta t} \qquad n \geq 1 \tag{7.24}$$

If we take the limit as $\Delta t \to 0$ we find

$$\frac{dp(n; t)}{dt} = -\lambda p(n; t) + \lambda p(n - 1; t) \qquad n \geq 1 \tag{7.25}$$

For $n = 0$,

$$p(0; t + \Delta t) = p(0; t)(1 - \lambda \Delta t) + o(dt)$$

With algebra and taking the limit as $\Delta t \to 0$, we find

$$\frac{dp(0; t)}{dt} = -\lambda p(0; t) \tag{7.26}$$

We see that this set of differential equations is a simplified form of equation (7.20). Equation (7.25) is called a differential-difference equation, because it contains a differential (in t) and a difference (in n). Although there are many approaches to solving this equation, we shall use z transforms on the difference equation and Laplace transforms on the differential equation.

The Laplace transform of a function $f(t)$, $(0 \leq t < \infty)$ is

$$F(s) = \int_0^\infty f(t)e^{-st}\, dt$$

Taking the Laplace transform of equations (7.25) and (7.26), we find

$$sP(n; s) - p(n; 0) = -\lambda P(n; s) + \lambda P(n - 1; s) \qquad n \geq 1 \qquad (7.27)$$
$$sP(0; s) - p(0; 0) = -\lambda P(0; s) \qquad\qquad\qquad\qquad (7.28)$$

Assume that at $t = 0$ no events have taken place: $p(0; 0) = 1$. We shall take the z transform of equation (7.27):

$$(s + \lambda)z^{-1}[P(s, z) - P(0; s)] - \lambda P(s, z) = 0 \qquad (7.29)$$

We may find $P(0; s)$ by solving equation (7.28). Since $p(0; 0) = 1$,

$$sP(0; s) - 1 = -\lambda P(0; s)$$
$$P(0; s) = \frac{1}{s + \lambda}$$

Substituting this in equation (7.29) and solving we find

$$P(z; s) = \frac{1}{(s + \lambda)[1 - (\lambda/s + \lambda)z]} \qquad (7.30)$$

The inverse z transform yields

$$P(n; s) = \frac{\lambda^n}{(s + \lambda)^{n+1}} \qquad (7.31)$$

Taking the inverse Laplace transformation,

$$p(n; t) = \frac{(\lambda t)^n e^{-\lambda t}}{n!} \qquad (7.32)$$

The state probability distribution has the form of the Poisson distribution with mean λt. Note that the mean number of events in an interval $(0, t)$ is a linear function of t.

In practice it is usually difficult to recognize identifiable physical properties in the form of the postulates that we used to specify the basic properties of the Poisson process. For this reason we shall examine other properties of the process.

Theorem: *Consider a stochastic process where random events cause the only possible changes in state to be from state i to state $i + 1$ for $i = 0, 1, 2, \ldots$. A necessary and sufficient condition for the stochastic process to be Poisson process is that the probability density of time intervals, τ, between transitions from state i to state $i + 1$ has the form*

$$a(\tau) = \lambda e^{-\lambda \tau}$$

where λ is a constant rate of transition from state i to $i + 1$, for all i.

PROOF. We shall consider the necessary conditions first. Suppose we have a Poisson process with a probability distribution given by equation (7.32). For $n = 0$,

$$p(0; t) = e^{-\lambda t}$$

This is the probability that no event occurs in the interval $(0, t)$, where $\tau = t - 0$. Alternatively, this is the probability that the time interval between events is greater than or equal to τ. The probability of an event in a time t or less is given by

$$A(\tau) = 1 - p(0; t)$$
$$= 1 - e^{-\lambda t}$$

But this is the cumulative distribution function of the time intervals between events. Therefore,

$$a(\tau) = \frac{dA(\tau)}{dt} = \lambda e^{-\lambda t}$$

Consider the sufficiency part of the proof. Suppose we have a stochastic process where random events cause the only possible changes in state to be from i to $i + 1$ for all i and the probability density of the time intervals between transitions, for all i, is

$$a(\tau) = \lambda e^{-\lambda t} \qquad \tau \geq 0 \qquad (7.33)$$

We now wish to show that the probability of one or more arrivals has the form of the basic postulates for the stochastic process

$$P[\text{one or more arrivals in } \Delta\tau] = \lambda e^{-\lambda \Delta\tau} \Delta\tau$$

$$= \lambda \Delta\tau \left(1 - \Delta\tau + \frac{(\lambda \Delta\tau)^2}{2!} \cdots \right)$$

$$= \lambda \Delta\tau + o(\Delta\tau)$$

But this has the form of the postulated stochastic process and hence is a Poisson process.

The theorem has demonstrated a basic property of the Poisson process. Namely, we have shown that probability density of the time intervals between transitions in the process is the negative exponential density. More important for practical applications and recognition of Poisson processes, we have shown this to be a necessary and sufficient condition.

7.5   Description of a Queueing System

To describe a queueing system, it is necessary to specify (1) the input or arrival process, (2) the service process, and (3) the queue discipline. We shall discuss each of these in detail.

Arrival Process

The arrival process refers to the basic properties of the arrivals of customers at a service facility. Normally, the character of these arrivals is specified in terms of their random or chance nature. Suppose customers arrive at the service facility at times $t_1, t_2, \ldots, t_n, \ldots$, where $t_n > t_{n-1} \cdots > t_2 > t_1 > 0$. These times are called *arrival times*. Let $\tau_n = t_{n+1} - t_n$ be the time between the arrival of the $(n + 1)$st and nth customers. These times are called *interarrival times*.

The simplest and most widely used arrival process is the Poisson arrival process. In this case the interarrival times follow the negative exponential density:

$$a(\tau) = \lambda e^{-\lambda\tau} \qquad \tau \geq 0$$

Also the number of customers arriving in the interval $(0, t)$ would follow the Poisson distribution:

$$p(n; t) = \frac{(\lambda t)^n e^{-\lambda t}}{n!}$$

Note that in this type of arrival process we are assuming that the rate λ is independent of the number of arrivals. In essence we assume arrivals from an infinite population. Problem 17 in this chapter discusses an example with a finite arrival population.

Service Process

We shall assume that the service process consists of one or more servers providing service to arriving customers at a service facility. In specifying the properties of the service process, we shall usually describe the operation of a single server. Examples of servers are a checkout counter at the supermarket, a runway at an airport, or a bed in a hospital.

Consider a server where the probability of a service completion during a time interval Δt is $\mu \Delta t$, where μ is the service rate. The probability of no service completion in Δt is $1 - \mu \Delta t$. Let $S(t)$ be the probability a service begun at $t = 0$ does not terminate in the interval $(0, t)$. Then we have

$$S(t + \Delta t) = (1 - \mu \Delta t)S(t)$$

Rearranging and taking the limit as $\Delta t \to 0$ we have

$$\frac{dS(t)}{dt} = -\mu S(t)$$

Solving this differential equation we find

$$S(t) = ce^{-\mu t}$$

Let $s(t)$ be the probability density of the time for service completion. $S(t)$ may be viewed as the probability that the time taken for a service completion is greater than or equal to t:

$$S(t) = 1 - \int_0^t s(t)\,dt$$

Taking the derivative of both sides and solving we find

$$\frac{dS(t)}{dt} = s(t) = c\mu e^{-\mu t}$$

Since the service must terminate sooner or later we require

$$\int_0^\infty c\mu e^{-\mu t}\,dt = 1$$

Solving we find $c = 1$ and

$$s(t) = \mu e^{-\mu t} \qquad t \geq 0 \tag{7.34}$$

Service times that follow the negative exponential density are commonly found and widely assumed in applications of queueing theory.

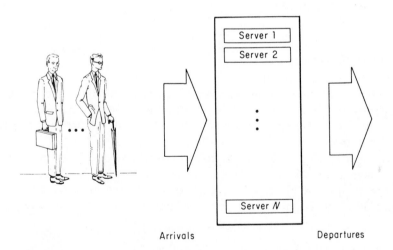

Arrivals — Server 1, Server 2, ⋮, Server N — Departures

Figure 7.7.

Another descriptor of the service process is the number of servers in the service facility and whether they are arranged in parallel as in Figure 7.7, or in series, or in tandem, as in Figure 7.8.

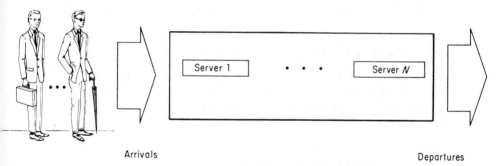

Arrivals   Departures

Figure 7.8.

Queue Discipline

The queue discipline is the manner in which customers form in a queue, the manner in which they behave while waiting, and the manner in which they are chosen for service. In this chapter we shall be concerned only with customers who are served in the order in which they arrive at the service facility. This is called a first come–first served discipline.

Although this chapter will be concerned only with a single discipline, it may be informative to discuss terms related to queue disciplines that are frequently seen in the literature:

Balking: This occurs when arriving customers elect not to join the queue. On occasion customers may balk because there is not sufficient waiting space.

Priorities: In certain applications some customers are served before others regardless of their order of arrival. These customers have priority over others. If the arrival of a customer causes the service to another to be interrupted, he is said to have a preemptive priority.

Reneging: This occurs when a waiting customer leaves the line.

Jockeying: Customers may jockey from one waiting line to another. We have all seen this occur in the supermarket.

Classification of Queues

Kendall [7] proposed a classification of queues that is receiving increased use. In his description the following are among the symbols used:

M—Poisson arrival process or exponential service times
G —No assumption made about service times
GI—General input: interarrival times are statistically independent and have some distribution function

We shall define other symbols as needed during the remainder of the text.
These symbols are then arranged to specify the queueing system as:

arrival process/service process/number of servers

For example, $M/M/1$ indicates a system with Poisson arrival process, exponential service times, and a single server in the service facility.

7.6   Single-Channel Queue: *M/M/1*

Consider a service facility with a single server whose service times follow a negative exponential density and where services are performed at a rate μ. The arrival process is a Poisson process and customers are served with a first come–first served discipline.

Recalling the properties of the Poisson arrival process and the service process with exponential service times, we know:

1. $P[\text{arrival in } \Delta t] = \lambda \Delta t + o(\Delta t)$.
2. $P[\text{service completion in } \Delta t] = \mu \Delta t + o(\Delta t)$.

It is clear that the stochastic process that we have formulated is a Markov process if we consider the conditional probability

$$p(n + 1; t + \Delta t \mid n; t, \ldots, n_1; t_1) = \lambda \Delta t(1 - \mu \Delta t) + o(\Delta t) \quad (7.35)$$

The term $o(\Delta t)$ includes terms corresponding to the past history of the process except for the immediately preceding state. If Δt is sufficiently small, these terms are negligible and the conditional probability depends only upon the immediately preceding state. We could develop similar arguments for $p(n - 1; t + \Delta t \mid n; t, \ldots, n_1; t_1)$ and $p(n; t + \Delta t \mid n; t, \ldots, n_1; t_1)$.

In this section our concern will be pointed toward finding the state probability distribution $p(n; t)$. Using the Chapman-Kolmogorov equation we can write

$$\begin{aligned}
p(n; t + \Delta t) = {} & p(n; t)(1 - \lambda \Delta t)(1 - \mu \Delta t) \\
& + p(n + 1; t)(1 - \lambda \Delta t)\mu \Delta t \\
& + p(n - 1; t)\lambda \Delta t(1 - \mu \Delta t) + o(\Delta t) \quad n \geq 1
\end{aligned}$$

The equation takes a slightly different form for $n = 0$; this case will be discussed later. Rearranging, subtracting $p(n; t)$ from both sides and dividing by Δt we find

$$\frac{p(n; t + dt) - p(n; t)}{\Delta t}$$

$$= -(\lambda + \mu)p(n; t) + \mu p(n + 1; t) + \lambda p(n - 1; t) + \frac{o(\Delta t)}{\Delta t} \quad n \geq 1$$

Taking the limit of both sides as $\Delta t \to 0$ we find the following differential-difference equation:

$$\frac{dp(n; t)}{dt} = -(\lambda + \mu)p(n; t) + \mu p(n + 1; t) + \lambda p(n - 1; t) \quad n \geq 1$$

$$(7.36)$$

We can find the boundary condition on the difference equation by considering the Chapman-Kolmogorov equation for $n = 0$:

$$p(0; t + \Delta t) = p(0; t)(1 - \lambda \Delta t) \cdot 1 + p(1; t)(1 - \lambda \Delta t)\mu \Delta t + o(\Delta t)$$

With algebra and taking the limit of both sides as $\Delta t \to 0$ we find

$$\frac{dp(0; t)}{dt} = -\lambda p(0; t) + \mu p(1; t)$$

We shall assume that at $t = 0$ there is no one waiting in line. That is, $p(0; 0) = 1$.

In Section 7.3 we noted that the solution of differential equations resulting from the Chapman-Kolmogorov equations had a steady state and a transient part. The steady-state portion is constant in time and the transient portion usually dies out as $t \to \infty$. We postponed a detailed discussion of the solution until the analysis of the queueing models. We should note that the differential-difference equations that have been derived for the single-channel queue are in fact describable by the vector differential equation (7.21). The solution to the differential-difference equation will have the form of equation (7.22). However, solution of the differential-difference equation directly is considerably easier and is usually used in the theory of queues whenever possible.

The solution to the differential-difference equation has the following form:

$$p(n; t) = p(n) + T(n; t)$$

$p(n)$ is the steady-state part. In the systems studied from this point on, $T(n; t)$ is the transient part that will die out, as $t \to \infty$. In the case of the single-channel queue, the derivation of the transient solution is beyond the scope of this book and will not be covered. However, we shall find the steady-state solution.

It can be shown (see Feller [8] for further discussion) that for the queueing systems describable as Markov processes in this text that the limits

$$\lim_{t \to \infty} p(n; t) = p(n)$$

exist and are independent of initial conditions. Furthermore, after letting $dp(n; t)/dt = 0$ and $p(n; t) = p(n)$ in equation (7.36) we may solve for the steady-state probability $p(n)$:

$$
\begin{aligned}
-(\lambda + \mu)p(n) + \mu p(n + 1) + \lambda p(n - 1) &= 0 \qquad n \geq 1 \\
-\lambda p(0) + \mu p(1) &= 0
\end{aligned}
\qquad (7.37)
$$

We will solve this linear homogeneous difference equation using z transforms. Taking the z transform of equation (7.37) and using the initial condition we find

$$P(z) = [(1 - z)(\mu - \lambda z)] - (1 - z)\mu p(0)$$

Rearranging and solving,

$$P(z) = \frac{p(0)}{1 - (\lambda/\mu)z} \tag{7.38}$$

Taking the inverse z transform we find

$$p(n) = \frac{\lambda^n}{\mu^n} p(0)$$

If we recall that

$$\sum_{n=0}^{\infty} p(n) = 1$$

then

$$\sum_{n=0}^{\infty} \frac{\lambda^n}{\mu^n} p(0) = 1$$

Solving,

$$p(0) = \frac{1}{\sum\limits_{n=0}^{\infty} \lambda^n/\mu^n}$$

If we recall that the series

$$\sum_{n=0}^{\infty} \frac{\lambda^n}{\mu^n} = \frac{1}{1 - \lambda/\mu} \qquad \lambda < \mu$$

we may easily verify that

$$p(0) = 1 - \lambda/\mu$$

We shall only consider cases where $\lambda < \mu$. Therefore,

$$p(n) = \frac{\lambda^n}{\mu^n} (1 - \lambda/\mu) \qquad n \geq 0 \tag{7.39}$$

Thus the steady-state probability distribution for the single-channel queue has the form of a geometric distribution with parameter λ/μ.

In many cases in the literature, we may observe the substitution $\rho = \lambda/\mu$, where ρ is called the *load factor* of the service system. With this notation

$$p(n) = \rho^n(1 - \rho) \qquad n \geq 0 \tag{7.40}$$

Note that we have only concerned ourselves with the case where the load factor $\rho = \lambda/\mu < 1$. Intuitively we assume that service is being performed at a faster rate than the rate of arrivals. We could show that this is comparable to assuming that a queue of infinite length will not occur.

7.7 Multiple-Channel Queue: *M/M/c*

In this section we consider a system with c servers in parallel using a first come–first served discipline. Service times for each server follow a negative exponential density with parameter μ. The arrival process is a Poisson process with parameter λ.

Using the same line of argument used in the case of a single-channel queue, we could show that the stochastic process that we have postulated is a Markov process. This is left to the reader as an exercise.

Using the Chapman-Kolmogorov equation we may express the state probability distribution as follows:

$$
\begin{aligned}
p(n; t + \Delta t) = {}& p(n; t)[1 - \lambda\,\Delta t][1 - n\mu\,\Delta t] \\
& + p(n - 1; t)[\lambda\,\Delta t][1 - (n - 1)\mu\,\Delta t] \\
& + p(n + 1; t)[1 - \lambda\,\Delta t][(n + 1)\mu\,\Delta t] + o(\Delta t) \\
& \hspace{6cm} 1 \le n < c \quad (7.41)
\end{aligned}
$$

Note that for $1 \le n < c$ the total service rate varies with the state of the system. However, when $n \ge c$ all c servers are busy and a waiting line forms. In this case we must express the state probability distribution in a different form:

$$
\begin{aligned}
p(n; t + \Delta t) = {}& p(n; t)[1 - \lambda\,\Delta t][1 - c\mu\,\Delta t] + p(n - 1; t)[\lambda\,\Delta t][1 - c\mu\,\Delta t] \\
& + p(n + 1; t)[1 - \lambda\,\Delta t][c\mu\,\Delta t] + o(\Delta t) \quad n \ge c \quad (7.42)
\end{aligned}
$$

Finally, the boundary condition, $n = 0$, may be expressed as

$$
p(0; t + \Delta t) = p(0; t)[1 - \lambda\,\Delta t] + p(1; t)[1 - \lambda\,\Delta t][\mu\,\Delta t] \quad (7.43)
$$

With algebra and taking the limit as $\Delta t \to 0$ we obtain the following differential-difference equations:

$$
\frac{dp(n; t)}{dt} = -(\lambda + n\mu)p(n; t) + \lambda p(n - 1; t) + (n + 1)\mu p(n + 1; t)
$$
$$
1 \le n < c
$$
$$
(7.44)
$$
$$
\frac{dp(n; t)}{dt} = -(\lambda + c\mu)p(n; t) + \lambda p(n - 1; t) + c\mu p(n + 1; t)
$$
$$
n \ge c
$$

$$
\frac{dp(0; t)}{dt} = -\lambda p(0; t) + \mu p(1; t)
$$

Analysis of the transient solution of these equations is beyond the scope of this text. We shall, however, determine the steady-state value $p(n)$. If we let $dp(n; t)/dt = 0$ and $p(n; t) = p(n)$ we obtain the following difference equations:

$$
\begin{aligned}
-(\lambda + n\mu)p(n) + \lambda p(n - 1) + (n + 1)\mu p(n + 1) &= 0 \quad & 1 \le n < c \\
-(\lambda + c\mu)p(n) + \lambda p(n - 1) - c\mu p(n + 1) &= 0 \quad & n \ge c \quad (7.45) \\
-\lambda p(0) + \mu p(1) &= 0 &
\end{aligned}
$$

Taking the z transform of these equations we find

$$-(\lambda + c\mu)P(z) + \lambda z P(z) + c\mu z^{-1}[P(z) - p(0)]$$
$$+ c\mu p(0) - (c - 1)\mu(1 - z)p(1) - (c - 2)\mu z(1 - z)p(2) - \cdots$$
$$- (c - n)\mu z^{n-1}(1 - z)p(n) - \cdots - \mu z^{c}(1 - z)p(c - 1) = 0$$

Multiplying both sides by z and collecting terms,

$$-(\lambda + c\mu)z p(z) + \lambda z^{2} P(z) + c\mu P(z) - \mu(1 - z)\sum_{n=0}^{c-1}(c - n)p(n)z^{n} = 0$$

Solving we find

$$P(z) = \frac{\mu(1 - z)\sum_{n=0}^{c-1}(c - n)p(n)z^{n}}{\lambda z^{2} - (\lambda + c\mu)z + c\mu} \tag{7.46}$$

Determination of the inverse transformation is beyond the scope of this text. The inverse z transform yields

$$p(n) = \frac{p(0)}{n!}\left(\frac{\lambda}{\mu}\right)^{n} \qquad 1 \le n < c$$

$$= \frac{p(0)}{c!}\left(\frac{\lambda}{c\mu}\right)^{n}c^{c} \qquad n \ge c \tag{7.47}$$

where

$$p(0) = \frac{1}{\sum_{n=0}^{c-1}\frac{c\lambda^{n}}{\mu}\Big/n! + \frac{c\lambda^{c}}{\mu}\Big/c!\left(1 - \frac{\lambda}{\mu}\right)} \tag{7.48}$$

7.8 Infinite-Channel Queue: $M/M/\infty$

We turn to a service facility with enough servers to serve all customers who arrive: an infinite number of servers. Each server has a negative exponential service time density and he performs service at a rate μ. The arrival process is a Poisson process, with rate λ, and customers are served with a first come–first served discipline. By constructing the transition probabilities we could easily show that this process is a Markov process. This verification is left as an exercise for the reader.

Using the Chapman-Kolmogorov equation we may write the following expression for the state probability distribution:

$$p(n; t + \Delta t) = p(n; t)[1 - \lambda \Delta t][1 - n\mu \Delta t]$$
$$+ p(n - 1; t)[\lambda \Delta t][1 - (n - 1)\mu \Delta t]$$
$$+ p(n + 1; t)[1 - \lambda \Delta t][(n + 1)\mu \Delta t] + o(\Delta t)$$
$$n \ge 1 \tag{7.49}$$

With algebra and taking the limit of both sides as $\Delta t \to 0$ we find

$$\frac{dp(n; t)}{dt} = -(\lambda + n\mu)p(n; t) + \lambda p(n - 1; t) + (n + 1)\mu p(n + 1; t)$$

$$n \geq 1 \qquad (7.50)$$

Using the Chapman-Kolmogorov equation for the case $n = 0$, it is easy to show

$$\frac{dp(0; t)}{dt} = -\lambda p(0; t) + \mu p(1; t) \qquad (7.51)$$

Once again we have generated a differential-difference equation with boundary conditions specified by equation (7.51) and $p(0; 0)$. In the case of the systems studied in Sections 7.6 and 7.7, the transient solution of the differential-difference equation was beyond the scope of this text. In the current system, we shall attempt to find the transient solution $p(n; t)$.

If we take the z transform of equation (7.50) we find the following partial differential equation:

$$\frac{\partial P(z, t)}{\partial t} = \mu(1 - z)\frac{\partial P(z, t)}{\partial z} - \lambda(1 - z)P(z, t) \qquad (7.52)$$

At this point we shall solve the equation directly without the use of the Laplace transform. It can be shown that a sufficient condition for $P(z, t)$ to satisfy equation (7.52) is that the following equations hold:

$$\frac{dt}{1} = \frac{dz}{-\mu(1 - z)} = \frac{dP(z, t)}{-\lambda(1 - z)P(z, t)} \qquad (7.53)$$

These equations are called the *Lagrange equations*. The problem of solving the partial differential equation has been reduced to solving the simultaneous ordinary equations given in (7.53).

The first equation we shall solve is

$$dt = \frac{dz}{-\mu(1 - z)} \qquad (7.54)$$

This equation is called *separable* and is quite easy to solve. We shall ask the reader to show as an exercise the solution

$$z = 1 - c_1 e^{-\mu t} \qquad (7.55)$$

where c_1 is some constant to be determined.

We shall now solve the second equation

$$\frac{dz}{-\mu(1 - z)} = \frac{dP(z, t)}{-\lambda(1 - z)P(z, t)} \qquad (7.56)$$

Once again the reader may show as an exercise that

$$P(z, t) = c_2 e^{\lambda z/\mu} \qquad (7.57)$$

where c_2 is a constant to be determined.

If we observe equation (7.55) at $t = 0$ we find

$$c_1 = 1 - z \tag{7.58}$$

Observing equation (7.57) at $t = 0$ we find

$$P(z, 0) = c_2 e^{\lambda z/\mu} \tag{7.59}$$

Note that $P(z, 0)$ is the z transform of $p(n; 0)$ or the initial state vector. If there are i people in the system at $t = 0$,

$$p(n; 0) = \begin{cases} 1 & n = 1 \\ 0 & n \neq 1 \end{cases}$$

In this case $P(z; 0) = z^i$, and

$$P(z; 0) = c_2 e^{\lambda z/\mu} = z^i \tag{7.60}$$

Using equation (7.58),

$$(1 - c_1 e^{-\mu t})^i = c_2 e^{(\lambda/\mu)(1 - c_1)} \tag{7.61}$$

Substituting equations (7.55), (7.58), and (7.60) into this equation we find

$$[1 - (1 - z)e^{-\mu t}]^i = P(z, t)e^{\lambda/\mu(1 - z)(1 - e^{-\mu t})} \tag{7.62}$$

Rearranging and solving,

$$P(z, t) = [1 - (1 - z)e^{-\mu t}]^i e^{-\lambda/\mu(1 - z)(1 - e^{-\mu t})} \tag{7.63}$$

This is the z transform of the state probability distribution if $n = i$ at $t = 0$. As a special case, consider $n = i = 0$:

$$P(z, t) = e^{-\lambda/\mu(1 - z)(1 - e^{-\mu t})} \tag{7.64}$$

Recall the form of z transform for the Poisson distribution (see, for example, Saaty [3])

$$P(z) = e^{-A(1 - z)}$$

If we let $A = \lambda/\mu(1 - e^{-\mu t})$, equation (7.64) has the form of the z transform of the Poisson distribution. Taking the inverse transform we find

$$p(n; t) = \frac{[\lambda/\mu(1 - e^{-\mu t})]^n e^{-\lambda/\mu(1 - e^{-\mu t})}}{n!} \tag{7.65}$$

Note that this is the state probability distribution for any time t and is called the transient solution of the differential-difference equation. We may find the steady-state solution by

$$\lim_{t \to \infty} p(n; t) = \frac{(\lambda/\mu)^n e^{-\lambda/\mu}}{n!} \tag{7.66}$$

which is also the Poisson distribution.

It may be helpful in understanding the nature of transient solutions to consider some examples of equation (7.65). Figure 7.9 displays the transient expressions $p(0; t)$ and $p(1; t)$ as functions of time for the infinite channel queue. These probabilities are plotted for $\lambda = 2$ and $\mu = 1$. Note the point at which the probabilities are constant. This is the steady-state portion of equation (7.65). These values may be found using equation (7.66).

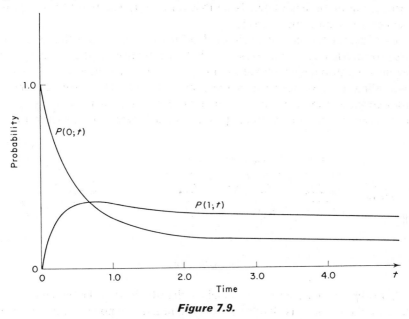

Figure 7.9.

7.9   Non-Markovian Queues

This section is concerned with selected types of service systems in which the state of the system is not a Markov process. A major portion of our effort will be concentrated on the simulation of these cases with a system whose state is a Markov process.

Arrival Distribution

Our discussion of queues up to this time has been concerned with systems where interarrival times follow a negative exponential density. Suppose we have a service system where the probability density of interarrival times is the k-Erlang density:

$$a(\tau) = k\lambda(k\lambda\tau)^{k-1}e^{-k\lambda\tau}/(k-1)! \qquad (7.67)$$

Recall that in Section 7.3 we have shown a necessary condition for a stochastic process to be a Markov process is that the probability density of time intervals between first transition from state i to state j, given the process is in state i, is a negative exponential density. Noting that equation (7.67) is the probability density of first transition from state i to state $i + 1$, the process is clearly not a Markov process, except when $k = 1$.

The mean time interval between arrivals in this case is $1/\lambda$, the same as the case of Poisson arrivals. However, the variance of the k-Erlang is $1/k\lambda^2$, which is less than the variance of the negative exponential density $1/\lambda$ for $k \geq 2$. The variance grows small as k becomes larger. We shall discuss this property in more detail later. Note that for $k = 1$, equation (7.67) becomes the negative exponential density.

Consider the service system pictured in Figure 7.10. Suppose that customers are provided from an infinite reservoir but, in order to enter the service system, we must go through an arrival timing channel with k phases. Customers are only allowed to go forward in the timing channel. Only one customer is allowed in the timing channel at one time. However, when one leaves phase 1 we assume that another enters phase k immediately from the reservoir.

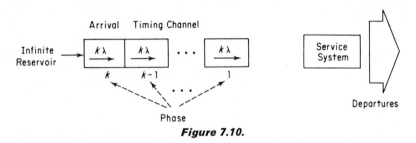

Figure 7.10.

Let τ_i be the time a customer spends in the ith phase of the timing channel. Assume the probability density of τ_i is the negative exponential density with parameter $k\lambda$.

$$a(\tau_i) = k\lambda e^{-k\lambda\tau_i} \tag{7.68}$$

This means that the rate of transition out of each phase is equal to $k\lambda$.

Let

$$\tau = \sum_{i=1}^{k} \tau_i$$

The Laplace transform of equation (7.68) is

$$A_i(s) = \frac{k\lambda}{s + k\lambda} \tag{7.69}$$

Therefore the Laplace transform of the probability density of τ is

$$A(s) = \prod_{i=1}^{k} A_i(s)$$

$$= \frac{(k\lambda)^k}{(s + k\lambda)^k} \tag{7.70}$$

We can easily verify that the inverse transformation yields equation (7.67). Hence the system we have postulated is one in which the interarrival times into the service system follow the k-Erlang density.

An example will serve to illustrate that the state of the postulated system is a Markov process and simulates the state of a non-Markov process. Consider a single exponential service channel with parameter μ, where interarrival times follow a k-Erlang density. Using Kendall's notation this system is described as $E_k/M/1$. Furthermore, suppose there is no waiting space in this system. When the single server is busy, the customers overflow and are lost.

The state of the system can be represented by two integers. The first indicates the phase that the next unit to arrive is in $(1, \ldots, k)$ as it flows through the timing channel. The second integer may have values 0, indicating the service channel is empty, or 1, indicating the channel is filled.

Consider the probability

$$p(r, 0; t + \Delta t \mid r - 1, 0; t) = k\lambda \, \Delta t + o(\Delta t)$$

We see that the conditional transition probabilities depend only on the immediately preceding state of the system. Hence the process generated by the system with a k-phase timing channel is a Markov process.

With the definitions above we may write the following Chapman-Kolmogorov equation:

$$p(r, 0; t + \Delta t) = p(r - 1, 0; t)k\lambda \, \Delta t + p(r, 1; t)\mu \, \Delta t(1 - k\lambda \, \Delta t) + o(\Delta t)$$
$$1 \le r < k$$

With algebra and making appropriate substitutions for steady-state solution, we obtain the following difference equation:

$$k\lambda p(r - 1, 0) + \mu p(r, 1) - k\lambda p(r, 0) = 0 \qquad 1 \le r < k \qquad (7.71)$$

The boundary condition for the state $(k, 0)$ is expressed in the following equation:

$$\mu p(k, 1) - k\lambda p(k, 0) = 0 \qquad\qquad (7.72)$$

We now consider equations describing the service channel when busy. Using the Chapman-Kolmogorov equation,

$$p(r, 1; t + \Delta t) = p(r - 1, 1; t)k\lambda \, \Delta t$$
$$+ \, p(r, 1; t)(1 - k\lambda \, \Delta t)(1 - \mu \, \Delta t) + o(\Delta t) \qquad 1 \le r < k$$

Using the usual procedure we find the following difference equation for finding the steady-state solution:

$$k\lambda p(r - 1, 1) - (\mu + k\lambda)p(r, 1) = 0 \qquad 1 \le r < k \qquad (7.73)$$

The boundary equation for state $(k, 1)$ is as follows:

$$k\lambda p(1; 0) + k\lambda p(1, 1) - (\mu + k\lambda)p(k, 1) = 0 \qquad\qquad (7.74)$$

Solutions of equations (7.71) and (7.72) give us $p(r, 0)$ and solution of equations (7.73) and (7.74) give $p(r, 1)$. Now note the form of the marginal probabilities:

$$p(0) = \sum_{r=1}^{k} p(r, 0)$$

This indicates that as long as the customer is in the timing channel he still is not viewed as having arrived until he leaves the channel. Similarly,

$$p(1) = \sum_{r=1}^{k} p(r, 1)$$

These solutions are left as an exercise. We shall simply state the results:

$$p(1) = \rho \left[1 - \left(1 + \frac{1}{k\rho} \right)^{-k} \right]$$
$$p(0) = 1 - p(1)$$

(7.75)

where $\rho = \lambda/\mu$, the load factor.

We have simulated a non-Markovian system with a Markov process. This simulation has allowed us to get the steady-state result given in equation (7.73) through the use of the theory of Markov processes. Extensions of this approach to arrival distributions will not be covered further. However, the problems at the end of the chapter contain several extensions.

It is also interesting to note the limiting form of the Erlang density. Consider the limit of its Laplace transform:

$$\lim_{k \to \infty} \frac{(k\lambda)^k}{(s + k\lambda)^k} = \lim_{k \to \infty} \frac{1}{(1 + s/k\lambda)^k} = e^{s/k\lambda}$$

(7.76)

This has the form of the Laplace transform of the normal density with mean $1/k\lambda$ and variance zero. This is the equivalent of regularly spaced, or scheduled, arrivals arriving every $1/k\lambda$ time units. Hence we see the limiting form of an Erlang arrival process is a deterministic process. In Kendall's notation, this type of process is identified with a D.

Service Distribution

To indicate how another type of non-Markovian system might be handled, we shall consider the effect of a non-exponential probability density for service times. Suppose we have a system with a Poisson arrival process, where the service times for each server follow the hyperexponential density:

$$s(t) = \alpha^2 \mu e^{-2\alpha\mu t} + (1 - \alpha)^2 \mu e^{-2(1 - \sigma)\mu t} \qquad 0 < 2\alpha < 1 \qquad (7.77)$$

This density still has the same mean service time, $1/\mu$, but has a variance

$$\text{var} (t) = \frac{1 - 2\alpha - 2\alpha^2}{\mu^2 (2\alpha - 2\alpha^2)}$$

which is larger than the variance for the negative exponential density, $1/\mu^2$.

Once again we recall the necessary condition for a stochastic process to be a Markov process: The probability density of time intervals between first transition from state i to state j, given the process is in state i, is a negative exponential density. Upon reflection of this condition, the state of the system under study is clearly not a Markov process. We shall simulate this non-Markov process with an expanded definition of the service system.

Consider a server where customers waiting for service enter either one of two parallel service channels, as shown in Figure 7.11. The customer goes to the branch serving at rate $2\alpha\mu$, a fraction α of the time. He goes to the

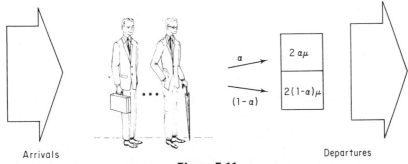

Arrivals   Departures

Figure 7.11.

branch serving at rate $2(1 - \alpha)\mu$ a fraction $1 - \alpha$ of the time. Service times for both branches follow the negative exponential density. The probability density for the total service process is the mixed exponential, or hyperexponential density, given by equation (7.77).

We will use an example [9] to show how this simulated service process generates a Markov process. Assume we are concerned with a single-channel service system with a Poisson arrival process, with parameter λ, a hyperexponential service process and a first come–first served discipline: $M/HE_2/1$. Furthermore, assume that no queue is allowed. That is, when the service channel is busy arrivals overflow and are lost.

We will define the following three states:

State	Condition
0	No unit, service channel idle
1_1	Unit undergoing service at rate 2α
1_2	Unit undergoing service at rate $2(1 - \alpha)$

With these definitions we may write the following Chapman-Kolmogorov equations:

$$p(0; t + \Delta t) = p(0; t)(1 - \lambda\,\Delta t)\cdot 1$$
$$+ \, p(1_1; t)(1 - \lambda\,\Delta t)2\alpha\mu\,\Delta t$$
$$+ \, p(1_2; t)(1 - \lambda\,\Delta t)2(1 - \alpha)\mu\,\Delta t + o(\Delta t) \quad (7.78)$$

$$p(1_1; t + \Delta t) = p(1_1; t)(1 - \alpha\lambda\,\Delta t)(1 - 2\alpha\mu\,\Delta t)$$
$$+ p(0; t)(\alpha\lambda\,\Delta t)\cdot 1 \qquad\qquad + o(\Delta t) \quad (7.79)$$

$$p(1_2; t + \Delta t) = p(1_2; t)[1 - \alpha\lambda\,\Delta t][1 - 2(1 - \alpha)\mu\,\Delta t]$$
$$+ p(0; t)[(1 - \alpha)\lambda\,\Delta t]\cdot 1 \qquad + o(\Delta t) \quad (7.80)$$

With algebra and taking the limit as $\Delta t \rightarrow 0$ we may generate three simultaneous differential equations. In the steady state, the resulting algebraic equations may be solved simultaneously to obtain

$$p(0) = \frac{1}{1 + \lambda/\mu} \tag{7.81}$$

$$p(1_1) = p(1_2) = \frac{\lambda/\mu}{2(1 + \lambda/\mu)} \tag{7.82}$$

Thus the steady-state solutions have been obtained through simulation of the stochastic process by a Markov process. This simulation has allowed us to take advantage of our knowledge of the Markov process during the analysis of these non-Markovian systems.

Other more complicated systems are not as easily analyzed and in general may not be simulated as Markov processes. The analysis of these systems is beyond the scope of this text. The interested reader should read an advanced text on queueing theory such as Prabbu [10].

7.10   Waiting Times

The theory of queues includes the analysis of many measures of effectiveness other than the state probability distribution for the service system. Although this distribution is usually of more frequent concern, other properties, such as the busy period, the number in queue, and the waiting time in the queue may be of interest. The customer waiting time seems to be of frequent interest and, for this reason, will be covered here. For analysis of other properties the reader is referred to the problems at the end of the chapter and to references [1, 2, 3, 4, 6, and 10].

Single-Channel Queue: M/M/1

The mode of analysis of the waiting times for service systems varies with the system. One of the less complex of these is the single-channel queue, $M/M/1$, which was discussed in Section 7.6. We wish to find the probability density of the time t that an arriving customer must wait for service.

Suppose that a customer arriving at this service system finds n people in the system, including the one being served. There are $n - 1$ customers waiting in line. The total time t that the arriving customer must wait is given by

$$t = t_1' + t_2 + \cdots + t_{n-1} + t_n$$

where $t_2, t_3, \ldots, t_n$ are the identically and independently $n \geq 1$ distributed negative exponential service times of the single server. t_1' is the period between the arrival of the $(n + 1)$st customer and the completion of service for the customer that was found in the service channel. The problems at the end of the chapter indicate that this residual service t_1' has the same probability density as the remaining service times. Therefore, t is the summation of n random variables following the negative exponential density.

Define $w(t)$ as the probability density of the waiting time t and $W(s)$ as its Laplace transform. Recall the Laplace transform of the negative exponential density:

$$W_i(s) = \frac{\mu}{s + \mu} \tag{7.83}$$

Therefore,

$$W(s) = \prod_{i=1}^{n} W_i(s)$$

$$= \frac{\mu^n}{(s + \mu)^n} \qquad n \geq 1 \tag{7.84}$$

Taking the inverse transform we find

$$w(t) = \frac{\mu(\mu t)^{n-1}e^{-\mu t}}{(n - 1)!} \qquad n \geq 1 \tag{7.85}$$

The case $n = 0$ will be discussed later.

Equation (7.85) has the form of the gamma probability density. We should note that this expression is conditioned on the fact that there are n customers in the system at the time of arrival of the $(n + 1)$st customer. In Section 7.6 we found that the random variable n followed, in the steady state, the geometric distribution

$$p(n) = \rho^n(1 - \rho) \qquad n \geq 0$$

To obtain a generalized waiting time density we must average equation (7.85) over all values of $n \geq 1$:

$$w(t) = \sum_{n=1}^{\infty} \frac{\mu(\mu t)^{n-1}e^{-\mu t}}{(n - 1)!} \rho^n(1 - \rho) \qquad \rho = \lambda/\mu$$

$$= \mu(1 - \rho)\rho e^{-\mu t} \sum_{n-1=0}^{\infty} \frac{\rho^{n-1}(\mu t)^{n-1}}{(n - 1)!}$$

$$= \rho(1 - \rho)\mu e^{-\mu t(1 - \rho)} \qquad t > 0 \tag{7.86}$$

The case for $t = 0$ corresponds to the occasion when $n = 0$; thus this density has a discontinuity at zero with[3]

$$W(0+) = (1 - \rho) \tag{7.87}$$

In summary,

$$W(t) = 1 - \rho \qquad\qquad t = 0$$
$$= \rho(1 - \rho)\mu e^{-\mu t(1-\rho)} \qquad t > 0 \tag{7.88}$$

We should note that this analysis is not as easy for the systems $M/M/c$ and $M/M/\infty$. In these systems the probability density of the times between successive service completions for the *total* system is needed.

Problems

1. Consider the stochastic process $X(t) = a + bt$, $t \geq 0$, where a and b are uniformly distributed independent random variables where $0 \leq a, b \leq 1$. Find the ensemble average and the covariance of the process.

2. Find the ensemble mean and covariance of a Poisson process $X(t)$, $t \geq 0$, with parameter λ.

3. Is the Poisson process a stationary process? Why?

4. Let $X(t)$, $t \geq 0$, be a Poisson process with parameter λ. Let k be a positive constant. Show that the process

$$Y(t) = X(t + k) - X(t)$$

is covariance stationary.

5. Consider the stochastic process

$$X(t) = a \sin t + b \cos t$$

where a and b are independent random variables with zero means and equal variances. Show the process is covariance stationary.

6. Is the stochastic process in Problem 5 ergodic? Why?

7. Derive the probability distribution of time intervals between transitions in a Markov chain.

8. Find the transient state probability distribution for a general two-state Markov chain with the following transition matrix. Assume an arbitrary initial state vector.

$$\pi = \begin{bmatrix} p & q \\ q & p \end{bmatrix}$$

9. Use the results of Problem 7 to conjecture how one might analyze simple discrete-time queues.

---

[3] There is a discontinuity at $t = 0$.

10. Consider a Markov chain with the transition matrix shown below:

$$\pi = \begin{bmatrix} 0.6 & 0.4 & 0 & 0 & 0 \\ 0 & 0 & 0.5 & 0.5 & 0 \\ 0.3 & 0.2 & 0.5 & 0 & 0 \\ 0.2 & 0 & 0 & 0.1 & 0.7 \\ 0.6 & 0 & 0 & 0.4 & 0 \end{bmatrix}$$

If the system is initially in state 1 find the steady-state probability of the system being in state 4.

11. Find the transient solution for a state probability distribution of a Markov process whose differential rate matrix is

$$\mathbf{A} = \begin{bmatrix} -\lambda & \lambda \\ \mu & -\mu \end{bmatrix}$$

Assume $\mathbf{P}(0) = (1, 0)$.

12. Consider a service facility with three parallel channels where service times for each channel follow a negative exponential density with parameter μ. The arrival process is a Poisson process with parameter λ. Derive all steady-state probabilities.

13. At a particular large airport there is a limousine service that has an automobile leaving the central depot every 15 minutes. Assuming that people arriving at the limousine depot follow a Poisson process with a mean arrival rate of eight people per hour and the capacity of each limousine is six persons:

(a) What is the probability that the limousine will leave no passengers?
(b) What is the probability that the limousine will leave with six persons?

14. A navigation lock has the capability of passing two tows every hour. The arrival process at the lock is Poisson with the average arrival rate being one per hour.

(a) What is the probability there will be three tows in the queue?
(b) What is the probability a tow will have to wait?

15. A gas station has two multiple-purpose pumps. Service times follow a negative exponential density with mean 4 minutes. Cars arrive in a Poisson arrival process at the rate of 10 per hour.

(a) What is the probability of having to wait for service?
(b) What is the average percentage idle time of the pumps?

16. Consider a service system with a Poisson arrival process, exponential service times for each server, and a first come–first served discipline. There are two parallel servers with no upper bound on queue length. Only one channel is attended until the number in the system reaches five, at which time the second channel is opened. When the number in the system drops to four the second channel is closed.

(a) Derive the differential-difference equation that describes the state probability distribution of this system.
(b) Find the steady-state solution.
(c) Show that the number of customers in the service system is a Markov process.
(d) How may the transient solution be found?
(e) Using a graph, conjecture a form for $p(3; t)$. Show where the steady-state solution may be used to approximate $p(3; t)$.

17. (a) Consider a set of M machines serviced by r repairmen. The time intervals between breakdowns for each machine follow a negative exponential density with parameter λ. The service times for each repairman follow a negative exponential density with parameter μ. Machines are serviced in the order in which they break down. Find the steady-state probability distribution of n machines being out of service in terms of $p(0)$ and the parameters for the system.
    (b) Is the stochastic process generated by this system a Markov process? Why?
    (c) Conjecture the form of $p(1; t)$ by drawing a graph. At what point would the steady-state probability found in (a) be a reasonable approximation for $p(1; t)$?

18. (a) Consider a self-service discount store where all the customers join a single line to pay for their merchandise at a single cash register. Assume that the arrival process is Poisson and the service time follows a negative exponential density. On the average, 9 customers arrive every 5 minutes and the cashier serves, on the average, 10 customers every 5 minutes.

    1. What is the average number of customers waiting for service?
    2. What is the average number of persons in the system?
    3. What is the average waiting time of a customer?
    4. What is the average time a customer spends in the system?
    5. Derive an expression for the expected number of arrivals during the first hour of operation.

    (b) If the store manager decides to add a second cash register to serve the queue and this new cashier has the same service rate as the other, what are 1, 2, 3, and 4 above? Give reference texts used in solution of this part.
    (c) Instead of adding a second register, would it have been better to just hire a new cashier who worked twice as fast as the original cashier? Base your decision upon 1, 2, 3, and 4.

19. Consider a Poisson arrival process. Suppose we start collecting data at $t = 0$ in an effort to estimate the parameter λ of the interarrival time density.

    (a) Can we use the time between $t = 0$ and the first arrival to estimate this density? Why?
    (b) Suppose we start collecting data between any two arrivals. Can the time until the first arrival be used to estimate λ? Why?

References Cited and Bibliography

[1] Morse, P. M. *Queues, Inventories and Maintenance.* New York: Wiley, 1958.

[2] Cox, D. R., and W. Smith. *Queues.* London: Methuen, 1961.

[3] Saaty, T. L. *Queueing Theory.* New York: McGraw-Hill, 1961.

[4] Parzen, E. *Stochastic Processes.* San Francisco: Holden-Day, 1962.

[5] Feller, W. *An Introduction to Probability Theory and Its Application*, Vol. II. New York: Wiley, 1966.

[6] Takacs, L. *Stochastic Processes.* London: Methuen, 1960.

[7] Kendall, D. G. "Stochastic Processes in the Theory of Queues and Their Analysis by the Method of the Imbedded Markov Chains." *Ann. Math. Statist.*, Vol. 24 (1953).

[8] Feller, W. *An Introduction to Probability Theory and Its Applications*, Vol. I. New York: Wiley, 1957.

[9] Morse, P. M. "Dynamics of Operational Systems." In (R. L. Ackoff, ed.), *Progress in Operations Research.* Vol. 1. New York: Wiley, 1963.

[10] Prabbu, N. V. *Queues and Inventories.* New York: Wiley, 1965.

CHAPTER 8

Decisions and Games

8.1 Decision Process

The discussion of the decision process contained in Chapter 1 identified certain basic properties and definitions related to decision making. These definitions were accomplished through the use of examples. This chapter contains a more explicit discussion of mathematical models of decision problems.

Before developing additional mathematical models it will be of value to review the basic components of a decision problem:

1. A *decision-maker*. Someone or some group must be identified as the decision-maker. Certain classes of problems may have two or more decision-makers.
2. *Objectives*. The decision-maker must have one or more objectives. These objectives may be defined as desired outcomes of his decision. In the case of multiple objectives some may conflict [4].

    Objectives may be viewed as being either qualitative or quantitative. An example of a qualitative objective would be a football team's desire to win a football game. We have all probably used the quantitative objective of maximizing profit or minimizing cost. We shall only be concerned with quantitative objectives. For further discussion of the analysis of qualitative objectives see Ackoff [2].
3. *Alternative courses of action*. The decision-maker must have two or more alternatives, or courses of action, from which to choose. In many decision problems there are an infinity of courses of action.

    A *strategy* has been loosely defined as a rule for decision making.

We shall assume that when the decision-maker decides to choose course of action a_i, this action actually occurs.

There are problems when the decision-maker does not have complete control over the actions he chooses. In both cases when a decision-maker decides on a single action as his strategy this is called a *pure strategy*. A *mixed strategy* occurs when the decision-maker decides to choose any one of several actions with some random selection procedure.

4. A *measure of effectiveness*. The decision-maker must have some measure of the level of attainment of his objectives for each course of action. Implicit in these definitions is the assumption that for a problem to exist this measure cannot be the same for all alternatives.

It is important to note that the environment in which the decision problem exists must be recognized. This is the total system concept discussed in Chapter 1. A more detailed discussion of the components of decision problems may be found in Chapter 5 of Churchman, Ackoff, and Arnoff [1] or in Ackoff [2].

Luce and Raiffa [3] indicate that "decision making is commonly partitioned according to whether a decision is made by (i) an individual or (ii) a group, and according to whether it is effected under conditions of (a) certainty (b) risk, or (c) uncertainty. To this last classification we really must add (d) a combination of uncertainty and risk in the light of experimental evidence. This is the province of statistical inference." This text will only be concerned with decision making by individuals. Those interested in group decision making should consult Luce and Raiffa [3] for additional discussion.

Decision making under certainty occurs when we are able to ascertain with certainty which outcome (possibly among several) will occur if a specific course of action is taken. In this case there are no random variables, either controllable or uncontrollable. The second kind of decision problem occurs where each action leads to any one of several outcomes. In this case each outcome may occur with a *known* probability. This is called *decision making under risk*. If each alternative action leads to any one of several outcomes when the outcomes occur with *unknown* probabilities, we are in the realm of *decision making under uncertainty*. In the following pages we shall discuss each class of decision problem in greater detail, define a mathematical notation for each, and cover alternative approaches for solution.

8.2   Decision Making under Certainty

Consider the case where we have one objective, O_1, and a finite number of alternative actions $a_1, \ldots, a_R$. For each of these actions we know with certainty the level of attainment or the outcome relative to O_1. In this situation we choose that action that comes closest to satisfying O_1. The more interesting case occurs where there are two or more conflicting objectives. The inventory problem of Chapter 1 is such a problem. It will be useful to redefine this problem in a decision theoretic framework.

The elements of Table 1.1 were called measures of efficiency. The numbers given in the table are the specific outcomes that result when choosing the various courses of action. These outcomes are known with certainty.

The numbers shown in Table 1.1 are specific values of what we call outcome variables. We found in Chapter 1 that

$$z_1 = \frac{q-1}{2} = \text{average inventory}$$

$$z_2 = \frac{r}{q} = \text{orders per month}$$

These are the outcome variables expressed as a function of the controllable variable q. One or more *outcome*, or *state*, *variables* express the level of attainment for each objective. The *control*, or *controllable*, *variables* represent those factors which may be manipulated, or controlled, by the decision-maker. In the inventory example, any action a_i corresponds to a pair of values of the outcome variables. In general, a_i corresponds to a consequent Q-tuple of values for the outcome variables. These will be denoted by a Q-component vector z.

At this stage in Chapter 1 we discussed the formulation of a measure of effectiveness for the inventory problem. We now turn to the more general subject of the construction of values.

Values

To complete the decision problem we must determine the value to the decision-maker of each action, $V(a_i) = V(z_1, z_2, \ldots, z_Q)$. This latter term is the value of the Q-tuple of outcomes associated with each action a_i, $i = 1, \ldots, R$. This is a more general definition of the measure of effectiveness discussed in Chapter 1.

In many situations it may be intuitively satisfying to say that

$$V(z_1, z_2, \ldots, z_Q) = V(z_1) + V(z_2) + \cdots + V(z_Q) \tag{8.1}$$

This relation requires an assumption of *valuewise independence* that is commonly ignored in the literature. We shall make such an assumption in this chapter. The reader desiring a more extensive discussion of the concept should see Fishburn [5]. Throughout our discussion, we shall usually assume some form of the value functions $V(z_i)$, $i = 1, \ldots, Q$. Note that in the inventory example we assumed

$$V(z_1) = c_1 z_1 = c_1 \frac{(q-1)}{2}$$

$$V(z_2) = c_2 z_2 = c_2 \frac{r}{q}$$

where c_1, c_2, and r are constants.

In most references to be found in the literature the words value and utility are used in the same context. Savage [7] defines *utility* as a function that quantifies the relation of preference among several courses of action. This definition is consistent with our own discussion of value. It is also similar to the definition used by von Neumann and Morgenstern [8] in their revival of modern utility theory. It may be of some benefit for us to briefly discuss the modern concept of utility, denoting deviations from this definition when they occur.

Early mathematical studies of probability were concerned mainly with gambling. In particular, they were concerned with the question of which of several available cash gambles is the most advantageous. It was the notion of early probabilists that the gamble with the highest expected winnings is best. In essence, they felt that wealth could be measured in dollars. This was called the principle of mathematical expectation.

Daniel Bernoulli was one of the first to develop an idea of utility as we have defined it [9]. He suggested that maximization of utility is a better criterion for decision than maximization of expected winnings. Prior to the time of Bernoulli, the principle of mathematical expectation had dominated theory of behavior in the face of risk and uncertainty. There are many examples indicating this theory is not applicable. The following is one that Bernoulli offered: "To justify these remarks, let us suppose a pauper happens to acquire a lottery ticket by which he may with equal probability win either nothing or 20,000 ducats. Will he have to evaluate the ticket as 10,000 ducats; and would he be acting foolishly, if he sold it for 9,000 ducats?"

Bernoulli claimed that a dollar that might be worthless to a millionaire would be precious to a pauper. This type of reasoning is an example of what is called the law of *diminishing marginal utility*.

Notice that the discussion of utility up to this point has been without reference of any kind to probability. Savage calls this era the period of "probability-less" utility [7]. The feeling among economists during this time was that among the available consequences a person prefers those that have the highest utility for him. Today, the probability-less concept of utility has been discredited in the eyes of most economists. The details of the controversy will not be covered here. They have had a full treatment by Stigler [9].

If there is a point in time to mark the transition from the classical economist's definition to the concept of utility from the view of modern decision theory it must be the appearance of the von Neumann–Morgenstern theory of utility [8]. Their theory indicated that having adopted any theory of probability, the existence of a function whose expected value controls choice may be deduced. This was the bone of contention—the idea of maximizing utility. As a theory of economic behavior, the maximization of utility is not to be viewed as a theory that cannot be overthrown. However, it has provided considerable insight into individual economic behavior.

Given some theory of utility that satisfies our intuition, we might wonder how we find these numbers called utilities. In many cases utility is expressed in a functional relationship by a curve. For example, an individual has a utility curve for money expressed over some range. The question is, how is this curve found?

Many experimental techniques for measuring utilities have been developed and tested. Articles on this subject may be found in journals related to economics, psychology, sociology, philosophy, and operations research. Despite this preponderance of attention given to quantification of utility, one of the main obstacles to wider application of modern decision theory is the lack of adequate value measurements. For some interesting comments on this subject the reader should see Bross [10].

In practice, the most frequently seen measure of value in the literature is dollars. A utility function that is a linear function of the outcome variable is usually implicitly assumed. As an example, consider the case of Mr. Jones, who has been very careful in providing for the future needs of his family. He estimates that in the next twenty years he will need $8000 in liquid assets to finance his children's education. At the moment he has accumulated $5000, but the prospect of additional saving is not good.

On a certain afternoon he is contacted by a real estate broker who offers him the following investment opportunity. He may invest $5000 in un- developed land that will be worth $8000 in the very near future. However, if for some reason the city planners should decide not to develop this particu- lar area the land will be devalued to only $1000. It is estimated that the probability that the area will be developed is 0.5.

If Mr. Jones makes the investment his expected assets are 0.5($8000) + 0.5($1000) = $4500. It seems likely that he would not choose to make the investment since his expected assets would be less than the $5000 he already has. Suppose that Mr. Jones' utility for dollars is shown in the graph of Figure 8.1. This graph reflects the fact that his utility is not related to dol- lars by some linear relationship. The expected utility of the investment is 0.5(0.01) + 0.5(1.0) = 0.505. The $-V(\$5000) = 0.3$. In this case Mr. Jones

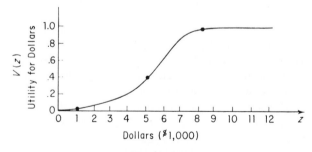

Figure 8.1.

would be likely to make the investment, because the expected utility of the investment exceeds the utility of his current assets.

This example is not intended to be a rigorous discussion of utility. It is used to demonstrate the effect that a value or utility function might have in the decision process. In this particular case, we have shown that the recognition of this fact may lead to a different decision.

Counteractions by an Adversary

In many decision problems the outcome of an action a_i depends on the reaction or counteraction b_j taken by an adversary. Consider the case of two decision-makers, A and B, each with a single objective. On occasion, we shall call these decision-makers *players*. The outcome variable is now a function of the decisions made by both decision-makers, $z = z(a_i, b_j)$. Here decision-maker A chooses a_i and decision-maker B chooses b_j. If each decision-maker has a finite number of courses of action we could construct a matrix of outcomes such as the one shown in Table 8.1. In this table we let $z_{ij} = z(a_i, b_j)$.[1]

TABLE 8.1

Matrix of all possible outcomes for two decision-makers, A and B

Decision-Maker A	Decision-Maker B				
	b_1	b_2 $\cdots$	b_j	$\cdots$	b_T
a_1	z_{11}	z_{12} $\cdots$	z_{1k}	$\cdots$	z_1
a_2	z_{21}	z_{22} $\cdots$	z_{2k}	$\cdots$	z_{2T}
$\vdots$	$\vdots$	$\vdots$	$\vdots$		$\vdots$
a_i	z_{i1}	z_{i2} $\cdots$	z_{ij}	$\cdots$	z_{iT}
$\vdots$	$\vdots$	$\vdots$	$\vdots$		$\vdots$
a_R	z_{R1}	z_{R2} $\cdots$	z_{Rj}	$\cdots$	z_{RT}

Given some value function $V(z)$ we could construct a similar *payoff matrix* such as that shown in Table 8.2. In this table we let $v_{ij} = V(a_i, b_j) = V[z(a_i, b_j)]$. This problem is decision making under certainty if we know exactly what decision-maker B's reaction will be for every a_i.

We shall consider a simple example with an infinite number of alternatives taken from Isaacs [17]. We shall be concerned with two armies who are trying to determine how to best allocate their resources. Army 1 is interested in minimizing the difference in the number of men each army has remaining after some time interval T. This difference will be expressed as

$$z_2 - z_1 \tag{8.2}$$

---

[1] We use this notation only when each player has a finite number of alternatives with decision making under certainty.

z_2 is a state variable expressing the number of men remaining in Army 2 whereas z_1 expresses the number of men remaining in Army 1.

Suppose that z_3 is the number of aircraft that Army 2 has available for the destruction of Army 1's forces. Suppose that at a certain time Army 2 decides to send a fraction, ψ_1, of these planes into the sector containing Army 1's forces. ψ_1 is a control variable. Assume that the expected number of casualties is given by $c_1\psi_1z_3$, where c_1 is a constant. On the other hand, we know Army 1 is sending new men into the sector at a fixed rate r.

TABLE 8.2

Matrix of values, or payoffs, for decision-maker A

Decision-Maker A	Decision-Maker B				
	b_1	b_2	$\cdots$	b_j	$\cdots$	b_T
a_1	v_{11}	v_{12}	$\cdots$	v_{1j}	$\cdots$	v_{1T}
a_2	v_{21}	v_{22}	$\cdots$	v_{2j}	$\cdots$	v_{2T}
$\vdots$	$\vdots$	$\vdots$		$\vdots$		$\vdots$
a_i	v_{i1}	v_{i2}	$\cdots$	v_{ij}	$\cdots$	v_{iT}
$\vdots$	$\vdots$	$\vdots$		$\vdots$		$\vdots$
a_R	v_{R1}	v_{R2}	$\cdots$	v_{Rj}	$\cdots$	v_{RT}

We assume that the quantities of the control and state variables are sufficiently large to consider their approximation by continuous variable as tenable. With some study we find the following equation expresses the state of Army 1's forces:

$$\frac{dz_1}{dt} = r - c_1\psi_1z_3 \qquad (8.3)$$

If we assume the game to be symmetrical, the same relation may be developed for Army 2:

$$\frac{dz_2}{dt} = u - c_2\phi_1z_4 \qquad (8.4)$$

where u is the rate at which Army 2 sends men into the sector, c_2 is a constant, ϕ_1 is the quantity.

We could develop further relationships here concerning control variables related to munitions, armor, and others. However, we will assume these to be the only pertinent constraints. Army 1 then wishes to minimize equation (8.2) subject to the constraints given by equations (8.3) and (8.4). This optimization problem may be solved with some of the optimization methods discussed in previous chapters. The particular type of decision problem discussed here is called a *differential game*. Those wishing further discussion should see Isaacs [17]. We will postpone a discussion of the solution of games until later.

8.3   Decision Making under Risk

Consider a decision problem where there is only one outcome variable for each alternative a_i, which is a random variable with probability density $f(z|a_i) - \infty < z < \infty$. We will only consider continuous random variables; the discussion may be interpreted for discrete variables with little difficulty.

We will call $f(z|a_i)$ an *efficiency function* after Churchman, Ackoff, and Arnoff [1]. Under risk, the form of $f(z|a_i)$ is known for all i.

We shall assume that the decision-maker will choose the course of action a_i that will yield the maximum expected value of his value function. Justification of this assumption is a philosophical question that will not be considered here. The reader wishing further discussion should see Ackoff [2] or Churchman [11].

In the case of a single outcome, the expected value function has the form

$$E_z[V(z|a_i)] = \int_{-\infty}^{\infty} f(z|a_i)V(z)\, dz \tag{8.5}$$

In the case of multiple outcomes, we must find the expected value:

$$E_z[V(z_1, \ldots, z_Q)|a_i] = \int_{-\infty}^{\infty} \cdots \int_{-\infty}^{\infty} V(z_1, \ldots, z_Q)f(z_1, \ldots, z_Q|a_i)\, dz_1, \ldots, dz_Q \tag{8.6}$$

where $f(z_1, \ldots, z_Q|a_i)$ is the joint probability density of outcomes $z_1, \ldots, z_Q$ given course of action a_i.

Under an assumption of valuewise independence of outcomes, this expression becomes

$$E_z[V(z_1, \ldots, z_Q|a_i)] = E_{z_1}[V(z_1|a_i)] + \cdots + E_{z_Q}[V(z_Q|a_i)] \tag{8.7}$$

In the case of multiple outcomes, we must have all outcome variables in common units before a value function $V(z_1, \ldots, z_Q)$ may be obtained. For this reason the mutual relationship between these variables must be determined. As an example Figure 8.2 shows two outcome variables plotted in a

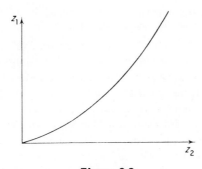

Figure 8.2.

functional relationship. Analysis of these relationships in the multiple-outcome case is beyond the scope of this text. We shall assume all outcome variables to be in common units unless stated otherwise. Those wishing further discussion should see Ackoff [2].

Counteractions by an Adversary

In the situation where we have an adversary, the efficiency function is conditioned by each of his reactions b_j. We must consider conditional probability densities of the form $f(z_1, \ldots, z_Q | a_i, b_j)$ over all $j = 1, \ldots, T$. Under risk we must know: (1) $P(b_j | a_i)$, $j = 1, \ldots, T$, if there is a finite or infinite number of discrete reactions, or (2) the probability density $p(b|a_i)$, if b is a continuous random variable.

Consider as an example the first case above. Decision-maker A will choose the action, a_i, which maximizes the expected value function of the form

$$\underset{z,b_j}{E}\left[V(\mathbf{z}|a_i)\right] =$$

$$\sum_{j=1}^{\infty} P(b_j|a_i) \int_{-\infty}^{\infty} \cdots \int_{-\infty}^{\infty} V(z_1, \ldots, z_Q) f(z_1, \ldots, z_Q | a_i, b_j)\, dz_1, \ldots, dz_Q \quad (8.8)$$

The optimal mixed strategy is obtained by maximizing

$$\sum_{i=1}^{R} P(a_i) \underset{z,b_j}{E}\left[V(\mathbf{z})|a_i\right]$$

subject to the requirements

$$\sum_{i=1}^{R} P(a_i) = 1$$

$$0 \le P(a_i) \le 1 \qquad i = 1, \ldots, R$$

Note that this is a bounded variable linear programming problem.

8.4   Decision Making under Uncertainty

In this section we are concerned with a decision problem where the decision-maker is ignorant of either the form of the efficiency functions $f(z_1, \ldots, z_Q | a_i, b_j)$ or the actions of his opponent, $P(b_j | a_i)$ or $p(b|a_i)$. We are also concerned with the situation where the decision-maker is ignorant of both the actions of his adversary and the efficiency functions.

Traditionally, problems under the heading uncertainty have been primarily concerned with the situation where the adversary is nature. In this situation the state of nature θ_j (corresponding to b_j) is stochastically independent of the action a_i of the decision-maker. Hence $P(\theta_j | a_i) = P(\theta_j)$. To simplify our discussion we shall only consider the case of a single outcome. If we have, or assume, a priori knowledge of the form of $P(\theta_j)$ or $p(\theta)$ the solution of the decision problem is simplified somewhat. We shall postpone discussion of this case until later in the chapter.

Under the conditions of uncertainty the expected value function of the decision-maker has the following form:

$$\underset{z, \theta_j}{E}\,[V(z|a_i)] = \sum_{j=1}^{T} P(\theta_j) \int_{-\infty}^{\infty} V(z)f(z|a_i, \theta_j)\,dz \qquad (8.9)$$

This expression assumes a finite number of states of nature. If θ is a continuous random variable, we have

$$\underset{z, \theta}{E}\,[V(z|a_i)] = \int_{-\infty}^{\infty} p(\theta) \int_{-\infty}^{\infty} V(z)f(z|a_i, \theta)\,dz\,d\theta \qquad (8.10)$$

We shall define $U(a_i, \theta_j)$ by

$$U(a_i, \theta_j) = \int_{-\infty}^{\infty} V(z)f(z|a_i, \theta_j)\,dz \qquad (8.11)$$

This is the expected value function for the decision-maker if he chooses action a_i and state of nature θ_j occurs. We should point out here that many discussions in the literature (for example, Luce and Raiffa [3]) do not allow z to be a random variable. Hence their discussion is made using only the equivalent of the function $U(a_i, \theta_k)$.

There are several proposed criteria for decision making when there is no information concerning the state of nature θ_j. The first of these is the *maximin criterion*. Using this criterion the worst possible outcome for each course of action is determined. The term a_i is chosen so that it maximizes the minimum gain. This may be stated mathematically as

$$\max_{a_i}\, \min_{\theta_j}\, [U(a_i, \theta_j)] \qquad (8.12)$$

This criterion is considered pessimistic, because it assumes that for any action a_i nature will act so as to minimize the value of the action to the decision-maker.

In an effort to develop a less pessimistic criterion for decision making under uncertainty, Hurwicz ([13], cited by Ackoff [2]) proposed the following:

$$\max_{a_i}\, \left\{ \alpha \max_{\theta_j} U(a_i, \theta_j) + (1 - \alpha) \min_{\theta_j} U(a_i, \theta_j) \right\} \qquad (8.13)$$

where α is some number between zero and 1. The term α is called the *coefficient of optimism*. For $\alpha = 0$ the criterion reduces to the maximin criterion. For $\alpha = 1$, we have a maximax criterion, which is pure optimism. The major problem here is that α must be estimated subjectively by the decision-maker.

Savage has proposed a *minimax regret criterion* [2]. We define the regret, $R(a_i, \theta_k)$ as follows:

$$R(a_i, \theta_j) = \max U(a_i', \theta_j) - U(a_i, \theta_j)$$

a_i' is the choice the decision-maker would have made had he known the state of nature θ_j in advance. The regret, $R(a_i, \theta_j)$, is the difference between the value of a given course of action and the value obtained had the decision-maker known beforehand what state of nature would prevail. Savage's criterion is to choose a_i such that

$$\min_{a_i} \max_{\theta_j} [R(a_i, \theta_j)] \tag{8.14}$$

A fourth criterion is based on the *principle of insufficient reason*. This principle takes the position that when the decision-maker is completely ignorant of the states of nature he should act as if all states are equally likely. Thus when θ_j is discrete and $j = 1, \ldots, T$ we choose a_i such that we have

$$\max_{a_i} \sum_{j=1}^{T} \frac{1}{T} U(a_i, \theta_j) \tag{8.15}$$

One of the faults of this criterion is that it is difficult to determine a meaningful interpretation of "equally likely" when the set of states of nature is infinite.

We shall not attempt a definitive comparison of these criteria for decision making under uncertainty. There is no unanimity of agreement on which criterion best approximates human behavior. The reader is referred to Luce and Raiffa [3] for further discussion.

One may question how frequently a decision-maker is forced to make decisions in complete ignorance. Quite often we may find that there is a priori knowledge, or information based on experimentation, that will aid us in the uncertainty situation. Our discussion will now turn to these cases.

Experimentation

Suppose that an a priori distribution of the states of nature $P(\theta_j)$, $j = 1, \ldots, T$, is known. Further, suppose we design an experiment to measure certain indicators of nature's behavior. As an example, a barometer reading is an indicator of rain. We use $e_1, \ldots, e_P$ to denote the P possible results of the experiment. For purposes of simplicity we shall assume it has only a single value for each $e_1, \ldots, e_r, \ldots, e_P$. By analyzing our observations we may find the conditional probabilities $P(e_r | \theta_j)$ for $r = 1, \ldots, P$ and $j = 1, \ldots, T$. We use Bayes' theorem or Bayes' rule [13] to find $P(\theta_j | e_r)$:

$$P(\theta_j | e_r) = \frac{P(e_r | \theta_j) P(\theta_j)}{\sum\limits_{j=1}^{T} P(e_r | \theta_j) P(\theta_j)} \tag{8.16}$$

We now use this value in equation (8.9):

$$E_{z, \theta_j} [U(a_i, \theta_j) | e_r] = \sum_{j=1}^{T} P(\theta_j | e_r) \int_{-\infty}^{\infty} V(z) f(z | a_i, \theta_j) \, dz \tag{8.17}$$

Thus when the decision-maker observes indicator e_r, he chooses that course of action a_i for which equation (8.17) is a maximum. An analogous argument may be developed for equation (8.10).

Comparison of Strategies

We will find it useful to let $x_i = P(a_i)$. A *strategy* is a decision rule that is most generally described by the vector $\mathbf{X} = (x_1, \ldots, x_i, \ldots, x_R)$,[2] where x_i is the frequency with which the decision-maker chooses course of action a_i. A *pure strategy* occurs when for some $i = p$, $x_p = 1$, and $x_i = 0$, $i \neq p$. Other cases are called *mixed strategies*.

Given some mixed strategy $\mathbf{X}$ we can write the general form of the expected value function for the decision-maker by using equation (8.9):

$$\underset{a_i, \theta_j, z}{E} [V(z)] = \sum_{i=1}^{R} x_i \sum_{j=1}^{T} P(\theta_j) \int_{-\infty}^{\infty} V(z) f(z \mid a_i, \theta_j) \, dz \qquad (8.18)$$

We shall define $r(\mathbf{X}; \theta_j)$ such that

$$\underset{a_i, \theta_j, z}{E} [V(z)] = \sum_{j=1}^{T} P(\theta_j) r(\mathbf{X}; \theta_j) \qquad (8.19)$$

A strategy $\mathbf{X}$ is said to *dominate* a strategy $\mathbf{Y}$ if $r(\mathbf{X}; \theta_j) \geq r(\mathbf{Y}, \theta_j)$ for all values of $j = 1, \ldots, T$. A strategy $\mathbf{X}$ is said to be *admissible* if it is not dominated by any other strategy.

$r(\mathbf{X}, \theta_j)$ may be viewed as the expected return to the decision-maker if he chooses the mixed strategy $\mathbf{X}$ and θ_j obtains. Using the definition of equation (8.12)

$$r(\mathbf{X}, \theta_j) = \sum_{i=1}^{R} x_i U(a_i, \theta_j)$$

Given some distribution $P(\theta_j)$, $j = 1, \ldots, T$, a strategy $\mathbf{X}$ is called a *Bayes strategy* relative to $P(\theta_j)$ if

$$\sum_{j=1}^{T} P(\theta_j) r(\mathbf{X}; \theta_j) \geq \sum_{j=1}^{T} P(\theta_j) r(\mathbf{T}; \theta_j)$$

for every other strategy $\mathbf{T}$.

Theorem: *Every admissible strategy is a Bayes strategy.*

The proof of the theorem may be found in Weiss [12]. The reader should be cautioned that there are Bayes strategies that are *not* admissible strategies.

---

[2] At this point the notation may disturb, if not confuse, the reader. However, it is consistent with some of the more popular texts in the field [3, 14].

This does not contradict the theorem above. For further discussion, see Weiss [12].

It is interesting to note that our definitions in this section hold under the conditions of experimentation. For example, the strategy of maximizing equation (8.17) is a Bayes strategy relative to the a priori distribution $P(\theta_j)$, $j = 1, \ldots, T$.

Construction of Bayes Strategies

The discussion of Bayes strategies above follows in the case where there are a finite number of states of nature θ_j and a finite number of alternative actions a_i. As an indication of how these strategies may be constructed, consider the following example.[3]

A public health program for control of a particular disease has chosen a diagnostic technique to be applied in mass screening. θ_1 will represent the true state of a patient having the disease. θ_2 will indicate the true state of a patient not having the disease. Studies have indicated that the diagnostic technique has the following characteristics:

States of Nature	$P(e_1\|\theta_k)$	$P(e_2\|\theta_k)$
θ_1	0.80	0.20
θ_2	0.90	0.10

Three actions may be taken on the basis of the test. The patient may be hospitalized (a_1), given outpatient clinic treatment (a_2), or given further tests (a_3). The loss table below, showing values of $U(a_i, \theta_j)$, has been derived after considerable study.

States of Nature	Actions		
	a_1	a_2	a_3
θ_1	1.0	0.5	2.0
θ_2	0.8	0.4	0

The elements in this table are values of $U(a_i, \theta_j)$. These values are plotted in Figure 8.3.

Note that a_1 is not admissible because it is dominated by a_2 and a_3. The shaded area is the convex set of all mixed strategies. Note that any mixed strategy also dominates a_1.

---

[3] This example is based on unpublished research of Charles D. Flagle.

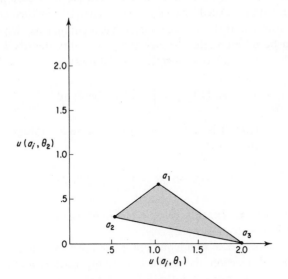

Figure 8.3. Expected Losses, $U(a_i, \theta_j)$.

A priori knowledge indicates that $P(\theta_1) = 0.10$ and $P(\theta_2) = 0.90$. Using this information we may construct the following probabilities using Bayes' theorem:

Observations	$P(\theta_1|e_r)$	$P(\theta_2|e_r)$
e_1	0.09	0.91
e_2	0.18	0.82

Given an indication for, for example, e_1 for a patient, we may find the Bayes strategy by examining the following expected losses:

$$\underset{\theta_j}{E}[U(a_1, \theta_j)|e_1] = U(a_1, \theta_1)P(\theta_1|e_1) + U(a_1, \theta_2)P(\theta_2|e_1)$$
$$= 1.0(0.09) + 0.8(0.91) = 0.82$$

Similarly,

$$\underset{\theta_j}{E}[U(a_2, \theta_j)|e_1] = 0.5(0.09) + 0.4(0.91) = 0.41$$
$$\underset{\theta_j}{E}[U(a_3, \theta_j)|e_1] = 2.0(0.09) + 0(0.91) = 0.18$$

Therefore a_3 would be the Bayes strategy if the patient presents indication e_1.

Consider the case where there is a nondenumerable infinity of states of nature. In this case θ may be considered a continuous random variable.

There is some philosophical concern in the literature over assuming that the states of nature are governed by chance. See Weiss [12] for further discussion. In this case assume that the state of nature has a cumulative density function $B(\theta)$ that can be differentiated to give the probability density $b(\theta)$. We will then define the expected value of $r(\mathbf{X}; \theta)$ as follows:

$$\underset{a_1, \theta, z}{E} [V(z)] = \int_{-\infty}^{\infty} r(\mathbf{X}; \theta) b(\theta) \, d\theta$$

We shall assume $r(\mathbf{X}; \theta)$ is continuous. In this case a strategy $\mathbf{X}$ is called a *Bayes strategy* relative to $B(\theta)$ if

$$\int_{-\infty}^{\infty} r(\mathbf{X}; \theta) \, d\theta \geq \int_{-\infty}^{\infty} r(\mathbf{Y}; \theta) \, d\theta \qquad (8.20)$$

for every strategy $\mathbf{Y}$. In this case, we cannot claim that all admissible strategies are Bayes strategies [12].

The cases related to a nondenumerable infinity of alternative actions follow from the discussion above. Those wishing further discussion should see Weiss [12].

8.5 Rectangular Games

Up to this point the discussion has been primarily concerned with building decision theoretic models of problem situations. Finding optimal strategies for these problems is a much more difficult matter. Rigorous analysis of these models usually requires assumptions to be made to facilitate use of the mathematical methods of optimization.

We have defined games, roughly, as decision problems where there are two or more decision-makers. The following sections, concerned with some of the less complex games, comprise part of what has traditionally been called the *theory of games*.

We shall only be concerned with games including two decision-makers, called *players*. We shall assume that the outcome of two concurrent actions by the players is known with certainty. For the sake of simplicity we shall assume only one objective for each player, to maximize the value or expected value of his return. The outcomes of the game for player A are shown in abstract fashion in Table 8.1. The corresponding table of values is given in Table 8.2. The entries in this table are usually called *payoffs*. Note that Table 8.2 gives player A's payoff matrix. Similarly, we can construct a payoff matrix for player B as shown in Table 8.3. Throughout the remainder of this chapter we shall assume a *linear utility function*. That is, we shall assume that when either player is faced with outcome z_1 with probability q and outcome z_2 with probability $1 - q$ we have

$$V(z_1, z_2) = q z_1 + (1 - q) z_2$$

For further discussion of this concept see Luce and Raiffa [3] or Fishburn [5].

TABLE 8.3

Payoff Matrix for Player B

Player B	Player A				
	a_1	$\cdots$	a_i	$\cdots$	a_R
b_1	u_{11}	$\cdots$	u_{1i}	$\cdots$	u_{1R}
$\vdots$	$\vdots$		$\vdots$		$\vdots$
b_j	u_{j1}	$\cdots$	u_{ji}	$\cdots$	u_{jR}
$\vdots$	$\vdots$		$\vdots$		$\vdots$
b_T	u_{T1}	$\cdots$	u_{Ti}	$\cdots$	u_{TR}

Games in which both players have a finite number of alternative actions are called *finite games*. Conversely, if either player has an infinite number of alternatives, the game is said to be infinite. If the sum of all payoffs to all players at the end of a game is zero, the game is called a *zero sum game*. In this case

$$v_{ij} = -u_{ji} \tag{8.21}$$

That is, player B loses the same quantity that player A wins. A *constant sum game* is one where the sum of all payoffs to all players is a constant. It can be shown that zero and constant sum games have equivalent properties and hence are both considered to be zero-sum games [14]. Finite, two-person, zero-sum games are called *rectangular games*. The process of finding a rectangular game equivalent to some arbitrary game is called *normalization*. The corresponding rectangular game is said to be in *normal form*. Arbitrary games are said to be in *extensive form* [14].

Saddle Points

We shall now turn to the analysis of rectangular games with saddle points. Since our attention is restricted to zero-sum games it will suffice to know only player A's payoff matrix. We use a shorthand notation for the matrix as follows:

$$\mathbf{V} = \begin{bmatrix} v_{11} & v_{12} & \cdots & v_{1T} \\ v_{21} & v_{22} & \cdots & v_{2T} \\ \vdots & \vdots & & \vdots \\ v_{R1} & v_{R2} & \cdots & v_{RT} \end{bmatrix} \tag{8.22}$$

It will be understood that player A's alternatives are listed vertically and player B's alternatives are listed horizontally. The payoff matrix will also occasionally be denoted as $\mathbf{V} = \{v_{ij}\}$, where $i = 1, \ldots, R$, $j = 1, \ldots, T$.

We shall also use the fact that the matrix $\mathbf{V}$ may be considered the real-valued function of two variables,

$$f(i, j) = v_{ij} \qquad i = 1, \ldots, R; \quad j = 1, \ldots, T \tag{8.23}$$

Theorem: *Let* $\mathbf{V} = \{v_{ij}\}$ *be an arbitrary* $R \times T$ *matrix. Then*

$$\max_i \min_j v_{ij} \leq \min_j \max_i v_{ij} \tag{8.24}$$

In order to see these relationships consider the following matrix:

$$\begin{bmatrix} 1 & 3 & 2 \\ 3 & 2 & 0 \end{bmatrix}$$

$$\max_i \min_j v_{ij} = 1 \quad \text{and} \quad \min_j \max_i v_{ij} = 2$$

Clearly, $1 \leq 2$.

The concept of a saddle point is important in the solution of rectangular games. Before examining conditions related to saddle points, we shall make the following definition:

Suppose the $f(x, y)$ is a real-valued function defined whenever $x \in A$, $y \in B$. Then a point (x^0, y^0), $x^0 \in A$, $y^0 \in B$, is called a *saddle point* if the following conditions are satisfied:

(1) $f(x, y^0) \leq f(x^0, y^0)$ all $x \in A$

(2) $f(x^0, y^0) \leq f(x^0, y)$ all $y \in B$

If we view a matrix as a real-valued function $f(x, y)$, the following theorem may be developed.

Theorem: *If* $\mathbf{V} = \{v_{ij}\}$ *is a matrix, then a necessary and sufficient condition that*

$$\max_i \min_j v_{ij} = \min_j \max_i v_{ij} \tag{8.25}$$

is that $\mathbf{V}$ *possess a saddle point.*

The proof of the theorem may be found in reference [14]. In different words the theorem indicates that if $v_{i_0 j_0}$ is a saddle point in V, then

$$v_{i_0 j_0} = \max_i \min_j v_{ij} = \min_j \max_i v_{ij}$$

$v_{i_0 j_0}$ is at the same time the minimum in a row of the matrix and a maximum in a column.

By considering the results of this theorem we may deduce a method for determining optimal strategies for each player when the payoff matrix for the game has a saddle point. $\min_j v_{ij}$ is the least player A can win for each course of action a_i. This follows, because we assume that player B has knowledge of player A's actions. Player A will choose the action that will maximize his minimum winnings. The same argument may be developed for player B's choice of a course of action. Hence if the game payoff matrix has a saddle point $v_{i_0 j_0}$, the player A will always choose action a_{i_0} and player B will always choose action b_{j_0}. $v_{i_0 j_0}$ is called the *value of the game*.

Example: Consider the payoff matrix

$$\begin{bmatrix} 6 & 5 & 4 & 7 \\ 8 & 6 & 3 & 2 \\ 0 & 2 & 3 & 6 \end{bmatrix}$$

$$\max_i \min_j v_{ij} = \min_j \max_i v_{ij} = v_{13} = 4$$

Hence player A will choose a_1 and player B will choose b_3 and the value of the game $v_{13} = 4$.

If we could be assured that all payoff matrices possessed saddle points, our discussion would be finished. Such is not the case. We now turn to games without saddle points.

Mixed Strategies

Recall that a mixed strategy for player A is defined by a vector $X = (x_1, \ldots, x_R)$, where the components of the vector represent the frequency with which player A will select actions a_1 through a_R. We require that $x_i \geq 0$, $i = 1, \ldots, R$, and

$$\sum_{i=1}^{R} x_i = 1$$

Similarly, we can define a mixed strategy for player B by the vector $Y = (y_1, \ldots, y_T)$. It is obvious that a pure strategy a_k is simply a mixed strategy X, where $x_i = 0$, $i \neq k$, and $x_k = 1$.

If player A uses mixed strategy X and player B uses mixed strategy Y, then the expected value of the game to player A is[4]

$$E(X, Y) = \sum_{i=1}^{R} \sum_{j=1}^{T} v_{ij} x_i y_j \qquad (8.26)$$

Definition: *If X^0 is an optimal strategy for player A and Y^0 is an optimal strategy for player B if for any other strategies X and Y, the following holds:*

$$E(X, Y^0) \leq E(X^0, Y^0) \leq E(X^0, Y) \qquad (8.27)$$

$E(X_0, Y_0)$ *is called the* value of the game.

---

[4] We remind the reader not to confuse this notation with the statistical definition of an expected value.

In other words, as far as player A is concerned, an optimal strategy $\mathbf{X}^0$ is one that makes $E(\mathbf{X}^0, \mathbf{Y})$ as large as possible. As far as player B is concerned, an optimal strategy $\mathbf{Y}^0$ is one that makes $E(\mathbf{X}, \mathbf{Y}^0)$ as small as possible. In general we shall define a set of strategies S_R for player A, $\mathbf{X} \in S_R$, and a set of strategies S_T for player B, $\mathbf{Y} \in S_T$. In searching for optimal mixed strategies we shall use a theorem known as the *minimax* or the *fundamental theorem* for rectangular games.

Theorem: *Let* $\mathbf{V} = \{v_{ij}\}$ *be any matrix and let* $E(\mathbf{X}, \mathbf{Y})$ *be defined by equation* (8.26) *for any* $\mathbf{X} = (x_1, \ldots, x_R)$ *and* $\mathbf{Y} = (y_1, \ldots, y_T)$ *for* $\mathbf{X} \in S_R$, $\mathbf{Y} \in S_T$. *Then the quantities*

$$\max_{\mathbf{X} \in S_R} \min_{\mathbf{Y} \in S_T} E(\mathbf{X}, \mathbf{Y})$$

$$\min_{\mathbf{Y} \in S_R} \max_{\mathbf{X} \in S_T} E(\mathbf{X}, \mathbf{Y}) \tag{8.28}$$

exist and are equal.

The proof of the theorem is given in McKinsey [14]. In reality the theorem tells us that every rectangular game has a value and a player of a rectangular game always has an optimal strategy. We still must develop methods of finding optimal strategies.

Theorem: *Let* $E(\mathbf{X}^0, \mathbf{Y}^0) = V^0$ *be the value of a rectangular game and* $\mathbf{X}^*$ *and* $\mathbf{Y}^*$ *be mixed strategies, where* $\mathbf{X}^* \in S_R$ *and* $\mathbf{Y}^* \in S_T$. *Then*

    (*a*) *A necessary and sufficient condition that* $\mathbf{X}^*$ *be optimal is that*

$$E(\mathbf{X}^*, \mathbf{Y}) \geq V^0 \tag{8.29}$$

    (*b*) *A necessary and sufficient condition for* $\mathbf{Y}^*$ *to be optimal is that*

$$E(\mathbf{X}, \mathbf{Y}^*) \leq V^0 \tag{8.30}$$

The proof of the theorem is given in [14]. It is sometimes useful to examine proposed solutions for optimality. The following theorem provides us with this capability. We shall let $\mathbf{X}_p$ and $\mathbf{Y}_p$ denote pure strategies for players A and B, respectively.

Theorem: *Let* V *be a number. Let* $\mathbf{X}^*$ *and* $\mathbf{Y}^*$ *be two mixed strategies. Then a necessary and sufficient condition for* $\mathbf{X}^*$ *and* $\mathbf{Y}^*$ *to be optimal is that*

$$\begin{aligned} E(\mathbf{X}_p, \mathbf{Y}^*) &\leq V \\ E(\mathbf{X}^*, \mathbf{Y}_p) &\geq V \end{aligned} \tag{8.31}$$

PROOF. The necessary condition will be considered first. By definition

$$E(\mathbf{X}, \mathbf{Y}^*) \leq E(\mathbf{X}^*, \mathbf{Y}^*) \leq E(\mathbf{X}^*, \mathbf{Y}) \tag{8.32}$$

if $\mathbf{X}^*$ and $\mathbf{Y}^*$ are optimal. The above relationship is simply a special case of this and the necessity follows.

We next consider the sufficient condition. We shall use $E(i, \mathbf{Y}^*)$ to denote the expected value function when player A chooses the pure strategy a_i. We know that

$$E(i, \mathbf{Y}^*) = \sum_{j=1}^{T} v_{ij} y_j^* \tag{8.33}$$

Operating on both sides of this expression we find

$$\sum_{i=1}^{R} E(i, \mathbf{Y}^*) x_i = \sum_{i=1}^{R} \sum_{j=1}^{T} v_{ij} y_j^* x_i$$

$$= E(\mathbf{X}, \mathbf{Y}^*) \tag{8.34}$$

By definition we know

$$E(i, \mathbf{Y}^*) \leq V$$

Since $x_i \geq 0$,

$$x_i E(i, \mathbf{Y}^*) \leq x_i V$$

Summing both sides we find

$$\sum_{i=1}^{R} x_i E(i, \mathbf{Y}^*) \leq \sum_{i=1}^{R} x_i V$$

Then using equation (8.34) we have

$$E(\mathbf{X}, \mathbf{Y}^*) \leq V$$

Similarly, we could show

$$E(\mathbf{X}^*, \mathbf{Y}) \geq V$$

Therefore,

$$E(\mathbf{X}, \mathbf{Y}^*) \leq E(\mathbf{X}^*, \mathbf{Y}^*) \leq E(\mathbf{X}^*, \mathbf{Y})$$

$\mathbf{X}^*$ and $\mathbf{Y}^*$ satisfy the conditions for optimality and the theorem is proved.

Before tackling an example one additional theorem will prove useful.

Theorem: *Let $E(\mathbf{X}, \mathbf{Y})$ be the expected value function and V the value for a rectangular game and let $\mathbf{X}^* = (x_1^*, \ldots, x_R^*)$ and $\mathbf{Y}^* = (y_1^*, \ldots, y_T^*)$ be optimal strategies for players A and B, respectively. Then for any i such that*

$$E(i, \mathbf{Y}^*) < V \tag{8.35}$$

we have $x_i^* = 0$. And for any j such that

$$E(\mathbf{X}^*, j) > V \tag{8.36}$$

we have $y_j^* = 0$.

The proof of the theorem is left for the reader as an exercise. Although the theorems discussed above provide clues to the solution of game problems, computations required for an arbitrary number of actions for each player are generally lengthy. The following example will serve to illustrate how the theory may be used in solution procedures.

Example: Consider a game with the following payoff matrix:

$$\begin{bmatrix} 3 & 2 \\ 4 & 1 \end{bmatrix}$$

We have shown that the following are necessary and sufficient conditions for optimality.

$$E(1, Y) = 3y_1 + 2y_2 \le V$$
$$E(2, Y) = 4y_1 + 1y_2 \le V$$
$$E(X, 1) = 3x_1 + 4x_2 \ge V$$
$$E(X, 2) = 2x_1 + 1x_2 \ge V$$

Note that we must require that

$$x_1 + x_2 = 1$$
$$y_1 + y_2 = 1$$

Rearranging we find the following:

$$y_1 + 2 \le V$$
$$3y_1 + 1 \le V$$
$$-x_1 + 4 \ge V$$
$$x_1 + 1 \ge V$$

First let us suppose that all inequalities hold as equalities. Solving we find

$$y_1 = \tfrac{1}{2}$$
$$x_1 = \tfrac{3}{2}$$

Hence the equality constraints are not consistent. One or more of the inequalities must hold as strict inequalities.

We shall use trial and error together with the last theorem and let two of the equalities be inequalities:

$$y_1 + 2 = V$$
$$3y_1 + 1 < V$$
$$-x_1 + 4 > V$$
$$x_1 + 1 = V$$

Using the last theorem this implies that $x_1 = 1$ and $y_1 = 0$. Hence we have $X^0 = (1, 0)$, $Y^0 = (0, 1)$, and $V^0 = 2$.

Dominance

The concept of dominance has been discussed before in the context of the general decision problem. In the context of a rectangular game, it may be possible to tell by inspection that certain actions will never enter into a mixed strategy except with probability zero. As an example consider the payoff matrix

$$\begin{bmatrix} -3 & 2 & 1 \\ 4 & 3 & 4 \\ 3 & 4 & 2 \end{bmatrix}$$

Note that whatever action player B chooses, player A will never choose action a_1. He can always do at least as well, or better, by choosing a_2 or a_3.

In game-theory language, a_s *dominates* a_t if $v_{sj} \geq v_{tj}$ for all j. a_s is said to *strictly dominate* a_t if $v_{sj} > v_{tj}$ for all j. In our example a_2 strictly dominates a_1. Similar definitions may be given for player B: b_p dominates b_q if $v_{ip} \geq v_{iq}$ for all i. b_p strictly dominates b_q if $v_{ip} > v_{iq}$ for all i.

Theorem: *If a_s dominates a_t, then there exists some optimal strategy $\mathbf{X}^0$ such that $x_t^0 = 0$. Likewise, if b_p dominates b_q, then there exists some optimal strategy Y^0 such that $y_q^0 = 0$.*

The theorem states formally the conjecture made in the example given above. It is also possible that some mixed strategy will be preferred to a pure strategy.

Theorem: *If the convex combination*

$$\sum_{\substack{i=1 \\ i \neq t}}^{R} \alpha_i v_{ij} \geq v_{tj} \qquad \text{for all } j \tag{8.37}$$

$$\alpha_i \geq 0 \qquad \sum_{\substack{i=1 \\ i \neq t}}^{R} \alpha_i = 1$$

then there exists an optimal strategy $\mathbf{X}^0$ such that $x_t^0 = 0$.

We may also state a similar theorem for player B:

Theorem: *If the convex combination*

$$\sum_{\substack{j=1 \\ j \neq q}}^{T} \alpha_j v_{ij} \leq v_{iq} \qquad \text{for all } i \tag{8.38}$$

$$\alpha_j \geq 0 \qquad \sum_{\substack{j=1 \\ j \neq q}}^{T} \alpha_j = 1$$

then there exists an optimal strategy $\mathbf{Y}^0$ such that $y_q^0 = 0$.

Example: Consider the payoff matrix

$$
\begin{bmatrix}
10 & 8 & 9 \\
4 & 9 & 5 \\
0 & 12 & 3
\end{bmatrix}
$$

Let $\alpha_1 = \frac{2}{3}$, $\alpha_2 = \frac{1}{3}$. Then for

$$
\begin{aligned}
i = 1 &: \tfrac{2}{3}(10) + \tfrac{1}{3}(8) > 9 \\
i = 2 &: \tfrac{2}{3}(4) + \tfrac{1}{3}(9) > 5 \\
i = 3 &: \tfrac{2}{3}(0) + \tfrac{1}{3}(12) > 3
\end{aligned}
$$

Therefore, the theorem above indicates $y_3^0 = 0$.

8.6   Linear Programming and Rectangular Games

One of the more efficient procedures for finding optimal strategies for the players of a rectangular game is to formulate and solve the corresponding linear programming problem. This section is concerned with theoretical justification for this approach.

First we consider the optimal strategy for player B. We have shown that a necessary and sufficient condition for some strategy $\mathbf{Y}$ to be optimal for player B is that when player A uses any pure strategy i, $i = 1, \ldots, R$, the following holds:

$$E(i, \mathbf{Y}) \le V \tag{8.39}$$

where V is the value of the game. Alternatively, the condition is

$$\sum_{j=1}^{T} v_{ij} y_j \le V \tag{8.40}$$

Note that we must also require

$$\sum_{j=1}^{T} y_j = 1 \tag{8.41}$$

$$y_j \ge 0, j = 1, \ldots, R$$

It is possible to assume without loss of generality that $V > 0$. We shall divide equations (8.40) and (8.41) by V to obtain

$$\sum_{j=1}^{T} v_{ij} \frac{y_i}{V} \le 1 \qquad i = 1, \ldots, R$$

$$\frac{y_j}{V} \ge 0 \qquad j = 1, \ldots, T \tag{8.42}$$

$$\sum_{j=1}^{T} \frac{y_j}{V} = \frac{1}{V}$$

Let $u_j = y_j/V$, $j = 1, \ldots, T$, and $z = 1/V$. We have seen that player B is attempting to minimize V or

$$\max z = \sum_{j=1}^{T} u_j \qquad (8.43)$$

subject to the constraints

$$\sum_{j=1}^{T} v_{ij} u_j \leq 1 \qquad i = 1, \ldots, R$$

$$u_j \geq 0 \qquad j = 1, \ldots, T \qquad (8.44)$$

This obviously is a linear programming problem.

Similarly, if we let $q = 1/V$ and $w_i = x_i/V$ we can formulate player A's objective to find optimal strategies as the search for the w_i in the following linear programming problem:

$$\min q = \sum_{i=1}^{R} w_i \qquad (8.45)$$

subject to

$$\sum_{i=1}^{R} v_{ij} w_i \geq 1 \qquad j = 1, \ldots, T$$

$$w_i \geq 0 \qquad i = 1, \ldots, R \qquad (8.46)$$

The derivation is left to the reader as an exercise. We immediately recognize player A's problem as the dual linear programming problem of player B. For an interesting alternative proof of the fundamental theorem of rectangular games using duality theory, see the problems at the end of the chapter.

It is possible to show that a linear programming problem has an equivalent two-person, zero-sum game. Unfortunately, space will not allow this topic to be covered here. The interested reader should see Dantzig [15].

Summary

Decision theory presents a global overview of the problems encountered by operations researchers. The subject is concerned with building mathematical models of general decision problems. The resulting models are quite frequently difficult to solve, thus requiring further study, perhaps further assumptions, until they are amenable to analysis with current mathematical methods.

A major value of decision theory is that through its study the implicit assumptions required to make a problem analyzable with existing mathematical techniques are pointed out. After reflection on these assumptions one realizes that there is a vast amount of work yet to be done before the formulation and solution of decision models closely approximates real life.

The existence of an adversary is a case in point. The complexity of the decision model grows drastically with the introduction of an opponent. Rectangular games are the simplest decision problems with an adversary. We have seen that the solution of these games may be accomplished only with some effort. However, the analysis of games in extensive form has not met with recognized success.

Differential games have yet to receive great attention in the O.R. literature. However, they have met with success in certain military applications. Isaacs [17] has published a definitive work in this area.

Problems

1. A man wishes to purchase new tires for his automobile. He finds that there are three types of tires available to him, types X, Y, and Z. Tire X sells for $15 and will last 15,000 miles. Tire Y costs $25 and has a life expectancy of 10,000 miles. Tire Z sells for $35 and will wear for 30,000 miles. The man performs a study to determine that every 2000 miles of wear is worth $1. He has two objectives: (1) maximize wear of his tires and (2) minimize his cash outlay for the tires. Formulate and solve his problem in a decision theoretic framework. Identify all terms and assumptions used.

2. Consider the problem of a decision-maker with three courses of action a_1, a_2, and a_3 with an adversary who can take two reactions r_1 and r_2. He knows that $P(r_1) = 0.3$ and $P(r_2) = 0.7$. The decision-maker has two objectives. Given the table of efficiences shown, which action should he choose? Assume $y(z) = z$.

	r_1		r_2	
	O_1	O_2	O_1	O_2
a_1	5	6	4	2
	5	3	4	4
	2	4	2	5

3. Mrs. Jones must decide on which type of dinner to serve her guests tomorrow night. She wants to decide among three different dinners: d_1, d_2, or d_3. The type of dinner she serves will affect the amount of guest satisfaction (O_1) and the mood of the guests after dinner (O_2). Since the weather plays an important role in the determination of which dinner would be most suitable, Mrs. Jones must anticipate the weather conditions for tomorrow night so she can purchase the food today. The probability of a cold evening is $P(\theta_1) = 0.3$,

the probability of a mild evening is $P(\theta_2) = 0.4$, and the probability of a hot evening is $P(\theta_3) = 0.3$. After some study she arrived at the table of values shown. All numbers are in common units. Which dinner should Mrs. Jones decide upon in hopes of maximizing satisfaction and mood?

	θ_1		θ_2		θ_3	
	O_1	O_2	O_1	O_2	O_1	O_2
d_1	5	3	4	7	9	6
d_2	1	6	9	7	4	5
d_3	7	2	8	5	8	6

4. Suppose the table of Problem 3 considered O_1 to be dinner satisfaction and O_2 to be the dinner cost, both of the objectives in common units. Since Mrs. Jones is a pennypincher as well as a good hostess, which dinner should she prepare for in this case?

5. A company producing bathing suits must decide upon what type and how many suits to produce. It has two alternatives to choose from: lot 1 or lot 2. Besides being different in quantity, the lots differ in types. The demand for bathing suits is dependent upon the trend of the summer weather. It was determined from past weather records that the probability of a warm summer (θ_1) is 0.65 and that of a cool summer (θ_2) is 0.35. The company wishes to maximize profit for the summer's sales. In the case of lot 1 (a_1) profit for a warm summer is described by the efficiency function $f(z_1|a_1, \theta_1)$ and in the case of a cool summer by $f(z_1|a_1, \theta_2)$. Similarly, for lot 2 (a_2) profit for a warm summer is described by $f(z_1|a_2, \theta_1)$ and for a cool summer by $f(z_1|a_2, \theta_2)$. Assume $v(z_1) = z_1^2$. Which lot should the company choose for the efficiency function given below?

$$f(z_1|a_1, \theta_1) = 6e^{-2z_1}$$

$$f(z_1|a_1, \theta_2) = \frac{1}{b - a}$$

$$f(z_1|a_2, \theta_1) = 2(e^{-z_1} - e^{-3z_1})$$

$$f(z_1|a_2, \theta_2) = \frac{2}{b - a}$$

In all cases $0 \le z_1 \le 4$, $b = 4$ and $a = 0$.

6. In Problem 5 assume the company identifies a second objective: to maximize good will. In the case of lot 1 (a_1), good will for a warm summer is described by $f(z_2|a_1, \theta_1)$ and for a cool summer $f(z_2|a_1, \theta_2)$. For lot 2 (a_2), good will for a warm summer is described by $f(z_2|a_2, \theta_2)$ and for a cool summer by

$f(z_2|a_2, \theta_2)$. Assume valuewise independence, where $v(z_i) = z_i^2$. Which lot should the company choose? The efficiency functions are shown below:

$$f(z_2|a_1, \theta_1) = \tfrac{1}{325}(z_2^2 + z_2)^2$$
$$f(z_2|a_1, \theta_1) = \tfrac{1}{138}(z_2^2 + 2z_2 + 5)$$
$$f(z_2|a_2, \theta_1) = \tfrac{1}{30}(z_2^2 - 3z_2 + 2)$$
$$f(z_2|a_2, \theta_2) = \tfrac{2}{275}(3z_2^2 - z_2)$$

In all cases $0 \le z_2 \le 5$.

7. The following example has been taken from Lechat and Flagle [16]. A group of patients with symptoms of leprosy are to be screened for a lepromatous condition. If found positive they may be hospitalized (a_1) or continued in outpatient care (a_2). If found negative they may be hospitalized, placed in outpatient care, or released from treatment (a_3). There are two states of nature: θ_1, the patient is lepromatous; θ_2, the patient is nonlepromatous. For each state of nature the screening process (experiment) yields the following results:

θ_1	
e_1	positive (lepromatous)
e_2	false-negative (nonlepromatous)

θ_2	
e_1	false-positive (lepromatous)
e_2	negative (nonlepromatous)

An experiment has resulted in the following probabilities being obtained:

States of Nature	$P(e_1|\theta_j)$	$P(e_2|\theta_j)$
θ_1	0.8	0.2
θ_2	0.0	1.0

After considerable study, the following loss table has been developed. The elements of this table are equivalent to the $U(a_i, \theta_j)$ discussed in Section 8.4.

States of Nature	Actions		
	a_1	a_2	a_3
θ_1	1.0	1.2	3.0
θ_2	1.0	0.4	0.5

Assume $P(\theta_1) = 0.9$ and $P(\theta_2) = 0.1$.

(a) What operations are implicitly assumed in the loss table for $U(a_i, \theta_k)$?
(b) Find the optimal Bayes strategy for each possible indication e_1 and e_2.

8. Suppose that in Problem 3 Mrs. Jones wants to find an optimal mixed strategy to be used in the long run. Formulate and solve the problem as a linear programming problem.

9. Find the optimal strategy for player A in a rectangular game whose payoff matrices are shown below:

(a) $\begin{bmatrix} 2 & 4 \\ 1 & 3 \end{bmatrix}$

(b) $\begin{bmatrix} 2 & 2 & 4 \\ 1 & 2 & 3 \end{bmatrix}$

(c) $\begin{bmatrix} 5 & 3 & 6 & 4 \\ 4 & 2 & 4 & 3 \\ 8 & 3 & 6 & 5 \\ 3 & 1 & 6 & 2 \end{bmatrix}$

(d) $\begin{bmatrix} 5 & 5 & 2 & 3 & 3 & 6 \\ 3 & 4 & 1 & 4 & 5 & 5 \\ 2 & 3 & 1 & 4 & 3 & 3 \\ 1 & 3 & 0 & 5 & 2 & 3 \\ 5 & 2 & 2 & 4 & 3 & 2 \\ 6 & 5 & 2 & 5 & 3 & 5 \end{bmatrix}$

10. Given the payoff matrix below formulate and solve for player A's optimal strategy using linear programming.

$$\begin{bmatrix} 6 & 4 & 3 \\ 4 & 5 & 1 \\ 3 & 4 & 6 \end{bmatrix}$$

11. Use the discussions of duality in Chapter 3 to develop an alternative proof for the minimax theorem.

12. Prove that the value of a game is unique.

13. A company has calculated the cost of providing storage facilities for inventory to meet seasonal peak demands. The inventory costs have been estimated as follows: $40,000 for a large inventory, $20,000 for a moderate inventory, and $10,000 for a small inventory. The net revenue, in thousands of dollars, associated with different inventories, taking into account price reductions

	Sales Peak		
Inventory	High	Medium	Low
Large	120	110	60
Moderate	60	50	70
Small	40	20	70

necessary to dispose of excess inventory, lost sales, and so on, are estimated here for three levels of sales peaks. Using game theory, determine how much inventory should be provided in advance of the seasonal sales peak. Justify all assumptions.

References Cited and Bibliography

[1] Churchman, C. W., R. L. Ackoff, and E. L. Arnoff. *Introduction to Operations Research.* New York: Wiley, 1957.

[2] Ackoff, R. L. *Scientific Method.* New York: Wiley, 1962.

[3] Luce, R. D., and H. Raiffa. *Games and Decisions.* New York: Wiley, 1958.

[4] Miller, D. W., and M. K. Starr. *Executive Decisions and Operations Research.* Englewood Cliffs, N.J.: Prentice-Hall, 1960.

[5] Fishburn, P. C. *Decision and Value Theory.* New York: Wiley, 1964.

[6] Chernoff, H., and L. E. Moses. *Elementary Decision Theory.* New York: Wiley, 1959.

[7] Savage, J. *The Foundations of Statistics.* New York: Wiley, 1954.

[8] von Neumann, J., and O. Morgenstern. *Theory of Games and Economic Behavior.* Princeton, N.J.: Princeton University Press, 1953.

[9] Stigler, G. J. "The Development of Utility Theory," *J. Political Econ.,* Vol. 58 (1950).

[10] Bross, I. D. *Design for Decision.* New York: Macmillan, 1953.

[11] Churchman, C. W. *Prediction and Optimal Decision.* Englewood Cliffs, N.J.: Prentice-Hall, 1961.

[12] Weiss, L. *Statistical Decision Theory.* New York: McGraw-Hill, 1961.

[13] Feller, W. *An Introduction to Probability Theory and Its Applications,* Vol. 1. New York: Wiley, 1957.

[14] McKinsey, J. C. C. *Introduction to the Theory of Games.* New York: McGraw-Hill, 1952.

[15] Dantzig, G. B. "A Proof of the Equivalence of the Programming Problem and the Game Problem." In *Activity Analyses of Production and Allocation* (T. C. Koopmans, ed.). New York: Wiley, 1951.

[16] Lechat, M. F., and C. D. Flagle. "Allocation of Medical and Associated Resources to the Control of Leprosy," *Acta Hospitalia,* Vol. II, No. 2 (June 1962).

[17] Isaacs, R. *Differential Games.* New York: Wiley, 1965.

CHAPTER 9

Graphs and Networks

9.1   Introduction

The theory of graphs, although having a rather lengthy history in engineering, has seen substantial use in operations research studies only during recent years. Because the use of graph theory in operations research is relatively new, most applications are found in the journals. Another indication of its relative age is the general disagreement on basic definitions. Our discussion here will be based on the texts of Busacker and Saaty [1], Ford and Fulkerson [2], Ore [3], and Berge [4]. Most definitions given in this chapter will be consistent with one of these references. However, the reader is cautioned that these arguments may not be consistent when he arbitrarily selects one of these texts. Whenever possible, we shall cite these inconsistencies.

Most applications of graphs in operations research have been in problems involving network flows. However, current research indicates a broader range of applications may be forthcoming. The general treatment of graphs found in this chapter is based on the foundation required to analyze networks and related concepts.

9.2   Definitions

A *graph* consists of two sets of basic elements: *vertices* and *edges*. There will be a set V of vertices that are connected in some way. Associated with this set of vertices is a set of edges, E. Each pair of vertices v and w connected by an edge e is said to be the end points of e. The edge e is said to join v and w.

A given graph may or may not take into account the order of the end points. The unordered product of a set S with itself, denoted S & S, is the set of all pairs of elements of the set S. In the unordered pairing there is no distinction between the pairs (s, t) and (t, s).

Summarizing, an *abstract graph* or *graph* consists of a nonempty set V, a set E that is disjoint from V and possibly empty, and a mapping, Φ of E into V & V. If $\Phi(e) = (v$ & $w)$, where $e \in E$ and $v, w \in V$, then e is said to be *incident* with the vertices v and w. A graph is said to be *finite* if V and E are finite sets. Otherwise, it is said to be infinite. Figure 9.1(a) shows an undirected graph.

Notice in the above definitions there is no direction associated with the *undirected edge e*. When concerned with ordered pairs of vertices, we must define a directed edge. The *ordered product* of a set S with itself, denoted $S \times S$, is the set of all distinct ordered pairs of elements of the set. In this case there is a distinction between the pairs (s, t) and (t, s), where $[s, t] \in S$.

A *directed graph* consists of a nonempty set V, a set A disjoint from V, and a mapping Δ of A into $V \times V$. The elements of V are called *vertices* or *nodes* and the elements of A are called *arcs*. The mapping $\Delta = \Delta(e) = (v, w)$ is called a *directed incidence* mapping. In Figure 9.1, $E = \{e\}$ is mapped into (a, b). a is called the *initial vertex* and b is called the *terminal* vertex.

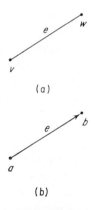

(a)

(b)

Figure 9.1.

It is possible to find references in the literature to *mixed graphs* [3]. These graphs, consisting of both directed and undirected edges, are not discussed here.

A *simple open curve* in E^N is a continuous, nonself-intersecting curve joining two distinct points in E^N. A *simple closed curve* is a continuous, non-self-intersecting curve whose end points coincide. A *geometric graph* in E^N is a set $V = \{v_i\}$ of points in E^N and a set $E = \{e_j\}$ of simple curves satisfying the following conditions:

1. Every closed curve in E^N contains precisely one point of V.

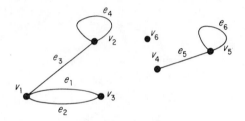

Figure 9.2.

2. Every open curve in E^N contains precisely two points of V and these are its end points.
3. The curves in E^N have no common points except for points of V.

Our discussion will only be concerned with geometric graphs.

9.3   Undirected Graphs

In this section we shall pay particular attention to undirected graphs. Although some of the discussion applies to directed graphs, the presentation may be facilitated if the concepts are introduced initially for the undirected case.

Graphs $G = (V, E)$ and $G' = (V', E')$ are said to be *isomorphic* to each other if there exist one-to-one correspondences between V and V', and E and E', that preserve incidences. If G is isomorphic to a geometric graph G', then G' is called the *geometric realization* of G. A graph is said to be *planar* if and only if it has a geometric realization in E^2. The graph shown in Figure 9.3(a) is planar because it has the geometric realization shown in Figure 9.3(b). Figure 9.4 is an example of a nonplanar graph.

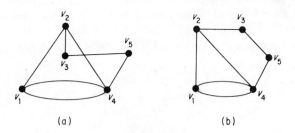

(a)   (b)

Figure 9.3.

If e joins vertices v and w, where $v = w$, then e is called a *loop*. Two loops are *parallel* if they are incident with the same vertex. Vertices v and w are said to be *adjacent vertices* if e joins v and w for at least one edge e. Edges e_1 and e_2 are *adjacent* if they have at least one common end point. As an

Figure 9.4.

example of the above definitions consider Figure 9.5. v_1 is adjacent to v_2. However, note that v_1 is not adjacent to v_4. e_2 and e_3 are examples of parallel edges. e_1 and e_7 are loops. The *degree* of a vertex v, denoted $\delta(v)$, is the number of edges incident with v with loops counted twice.

At this point we must make some definitions that vary with each text consulted. Our aim here is to facilitate the continuity of our own discussion without needless detail.

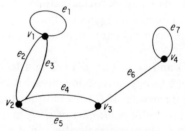

Figure 9.5.

A *path* is a sequence of edges, $e_1, e_2, \ldots, e_n$, of a graph such that there exists an appropriate sequence of vertices $v_0, v_1, \ldots, v_n$ so that e_i joins v_i and v_{i+1}. If the edges and vertices are distinct, the path is said to be *simple*. If, in the above definition $v_0 = v_n$, the sequence is said to be a *circuit*. If all edges and vertices are distinct except for v_0 and v_n, the circuit is *simple*.

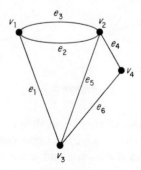

Figure 9.6.

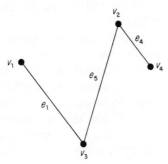

Figure 9.7.

A graph is *connected* if every pair of distinct vertices is joined by at least one *path*.

A graph is said to be a *tree* if it is connected and has no circuits. If a tree, T, is a subgraph of a graph G, the edges of G that appear in T are called *branches* relative to T. The edges not included in T are called *chords* relative to T. If all vertices of G are included in T, then T is said to *span* G.

Consider the connected graph in Figure 9.6. Figure 9.7 shows a tree constructed from this graph. e_1, e_4, and e_5 are called branches and e_2, e_3, and e_6 are chords.

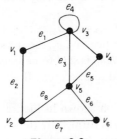

Figure 9.8.

If the graph $G = (V, E)$ is connected and if V is partitioned into non-empty sets W and $W' = V - W$, the set of edges joining W with W' is called the *cut set*. Consider the graph shown in Figure 9.8. Let $W' = (v_3, v_4, v_5)$ then the cut set is the set of edges, (e_1, e_6, e_8).

9.4 Directed Graphs

Recall that the basic structural difference of directed graphs, over undirected graphs, is that the end points constitute ordered pairs of vertices. The ordering relationships are designated by directed edges. Given a directed graph $D = (V, A)^1$ the associated undirected graph is obtained by

---

[1] For convenience we shall usually omit the notation for the incidence mapping, Δ.

disregarding the ordering of the end points. Directed edges, denoting this ordering, will usually be called *arcs*.

All the structural terms, such as adjacent and parallel edges, defined for undirected graphs hold for directed graphs. If arc a_1 joins v to w and arc a_2 joins v to w, then a_1 and a_2 are *strictly parallel*. On the other hand, if a_1 joins w to v and a_2 joins v to w, a_1 and a_2 are *parallel* but not strictly parallel.

If arc a joins v to w it is said to be *positively incident* with v and *negatively incident* with w. The number of arcs that are positively incident with v is called the *positive degree* of v, $\delta^+(v)$. The number of arcs that are negatively incident with v is called the *negative degree* of v, $\delta^-(v)$. The unsigned degree is defined as

$$\delta(v) = \delta^+(v) + \delta^-(v)$$

Directed graphs $D = (V, A, \Delta)$ and $D' = (V', A', \Delta')$ are said to be *isomorphic* if the elements of V and A can be placed in a one-to-one correspondence with those of V' and A' in such a way that

$$\Delta'(a') = (v', w')$$

if and only if $\Delta(a) = (v, w)$. If D and D' are isomorphic directed graphs and if D' is a directed geometric graph, the D' is called a *geometric realization* of D. A directed graph is *planar* if and only if its associated undirected graph is planar.

A *chain* is a sequence of arcs $a_1, a_2, \ldots, a_n$ of a graph if there exists an appropriate sequence of vertices $v_0, v_1, \ldots, v_n$ such that a_i joins v_i to v_{i+1}. If the arcs are distinct, the *chain* is said to be *simple*. If in the above definition $v_0 = v_n$, the sequence is said to be a *cycle*. If all arcs and vertices are distinct, the cycle is *simple*.

Consider the directed graph shown in Figure 9.9. The sequence a_3, a_6 is a chain from v_2 to v_1. A cycle is formed by the sequence a_3, a_6, a_1.

The concept of a path may be used in a directed graph. A path differs from a chain in that it allows the possibility of traversing an arc in the opposite direction to its orientation. In Figure 9.9 the sequence $a_3 a_5$ is a path from v_2 to v_1.

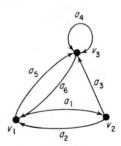

Figure 9.9.

When the terms tree and cut-set are used in directed graphs, directions are ignored. A directed graph is said to be a *directed tree* rooted a v_0 if (1) it forms a tree in the undirected sense and (2) the unique path determined by v_0 and any other vertex w is a chain from v to w.

9.5   Partitions and Distances

A *covering* is the partitioning of the edges of an undirected graph into disjoint subsets each of which is either a path or a circuit. Coverings including the fewest possible paths or circuits are called *minimal coverings*.

A circuit that covers a graph is called an *Euler circuit*. A graph containing an Euler circuit is called an *Euler graph* (after Ore [3]). For directed graphs, partitioning the arcs into disjoint chains or cycles is called a *covering*.

A problem relating to Euler circuits is that of determining a path or circuit incident with every vertex. If such a path is simple, it is called a *hamiltonian path*. Similarly if the circuit is simple, it it is called a hamiltonian circuit.

In directed graphs a simple chain or cycle that is incident with every vertex is called a *hamiltonian chain* or *cycle*. These definitions correspond to hamiltonian circuits or paths but also require consistency of direction.

If $v \neq w$ in a connected graph $G = (V, E)$, the *distance* between v and w, $d(v, w)$, denotes the minimum number of edges contained in any path joining v and w where $d(v, v) = 0$. In a connected directed graph $d(v, w)$ is the distance between v and w in the associated undirected graph.

An example of problems related to hamiltonian circuits is the traveling salesman problem discussed in Chapter 1. Consider the graph shown in Figure 9.10. The vertices represent cities. The numbers on the edges represent the distances between cities. The salesman is currently at v_0.

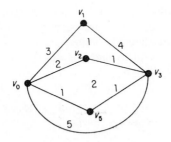

Figure 9.10.

The problem is to find a circuit that visits every city and returns to v_0 but contains the minimum distance of all such circuits. Alternatively, the problem is to find the hamiltonian circuit with minimum distance traveled. The details of solution will not be covered here. References may be found in Chapter 1.

9.6   Planar Graphs[2]

In Section 9.1 we saw that a planar graph can be drawn in a plane so that none of its edges intersects except at the vertices of the graph. In this section we shall extend these concepts. Two examples of nonplanar graphs,

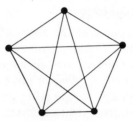

Figure 9.11.

sometimes called Kuratowski graphs, are shown in Figures 9.11 and 9.12. The graph in Figure 9.12 has been called a utility graph [1] because the top vertices could be viewed as houses and the bottom vertices as utilities. The edges connect all utilities to all houses.

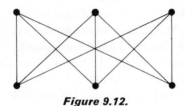

Figure 9.12.

If an edge is divided into two edges by the insertion of a new vertex of degree two, the planarity of a graph is not affected. Similarly, if two edges incident with a vertex of degree 2 are combined into one edge by removing a vertex, planarity is not affected.

Graphs G and G' are said to be *isomorphic to within degree 2* if they are isomorphic or if they can be transformed into isomorphic graphs by repeated application of the above transformations. For example, in Figure 9.13 (a) can be made isomorphic with (b) by removing vertices v_2 and v_4. The following theorem frequently proves useful in determining whether or not a graph is planar.

Theorem: *A necessary and sufficient condition for a graph G to be planar is that it should contain no subgraph, which is isomorphic to within degree* 2, *to either of the Kuratowski graphs.*

Proof of the theorem may be found in Berge [4] or Busacker and Saaty [1].

---

[2] This section may be skipped without loss of continuity.

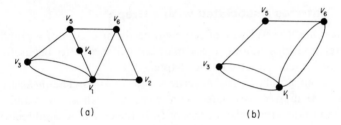

Figure 9.13.

9.7   Dual Graphs[3]

The concepts of dual relationships have already been of some concern in this text. Frequently, these concepts yield insight into the analysis and solution of graph problems.

Dual graphs are normally associated with planar graphs. They may be obtained by using the following procedure: Consider a planar graph G with regions R_i, $i = 1 \cdots N$. Assign a point p_i to every region R_i. If two regions R_i and R_j are adjacent join p_i to p_j which cross the common boundary edges of R_i and R_j. The edge that crosses the boundary will have no other point in common with any other boundary of the graph. An edge of G that is not the boundary of a region lies in a region and yields a loop.

An example of a graph and its dual is shown in Figure 9.14. Note that the dual graph has four vertices including the one corresponding to the outside region.

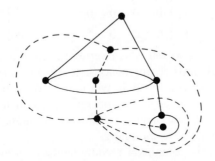

Figure 9.14.

Theorem: *A necessary and sufficient condition for a graph to be planar is that it have a dual.*

Proof of the theorem is cited in Busacker and Saaty [1].

---

[3] This section may be skipped without loss of continuity.

9.8   Matrices Associated with a Graph[4]

Matrices are a useful way of representing the structure of a graph. Many of the relationships among these matrices will prove to be useful in the applications discussed later in the chapter.

Suppose our graph, G, has N vertices and M edges. The *incidence matrix* is an $N \times M$ matrix, associated with a graph G, whose rows and columns correspond to the vertices and edges of G. In the case of an undirected graph, each entry of the matrix, s_{ij}, is either 1 or 0 depending on whether or not the

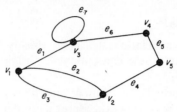

Figure 9.15

jth edge is incident with the ith vertex. In the case of a loop every entry in a column of the matrix is zero. Consider the graph shown in Figure 9.15. The incidence matrix for this graph has the following form:

$$\mathbf{S} = \begin{array}{c} \\ v_1 \\ v_2 \\ v_3 \\ v_4 \\ v_5 \end{array} \begin{array}{c} \begin{array}{ccccccc} e_1 & e_2 & e_3 & e_4 & e_5 & e_6 & e_7 \end{array} \\ \left[\begin{array}{ccccccc} 1 & 1 & 1 & 0 & 0 & 0 & 0 \\ 0 & 1 & 1 & 1 & 0 & 0 & 0 \\ 1 & 0 & 0 & 0 & 0 & 1 & 0 \\ 0 & 0 & 0 & 0 & 1 & 1 & 0 \\ 0 & 0 & 0 & 1 & 1 & 0 & 0 \end{array} \right] \end{array} \qquad (9.1)$$

Note there is no way to tell which vertex the loop is incident with. For this reason, we shall restrict our concern to graphs without loops. Every other column of the matrix has only two unit entries corresponding to the vertices incident with the edge. All operations on incidence matrices for undirected graphs will use binary arithmetic. In more specific terms all operations will be reduced to modulo 2.

The incidence matrix contains a predominance of zeros. For this reason it is always possible to rearrange rows and columns so that the matrix has the angular form:

$$\mathbf{S} = \begin{bmatrix} S_1 & 0 & \cdots & 0 \\ 0 & S_2 & \cdots & 0 \\ \vdots & \vdots & & \vdots \\ 0 & 0 & \cdots & S_k \end{bmatrix} \qquad (9.2)$$

---

[4] This section may be skipped without loss of continuity.

In the case of directed graphs the incidence matrix has a slightly different form. The elements, s_{ij}, may have the values $-1, 0, +1$, under the following conditions:

1. $s_{ij} = 0$ if the arc is not incident with a vertex.
2. $s_{ij} = +1$ if the arc is oriented away from the vertex.
3. $s_{ij} = -1$ if the arc is oriented toward the vertex.

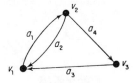

Figure 9.16.

Consider the directed graph shown in Figure 9.16. The corresponding incidence matrix is shown below:

$$S = \begin{array}{c} \\ v_1 \\ v_2 \\ v_3 \end{array} \begin{array}{cccc} a_1 & a_2 & a_3 & a_4 \\ \left[\begin{array}{cccc} +1 & -1 & -1 & 0 \\ -1 & +1 & 0 & +1 \\ 0 & 0 & +1 & -1 \end{array}\right] \end{array} \qquad (9.3)$$

A circuit matrix contains columns corresponding to edges and rows corresponding to the circuits. The circuit matrix for the graph shown in Figure 9.17 is given below:

$$C = \begin{array}{c} \\ c_1 \\ c_2 \\ c_3 \\ c_4 \\ c_5 \\ c_6 \end{array} \begin{array}{cccccc} e_1 & e_2 & e_3 & e_4 & e_5 & e_6 \\ \left[\begin{array}{cccccc} 1 & 1 & 0 & 0 & 0 & 0 \\ 1 & 0 & 1 & 0 & 1 & 1 \\ 0 & 0 & 1 & 1 & 1 & 0 \\ 0 & 1 & 0 & 1 & 0 & 1 \\ 0 & 1 & 1 & 0 & 1 & 1 \\ 0 & 1 & 0 & 1 & 0 & 1 \end{array}\right] \end{array} \qquad (9.4)$$

The circuits are defined as follows: $c_1 = \{e_1, e_2\}$, $c_2 = \{e_1, e_3, e_5, e_6\}$, $c_3 = \{e_3, e_4, e_5\}$, $c_4 = \{e_2, e_4, e_6\}$, $c_5 = \{e_2, e_3, e_5, e_6\}$, $c_6 = \{e_2, e_4, e_6\}$.

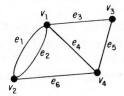

Figure 9.17.

Although it is possible to define several additional matrix representations of graphs [1], we will conclude this section by discussing one further matrix: the *connection matrix*. This matrix, denoted by $\mathbf{K} = \{k_{ij}\}$, has one row and one column for each node of the graph [2]. Our only use of this matrix

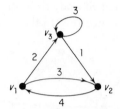

Figure 9.18.

will be in connection with directed graphs. k_{ij} will be the number, value, etc., associated with the arc directed from vertex i to vertex j. The connection matrix for the graph shown in Figure 9.18 has the form:

$$\mathbf{K} = \begin{array}{c} \\ u_1 \\ u_2 \\ u_3 \end{array} \begin{array}{c} \begin{array}{ccc} v_1 & v_2 & v_3 \end{array} \\ \begin{bmatrix} 0 & 3 & 2 \\ 4 & 0 & 0 \\ 0 & 1 & 3 \end{bmatrix} \end{array} \qquad (9.5)$$

9.9   Signal Flow Graphs[5]

A *signal flow graph* consists of directed edges, or arcs, connected at vertices we shall call *nodes* [6]. Concern for flow graphs has evolved primarily in electrical engineering as a device to facilitate the analysis of complex feedback systems. In operations research flow graphs have been subject to discussion more than anything else. They have been used primarily as a teaching device. There are only a few references to their application in the literature. These have been centered around queueing theory (e.g., [7]).

Basically a flow graph is used to represent a causal relationship such as $y = ax$. This equation is shown in flow graph form in Figure 9.19. The

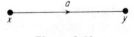

Figure 9.19.

direction of the arc indicates that y is the dependent variable and x is the independent variable. In the analysis of flow graphs, the convention is to place the arrowhead in the center of the arc. We shall retain this in an effort to differentiate this discussion from that of network flows which is to follow.

---

[5] This section may be skipped without loss of continuity.

The word signal that we have been using stems from the original application of flow graphs. Usually nodes correspond to signals. The dependency between nodes (or signals) is pictured by a directed edge, or arc. In this section we shall be concerned only with linear relationships. The flow graphs corresponding to such relationships are sometimes referred to as *linear signal flow graphs*.

We shall develop an abstract framework for the analysis of flow graphs and then follow this by an example. Consider a set of N equations in N unknowns that are consistent and not redundant

$$\mathbf{Fx} = -\mathbf{y} \tag{9.6}$$

where $\mathbf{y} = \{y_i\}$, $\mathbf{x} = \{x_i\}$, $\mathbf{F} = \{f_{ij}\}$ for $i, j = 1, \ldots, N$.

Rearranging we have

$$\mathbf{Fx} + \mathbf{y} = 0$$

Add $\mathbf{x}$ to both sides

$$\mathbf{Fx} + \mathbf{x} + \mathbf{y} = \mathbf{x} \tag{9.7}$$

Rearranging this equation we obtain

$$[(\mathbf{F} + \mathbf{I}), \mathbf{I}]\begin{bmatrix} \mathbf{x} \\ \mathbf{y} \end{bmatrix} = \mathbf{x} \tag{9.8}$$

We shall define a connection matrix for this set of equations as follows [5]:

$$\mathbf{K} = \begin{bmatrix} (\mathbf{F} + \mathbf{I}) & \mathbf{I} \\ 0 & 0 \end{bmatrix}^T = \begin{bmatrix} (\mathbf{F}^T + \mathbf{I}) & 0 \\ \mathbf{I} & 0 \end{bmatrix} \tag{9.9}$$

On many occasions the expression of equation (9.7) will have $\mathbf{y} = \mathbf{h}y_0$. Where $\mathbf{h} = [h_i]$ is a column vector with N parameters. In this case equation (9.8) has the form

$$[(\mathbf{F} + \mathbf{I}), \mathbf{h}]\begin{bmatrix} \mathbf{x} \\ y_0 \end{bmatrix} = \mathbf{x} \tag{9.10}$$

The connection matrix for this case is

$$\mathbf{K} = \begin{bmatrix} \mathbf{F} + \mathbf{I} & \mathbf{h} \\ 0 & 0 \end{bmatrix}^T = \begin{bmatrix} \mathbf{F}^T + \mathbf{I} & 0 \\ \mathbf{h}^T & 0 \end{bmatrix}$$

As an example of this case consider a set of equations discussed by Huggins [8]:

$$
\begin{aligned}
x_1 &= ay_0 && + gx_2 + fx_3 \\
x_2 &= bx_1 + cx_2 \\
x_3 &= ex_1 + dx_2 \\
x_4 &= && x_3
\end{aligned}
$$

Here we have

$$\mathbf{F} + \mathbf{I} = \begin{bmatrix} 0 & g & f & 0 \\ b & c & 0 & 0 \\ e & d & 0 & 0 \\ 0 & 0 & 1 & 0 \end{bmatrix}$$

$$\mathbf{h} = \begin{bmatrix} a \\ 0 \\ \vdots \\ 0 \end{bmatrix}$$

The connection matrix has the following form

$$\mathbf{K} = \begin{array}{c} \\ x_1 \\ x_2 \\ x_3 \\ x_4 \\ y_0 \end{array} \begin{array}{c} \begin{array}{ccccc} x_1 & x_2 & x_3 & x_4 & y_0 \end{array} \\ \begin{bmatrix} 0 & b & e & 0 & 0 \\ g & c & d & 0 & 0 \\ f & 0 & 0 & 1 & 0 \\ 0 & 0 & 0 & 0 & 0 \\ a & 0 & 0 & 0 & 0 \end{bmatrix} \end{array}$$

The corresponding flow graph is shown in Figure 9.20. The rows of $\mathbf{K}$ indicate where an arc originates and columns indicate which node is connected by the arc. For example $\mathbf{K}$ indicates there is an arc between node x_1 and node x_2 with associated value b.

At this point we shall make certain definitions related to signal flows. We note that there are specific conflicts between definitions of the flow graph literature [6, 9] and the literature on network flows such as Ford and Fulkerson [2]. One conflict is that the flow graph literature defines a path in the same way we have defined a chain here. The reader pursuing the flow graph literature should note these differences.

Using Figure 9.20 we review some old definitions and make new ones. An example of a chain is $a, e, 1$. A closed chain, or circuit, is a, b, g, a. The parameters assigned to each arc a, b, c, d, e, f, b are called *transmittances*. The product $a \cdot e \cdot 1$ is called a *chain transmittance*. The node y_0 is called a *source* or *independent node*. It is a node for which $\delta^-(y_0) = 0$. Likewise, x_4 is called a *sink* or *dependent node*. Note that $\delta^+(x_4) = 0$.

The *graph* transmittance, G_t, is defined as the ratio of the dependent node to the independent node. In our example

$$\frac{x_4}{y_0} = G_t$$

In the solution of a set of linear equations it will be our goal to express the

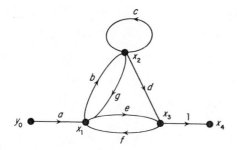

Figure 9.20.

dependent variable as a function of the independent variable and the parameters of the system:

$$x_4 = G_t y_0$$

Mason [9] has developed a fundamental relationship for finding the graph transmittance. This is stated without proof in the following theorem.

Theorem: *The graph transmittance, G_t, between a source and sink is given by*

$$G_t = \frac{\sum_k P_k \Delta_k}{\Delta} \tag{9.11}$$

where:

1. P_k is the *chain transmittance* from source to the sink of concern
2. Δ is the *graph determinant*, where

$$\Delta = (1 - C_1)(1 - C_2)\cdots(1 - C_n)^* \tag{9.12}$$

c_i is the cycle transmittance of the ith cycle and the asterisk indicates that products including two or more cycles with a common node are not included.

3. Δ_k is the *chain factor*. It is found from the graph determinant by striking out all cycles that touch nodes incident to the path of concern.

Note that an alternative form of the graph determinant is

$$\Delta = \left(1 - \sum_i C_i + \sum_{i,j} C_i C_j - \sum_{i,j,k} C_i C_j C_k + \cdots\right)^* \tag{9.13}$$

where the asterisk still has the same meaning. In the example there are four cycles:

$$C_1 = bg \qquad C_2 = ef \qquad C_3 = C \qquad C_4 = bdf$$

Therefore

$$\Delta = 1 - (C_1 + C_2 + C_3 + C_4) + C_2 C_3$$
$$= 1 - bg - ef - c - bdf + cef$$

$$G_t = \frac{x_4}{x_0} = \frac{(1 - C_3)P_1 + P_2}{\Delta}$$

$$G_t = \frac{(1 - c)ae + abd}{1 - bg - ef - c - bdf + cef}$$

The process of forming the graph transmittance has analogous operations in the solution of linear equations. The interested reader should see Seshu and Reed [5] or Lorens [10]. Note that determination of a graph transmittance requires the existence of a source and a sink. However, it is also interesting that in the example these are artificial in the sense that they are identical with other nodes in the graph. Using this artificial node concept it seems that we could express any dependent node as a function of the graph transmittance and independent node. This will be our main concern in the discuscussion to follow.

Markov Chains

We consider the example of a Markov chain discussed in Section 7.3. The transition probability matrix has the following form:

$$\pi = \begin{bmatrix} 0.4 & 0.6 \\ 0.3 & 0.7 \end{bmatrix}$$

The initial state vector $P(0) = (1, 0)$. The difference equations corresponding to equation (7.3) are as follows:

$$p(1; t + 1) = 0.4p(1; t) + 0.3p(2; t)$$
$$p(2; t + 1) = 0.6p(1; t) + 0.7p(2; t) \tag{9.14}$$

The z-transform of these equations yields

$$z^{-1}[P(1; z) - p(1; 0)] = 0.4P(1; z) + 1.3P(2; z)$$
$$z^{-1}[P(2; z) - p(2; 0)] = 0.6P(1; z) + 0.7P(2; z)$$

Rearranging

$$P(1; z) = p(1; 0) + 0.4zP(1; z) + 0.3zP(2; z)$$
$$P(2; z) = p(2; 0) + 0.6zP(1; z) + 0.7zP(2; z)$$

These equations have the form of equation (9.7) where $\mathbf{y}$ corresponds to the initial state vector $\mathbf{P}(0)$. In matrix notation $\mathbf{P}(z) = \mathbf{P}(0) + z\pi\mathbf{P}(\mathbf{z})$. The nodes of the flow graph correspond to the functionals $P(1; z)$ and $P(2; z)$. Sources correspond to the elements of the initial state vector $\mathbf{P}(0) = [p(1; 0), p(2; 0)]$.

The connection matrix is shown below:

$$\mathbf{K} = \begin{bmatrix} 0.4z & 0.6z & 0 & 0 \\ 0.3z & 0.7z & 0 & 0 \\ 1 & 0 & 0 & 0 \\ 0 & 1 & 0 & 0 \end{bmatrix} \tag{9.15}$$

The columns of zeros are indicative of source nodes. The flow graph for this example is shown in Figure 9.21. The relationship $P(1; z) = P(1; z)$ has been added so that we may ultimately obtain $P(1; z)$.

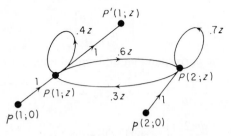

Figure 9.21.

From Mason's theorem we get

$$G_t = \frac{1 - 0.7z}{1 - 0.4z - 0.18z^2 + 0.28z^2} \tag{9.16}$$

$$= \frac{\frac{1}{3}}{1 - z} + \frac{\frac{2}{3}}{(1 - 0.1z)} \tag{9.17}$$

By turning to Section 7.3 the reader may verify that G_t yields elements of the matrix $(\mathbf{I} - z\pi)^{-1}$ and that

$$P(1; z) = p(1; 0) \qquad G_t = p(1; 0)\left[\frac{\frac{1}{3}}{1 - z} + \frac{\frac{2}{3}}{1 - 0.1z}\right]$$

It is not difficult to deduce that for some arbitrary transition probability matrix, π,

$$\mathbf{K} = \begin{bmatrix} z\pi & 0 \\ \mathbf{I} & 0 \end{bmatrix}$$

Actually we have another method of finding transient solutions to Markov chains. However, this is only part of the value of the technique. The flow graph is a picture of all possible transitions in the chain. Also, ignoring source and sink nodes the transmittances are simply the elements of the stochastic matrix π each of which has been multiplied by z.

The implications are apparent. If we know the transition matrix and initial state vector for a Markov chain, we can write down the corresponding flow graph immediately. There is no need to write equations describing the system.

Continuous Time Markov Processes

The analysis of continuous time Markov processes is completely analogous to the discrete time case, because the Laplace transform generates a system of linear algebraic equations from a set of simultaneous differential equations.

Suppose we have a Markov process with the following differential rate matrix:

$$\mathbf{A} = \begin{bmatrix} -\lambda & \lambda \\ \mu & -\mu \end{bmatrix}$$

Let $\mathbf{P}(0) = (1, 0)$. The corresponding differential equations are

$$\frac{dp(1;t)}{dt} = -\lambda p(1;t) + \mu p(2;t)$$

$$\frac{dp(2;t)}{dt} = \lambda p(1;t) - \mu p(2;t)$$

Taking the Laplace transform yields

$$s[P(1;s) - p(1;0)] = -\lambda P(1;s) + \mu P(2;s)$$
$$s[P(2;s) - p(2;0)] = \lambda P(1;s) - \mu P(2;s)$$

Rearranging

$$P(1;s) = (1/s)p(1;0) - (\lambda/s)P(1;s) + (\mu/s)P(2;s)$$
$$P(2;s) = (1/s)p(2;0) + (\lambda/s)P(1;s) - (\mu/s)P(2;s)$$

The connection matrix is

$$\mathbf{K} = \begin{bmatrix} -\lambda/s & \mu/s & 0 & 0 \\ \lambda/s & \mu/s & 0 & 0 \\ 1/s & 0 & 0 & 0 \\ 0 & 1/s & 0 & 0 \end{bmatrix} \tag{9.18}$$

The corresponding flow graph is shown in Figure 9.22. The graph transmittance yields

$$G_t = \frac{\lambda/s^2}{1 + \lambda/s - \lambda\mu/s^2 + \mu/s + \lambda\mu/s^2}$$

$$= \frac{\lambda}{s(s + \lambda + \mu)}$$

Recall that $G_t = [P'(2; s)/p(1; 0)]$. Thus $P(2; s) = p(1; 0)G_t$. This is the Laplace transform of the probability of being in state 2 at a time t given the system was initially in state 1 at $t = 0$.

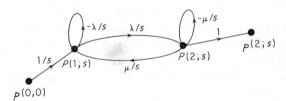

Figure 9.22.

Once again the flow graph could have been drawn without using the equations describing the system. In this case the first step is again to draw a picture of all possible transitions. The transmittances are obtained by multiplying the elements of the differential rate matrix by $1/s$. These become the transmittances of the graph.

The methods discussed here are particularly helpful when the number of states in the process is small and the differential rate matrix contains many zeros. When one or both of these conditions do not hold, finding the graph transmittance becomes practically impossible. Until an efficient algorithm is developed for finding the graph transmittance, the flow graph will be of only occasional value in finding closed form transient solutions for Markov processes.

The signal flow graph for a Markov process has a one-to-one correspondence with the wiring diagram for an analog computer [7]. Thus, the wiring diagram for transient analysis of Markov processes can be obtained from the flow graph without writing the differential equations describing the system.

9.10   Network Flows

By far the most attention to graph theory by operations researchers has been directed toward the analysis of *networks*. The formal structure of these problems is not new to us. Networks consist of a set of vertices, which we call *nodes*, connected by a set of arcs. Normally there is some number associated with each arc that may be cost, time, distance, and so on.

Although there are certain general results in this area, many problems considered are highly specialized. Efficient algorithms have been developed for solving these problems. Because of the diverse nature of the applications of graph theory in this area we must direct our attention toward the conceptual areas of problem formulation and analysis. We shall not attempt to develop algorithms for all problems discussed. As far as possible many of these will be left to the exercises.

Maximal Flow

For each arc directed from node i to node j our network will have a capacity $c_{ij} \geq 0$. We shall be concerned only with networks having one source and one sink: networks G, having a set of nodes, N, and a set of arcs, $A : G(N, A)$.

One of our first concerns is the maximal flow in a network: Given a network G and the capacity restrictions c_{ij}, what is the maximal flow from source to sink? Let n_1 be the source and n_N be the sink. A *flow, of amount v from n_1 to n_N*, is function x having components x_{ij} for all i and j that satisfies the following equations

$$\sum_{j=1}^{N} x_{ij} - \sum_{j=1}^{N} x_{ji} = \begin{matrix} v & i = 1 \\ -v & i = N \\ 0 & i \neq 1, N \end{matrix} \qquad (9.19)$$

where

$$0 \leq x_{ij} \leq c_{ij} \qquad (9.20)$$

x_{ij} is the quantity of flow from n_i to n_j. Our problem is to maximize the flow v subject to constraints (9.19) and (9.20).

A *cut* separating n_1 and n_N is a partitioning of the nodes into two complementary sets say I and J such that there are no chains joining n_1 and n_N. The set of arcs joining I and J is sometimes called a *cut* [2]. It will be denoted (I, J). This should not be confused with a cut set that is defined for the equivalent undirected graph. The capacity of the cut is

$$\sum_{\substack{n_i \in I \\ n_j \in J}} c_{ij}$$

The cut, separating source and sink, of minimum capacity is a *minimal cut*.

Consider the example in Figure 9.23(a). The first number in each pair beside the arc is the capacity. The second number is the arc flow. If $I = \{n_1, n_3, n_4\}$ the cut capacity is $c_{12} + c_{35} + c_{46} = 17$. Note that the cut capacity is the sum of the capacities of the members of the cut.

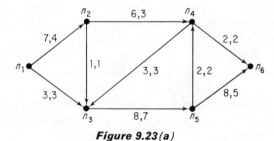

Figure 9.23(a)

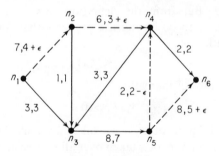

Figure 9.23(b)

Lemma: *Let v be a flow from n_1 to n_N in a network $(N:A)$. If I, J, is a cut separating n_1 and n_N then*

$$v = \sum_{\substack{n_i \in I \\ n_j \in J}} (x_{ij} - x_{ji}) \le \sum_{\substack{n_i \in I \\ n_j \in J}} c_{ij} \qquad (9.21)$$

Intuitively this theorem says that, for any flow and an arbitrary cut, the flow across the cut is equal to the flow from the source, v, and that this flow is bounded from above by the cut capacity. Proof of the lemma may be found in reference [2]. The theorem below gives the conditions under which the equality holds. In turn it provides a basis for finding maximal flow.

Theorem: *For any network, the maximal flow amount from source to sink is equal to the minimal cut capacity relative to the source and sink.*

PROOF. From the previous lemma we see that the theorem is proved if we can find a flow x and a cut (I, J) for which the equality flow value and cut capacity hold. For a cut (I, J) suppose maximum flow is equal to cut capacity:

$$\sum_{\substack{n_i \in I \\ n_j \in J}} x_{ij} = \sum_{\substack{n_i \in I \\ n_j \in J}} c_{ij} \qquad (9.22)$$

where

$$\sum_{\substack{n_j \in J \\ n_i \in I}} x_{ji} = 0 \qquad (9.23)$$

Under conditions of maximal flow, suppose the cut is defined as follows:

1. $n_i \in I$.
2. If $n_i \in I$ and $x_{ij} < c_{ij}$ then $n_j \in I$.
3. If $n_i \in I$ and $x_{ji} > 0$ then $n_j \in I$.

Now we wish to show that $n_N \in J$. In order to do this, we suppose it is not. This means $n_N \in I$. But from the definitions above, this indicates there exists a path from n_1 to n_N having the property that for all forward arcs, (n_i, n_{i+1}) of the path

$$x_{i,i+1} < c_{i,i+1}$$

and for all reverse arcs of the path

$$x_{i+1,i} > 0$$

Let ϵ_1 be the minimum of $c_{ij} - x_{ij}$ taken over all forward arcs of the path. Let ϵ_2 be the minimum of x taken over all reserve arcs. Define

$$\epsilon = \min(\epsilon_1, \epsilon_2) > 0$$

Now we will alter the flow x as follows: (1) increase x by ϵ on all forward arcs of the path, (2) decrease x by ϵ on all reverse arcs. It is easy to deduce that the new flow from n_1 to n_N is $v + \epsilon$. But this means the original flow was not maximal, which contradicts the original assumption. Hence $n_N \in J$.

This means that (I, J) is a cut separating source, n_1, and sink, n_N. From the definition above of the cut, then it follows

$$x_{ij} = c_{ij} \qquad (n_i, n_j) \in (I, J)$$

$$x_{ij} = 0 \qquad (n_j, n_i) \in (J, I)$$

Therefore

$$\sum_{\substack{n_i \in I \\ n_j \in J}} x_{ij} = \sum_{\substack{n_i \in I \\ n_j \in J}} c_{ij} \tag{9.24}$$

$$\sum_{\substack{n_i \in I \\ n_j \in J}} x_{ij} = 0 \tag{9.25}$$

and the theorem is proved.

This theorem is sometimes called the *max flow min cut theorem*. The proof is taken from Ford and Fulkerson [2].

A path from n_1 to n_N is a *flow-augmenting path* with respect to a flow x if $x_{ij} < c_{ij}$ on forward arcs of the path and $x_{ij} > 0$ on reverse arcs of the path. The dotted lines in Figure 9.23(b) indicate a flow-augmenting path in our example.

In this section we are concerned with examining cuts for minimal cut capacity or maximum flow. The following theorem is useful in determining when maximal flow has been reached.

Theorem: *A flow v from source to sink is maximal if and only if there is no flow-augmenting path with respect to v.*

Proof of the theorem is found in [2]. We will use the previous example to demonstrate the use of this theorem.

We would like to make the flow change, ϵ, as large as possible. With inspection of Figure 9.24 we see this is $\epsilon = 2$. A labeling process has been developed to systematically search for flow-augmenting paths [2]. If no such paths exists, the process terminates by locating a minimal cut. The following theorem will prove useful later. Proof may be found in [2]:

Theorem: *A cut (I, J) is minimal if and only if every maximal flow x saturates $(x_{ij} - c_{ij})$ all arcs (I, J) where all arcs (J, I) are flowless $(x_{ji} = 0)$.*

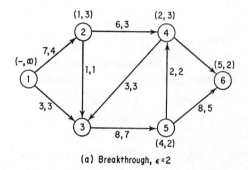

(a) Breakthrough, $\epsilon = 2$

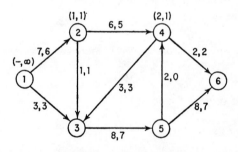

(b) Terminate, maximal flow = 9

Figure 9.24. Example of labeling process. Circles numbers indicate node numbers.

Labeling

We can start the algorithm assuming zero flow or some other feasible flow. Also, capacity restrictions will be assumed to have integer values. This restriction presents no loss in generality [2]. The process has two parts: (1) a labeling sequence that can terminate if a flow is maximal or go to (2) which results in a flow of higher value. A *label* consists of assigning the flow change ϵ to an arc.

Routine 1: This routine is the labeling process.

(a) Label the source $(-, \infty)$.

(b) (i) If n_i is a labeled node, n_j an unlabeled node, and if $x_{ij} < c_{ij}$ label n_j with $[n_i, \epsilon(n_j)]$ where $\epsilon(n_j) = \min [\epsilon(n_i), c_{ij} - x_{ij}]$. This rule holds when the arc from n_i to n_j is in the same direction as the path.

(ii) If n_i is a labeled node, n_j an unlabeled node, and if $x_{ji} > 0$ label n_j with $[n_i, \epsilon(n_j)]$ where $\epsilon(n_j) = \min [\epsilon(n_i), x_{ij}]$.

(c) Repeat (b) (i) or (b) (ii) until:

(i) The sink is labeled. Go to Routine 2.

(ii) No more labels can be assigned and the sink is unlabeled. Terminate. Flow is maximal.

Routine 2: This is the flow change routine.

(a) For nodes labeled in (b)(i), flow will be added $x_{ij} + \epsilon$.

(b) For nodes labeled in (b)(ii), flow will be decreased, $x_{ji} - \epsilon$.

(c) Choose $\epsilon = \epsilon(N)$.

This algorithm will continue to yield flow-augmenting paths until it terminates at labeled sink. This occasion is called a *breakthrough* and indicates that a maximal flow has been obtained. Its value may be obtained from the minimal cut capacities. In Figure 9.24 the labeling process has been applied to the network shown in Figure 9.23(a).

The next theorem is of some use in determining what values to assign to ϵ during this process.

Theorem: *If arc capacities are integers, there exists a maximal flow that is integer valued.*

Proof of this theorem is found in [2].

Minimal Cost Flows

Consider a network $D = (N, A)$ where each arc has a capacity c_{ij} and a unit cost k_{ij}. We wish to construct a flow from source to sink that minimizes the total flow cost

$$\min \sum_{\text{all } i,j} k_{ij} x_{ij}$$

We require however that we send v units from source to sink. Here we treat v as a parameter. The following theorem is central in finding minimal cost flows.

Theorem: *Let x be a minimal cost flow from source to sink of amount v. Then the flow obtained from x by adding $\epsilon > 0$ to the flow in the forward arcs of a minimal cost flow-augmenting path and subtracting the flow in reverse arcs of this path is a minimal cost flow of amount $v + \epsilon$.*

The proof of this theorem has been cited by Fulkerson [13]. With this statement we can now see how to set an algorithm for minimal cost flows. If all costs, k_{ij}, are nonnegative we could obtain minimal cost flows, using this theorem, for specific values of v. However, we still must develop a method for finding a minimal cost flow-augmenting path. The *out-of-kilter algorithm* of Ford and Fulkerson [2] is one such algorithm that has received considerable attention. Space does not allow this method to be covered here.

9.11   Shortest Route Problems

The *shortest route problem* has been a traditional area of concern in operations research. At this time there are numerous algorithms for solution of this problem—some have been summarized by Pollock and Wiebenson [14]. We shall derive an algorithm presented by Busacker and Saaty [1]. It is presented not as an efficient algorithm but simply as an indication of the application of graph theory in this area.

We shall be concerned with a network $D = (N, A)$ where every two nodes are connected. Associated with every arc is a real number called its *length*. We will assume the lengths are additive. Given node n_0 we wish to find the shortest chain from n_0 to every other node in D reachable from n_0. We will define $\lambda(a)$ to be the length of the arc a.

It is easy to see that if there is a cycle C_1 in the network such that $\lambda(C_1) > 0$ where C_1 is incident with one of the vertices reachable from n_0 the distance is unbounded. Hence we assume that for all cycles $\lambda(C_1) > 0$. This then will exclude all cycles from consideration and we shall be concerned only with simple chains.

We define a *shortest distance tree* T relative to reference node n_0 as a directed tree rooted at n_0, such that the tree chain from n_0 to each tree vertex $w \neq n_0$ is the shortest chain from n_0 to w. We want to find the *maximal shortest distance tree*, which is a shortest distance tree that includes every vertex reachable from n_0.

Theorem: *Let T be a tree in a directed graph $D = (N, A)$ rooted at n_0 and containing all vertices reachable from n_0. If n is any node of T, $L(n)$, denote the tree distance from n_0 to n with $L(n_0) = 0$. Then T is the shortest distance tree relative to n_0, if and only if every chord (n, w), whose end points are both in T satisfies*

$$L(w) \leq L(n) + \lambda(n, w) \tag{9.26}$$

PROOF. *Necessity.* If $L(w) > L(n) + \lambda(n, w)$, $L(w)$ is clearly not the minimum distance tree. This follows since we could construct a new tree from $L(n)$ and the chord (n, w).

Sufficiency. This part of the argument will be proved by contradiction.

Suppose T is not the shortest distance tree. Let $P = a_1 \cdots a_n$ be the shortest chain. Let $a_{i+1} = (n_i, n_{i+1})$ be the first arc of P that is not an arc of T.

Because P is the shortest distance from n_0 to n, it must be the shortest chain as far as n_j, $j = 1, \ldots, N$. But this means that $\lambda(P_i) = L(n_i)$ because the chain and tree intersect at n_i.

We have assumed $L(n_{i+1})\lambda(P_{i+1})$. But $(P_{i+1}) = L(n) + (a_{i+1})$. Therefore we have produced an arc a_{i+1} such that its end points satisfy

$$L(w) > L(n) + \lambda(n, w)$$

But this contradicts our original statement and thus the theorem is proved.

We will now develop an algorithm, given by Busacker and Saaty [1] for finding the maximal shortest distance tree:

STEP 1. Take T_0 as any tree rooted at n_0 that includes all vertices reachable from n_0.

STEP 2. Given any tree T_i let $L_i(n)$ denote the distance from n_0 to n through T_i. If every chord (n, w) satisfies

$$L_i(w) \leq L_i(n) + \lambda(n, w) \qquad (9.27)$$

then the theorem above tells us T_i is the maximal shortest distance tree.

STEP 3. If Step 2 is not satisfied, let (n^*, w^*) be a chord such that

$$L_i(w^*) > L_i(n^*) + \lambda(n^*, w^*) \qquad (9.28)$$

Let T_{i+1} be the tree obtained from T_i by adding chord (n^*, w^*) and deleting the arc from T_i whose terminal vertex is w^*. Note that T_{i+1} is rooted at n_0.

STEP 4. Return to Step 2. We should also point out that we know that the algorithm will converge to an optimum since there are no chains from n_0 to n that have infinitely small lengths. Therefore, at some iteration we must have

$$L_i(w) \leq L_i(n) + \lambda(n, w) \qquad (9.29)$$

for every chord relative to T_i, (v, w).

Example: As an example consider the graph shown in Figure 9.25. (a) shows the original graph. (b) indicates the initial tree T_0. The branch (n_0, n_1) was explored initially. At the next iteration we have

$$L_0(n_3) > L_0(n_4) + \lambda(n_4, n_3)$$

Hence the chord (n_4, n_3) is added and branch (n_1, n_3) is deleted to form T_1.
(c) and (d) show successive steps in the algorithm until the maximal
shortest distance tree is reached in (d).

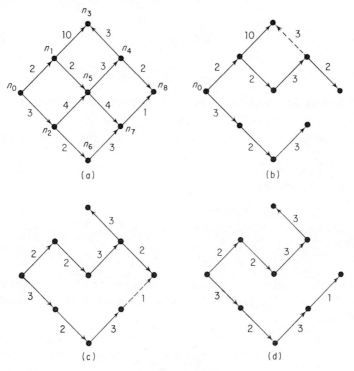

Figure 9.25.

9.12   Transportation Problems

A special class of minimum cost flow problems receiving considerable
attention in the literature are transportation problems. We consider here the
classical transportation problem or the *Hitchcock problem*.

Suppose we have a problem with M sources, each of which has an available
supply a_i, $i = 1, \ldots M$. We have N destinations, or sinks, each of which
has a demand, $b_j, j = 1, \ldots, N$. There is a unit shipping cost, k_{ij}, for shipping
one unit from source i to destination j. The problem is to determine how to
allocate goods from the sources to the destinations in order to minimize
shipping cost and meet demand and supply restrictions. The problem is
stated mathematically as follows:

$$\min z = \sum_{i=1}^{M} \sum_{j=1}^{N} k_{ij} x_{ij} \qquad (9.30)$$

subject to

$$\sum_{j=1}^{N} x_{ij} \leq a_i \qquad i = 1, \ldots, M \tag{9.31}$$

$$\sum_{i=1}^{M} x_{ij} \geq b_j \qquad j = 1, \ldots, N \tag{9.32}$$

$$x_{ij} \geq 0 \qquad \text{all } i \text{ and } j \tag{9.33}$$

The following assumptions can be made without loss of generality:

1. $\displaystyle\sum_{i=1}^{M} a_i \geq \sum_{j=1}^{N} b_j.$

2. $k_{ij} \geq 0 \qquad$ all i and j

3. $a_i, b_j, k_{ij} \quad$ are integers.

Multiplying equation (9.31) by -1

$$-\sum_{j=1}^{N} x_{ij} \geq -a_i \qquad i = 1, \ldots, M \tag{9.34}$$

Consider the problem of minimizing equation (9.30) with constraints (9.34), (9.32), and (9.33). The reader should convince himself that the dual of this problem is

$$\max g = -\sum_{i=1}^{M} a_i u_i + \sum_{j=1}^{N} b_j v_j$$

subject to

$$-u_i + v_j \leq k_{ij} \qquad \text{all } i \text{ and } j$$
$$u_i, v_j \geq 0 \qquad \text{all } i \text{ and } j$$

The complementary slackness conditions at optimality provide the following results:

1. $-u_i + v_j < k_{ij} \qquad$ implies $x_{ij} = 0.$

2. $u_i > 0 \qquad\qquad$ implies $\displaystyle\sum_{j=1}^{N} x_{ij} = a_i.$

3. $v_j > 0 \qquad\qquad$ implies $\displaystyle\sum_{i=1}^{M} x_{ij} = b_j.$

As an example of these relationships consider Table 9.1 taken from [2]. The elements of the array are the unit costs, k_{ij}. The elements across the top row are the demands b_j; the first column contains the available supply a_i.

TABLE 9.1

Costs, Supply, and Demand for a Hitchcock Problem

a_i \ b_j	Demand					
	3	3	6	2	1	2
Supply 4	5	3	7	3	8	5
5	5	6	12	5	7	11
3	2	8	3	4	8	2
9	9	6	10	5	10	9

A feasible primal solution is shown in Table 9.2. The elements correspond to flows x_{ij}.

TABLE 9.2

A Feasible Primal Solution

i \ j	1	2	3	4	5	6
1		2	0			2
2	3	0		1	1	
3			3			
4		1	3	1		

The value of the primal objective function is $z = 93$. Table 9.3 shows a feasible dual solution for the primal solution given in Table 9.2.

TABLE 9.3

A Feasible Dual Solution

u_i \ v_j	5	6	10	5	7	8
3	5	③	⑦	3	8	⑤
0	⑤	⑥	12	⑤	⑦	11
7	2	8	③	4	8	2
0	9	⑥	10	5	10	9

The reader should satisfy himself that the values of v_j shown across the top row, and those of u_i in the first column, are consistent with the complementary slackness conditions. With further examination we find that the value of the dual objective function is $g = 93$. The Fundamental Dual Theorem indicates that the primal and dual solutions given are optimal because the primal and dual objective functions are equal. The elements of Table 9.3 are the unit costs, k_{ij}. The circles correspond to those dual constraints that hold as equalities.

The example is an indication of the strategy we shall use in developing an algorithm. We shall define a feasible dual solution and then try to find a feasible primal solution that satisfies the complementary slackness conditions.

It will be of value to discuss in greater detail the generation of a feasible primal solution once a dual solution is obtained. Consider Figure 9.26

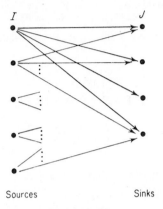

Figure 9.26.

which shows a transportation network with an arbitrary number of sources and an arbitrary number of sinks. In general it is possible to have a flow from every source to every sink. Associated with each arc are a capacity c_{ij} and a unit cost k_{ij}. In our case $c_{ij} = \infty$.

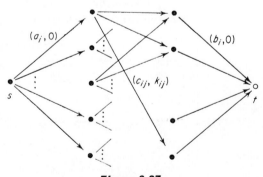

Figure 9.27.

Our approach will be to define a new network as shown in Figure 9.27. This is sometimes called a *reduced network*. We have added a source s having an arc lead to each source with capacity a_i and zero shipping cost. Likewise, we have added a sink with capacity b_j for all j and zero shipping cost.

It can be shown [2] that a maximum flow from s to t will saturate arcs leading to t. That is, for maximum flow $x_{jt} = b_j$ for all j. It is clear then that given a dual feasible solution, we can find a feasible primal solution by solving a maximum flow problem. Mathematically we wish to solve the following:

$$\max z = \sum_{i=1}^{M} \sum_{j=1}^{N} x_{ij} \qquad (9.35)$$

subject to

$$\sum_{j=1}^{N} x_{ij} \le a_i \qquad i = 1, \ldots, M \qquad (9.36)$$

$$\sum_{i=1}^{M} x_{ij} \le b_j \qquad j = 1, \ldots, N \qquad (9.37)$$

$$x_{ij} = 0 \qquad \text{if } -u_i + v_j < k_{ij} \qquad (9.38)$$

$$x_{ij} \ge 0 \qquad \text{otherwise} \qquad (9.39)$$

Arcs corresponding to dual constraints that hold as equalities are called *admissible arcs* in which $x_{ij} \ge 0$. For dual constraints that hold as inequalities we have *inadmissible arcs* where we require $x_{ij} = 0$. The algorithm developed will contain within it a maximum flow problem.

INITIAL SOLUTION: This generates a feasible dual solution.
   Take $u_i = 0$, $v_j = \min_i k_{ij}$, $x_{ij} = 0$ for all i and j.

   ROUTINE 1. Labeling process.

(a) Assign labels $(-, \epsilon_i)$ where

$$\epsilon_i = a_i - \sum_j x_{ij}$$

to all rows i for which

$$\sum_j x_{ij} < a_i$$

(b) Select a labeled row, say row i, and scan it for unlabeled columns j such that cell ij is admissible. Label these (i, δ_j) where $\delta_j = \epsilon_i$. Repeat until all labeled rows have been scanned.
(c) Select a labeled column, say column j. Scan it for unlabeled rows i such that $x_{ij} > 0$. Label these rows with (j, ϵ_i) where $\epsilon_i = \min(x_{ij}, \delta_j)$. Repeat until labeled columns have been scanned.
(d) Repeat (b) for newly labeled rows.
(e) When a column is labeled for which

$$\sum_i x_{ij} < b_j$$

a breakthrough has occurred. Go to Routine 2.
(f) If the process is continued until no more labels can be assigned and (e) is not reached, go to Routine 3.

ROUTINE 2. Flow change

(a) In this case we have labeled columns j with (i, δ_j) where

$$\sum_i x_{ij} < b_j$$

Let

$$\epsilon = \min\left(\delta_j, b_j = \sum_i x_{ij}\right)$$

Add ϵ to x_{ij}.
(b) Proceed in the row to the column singled out by the first member of the label on row i and subtract ϵ.
(c) Proceed in the column to the row singled out by the first member of its label. Add ϵ.
(d) Continue until initially labeled row has been reached.
(e) If all column demands have been satisfied, terminate optimum solution has been obtained. If all demands are not satisfied, discard old labels and go to Routine 1.

ROUTINE 3. Dual variable change. We use this routine when the labeling process has not resulted in a breakthrough.

(a) Let P and Q be the index sets of labeled rows and columns where $\bar{P}$ and $\bar{Q}$ are the complements of P and Q respectively. Define new dual variables by

$$\hat{u}_i = \begin{cases} u_i & i \in P \\ u_i + \delta & i \in \bar{P} \end{cases} \qquad (9.40)$$

$$\hat{v}_j = \begin{cases} v_j & j \in Q \\ v_j + \delta & j \in \bar{Q} \end{cases} \qquad (9.41)$$

where

$$\delta = \min_{P\bar{Q}} (k_{ij} + u_i - v_j)$$

(b) Return to Routine 1 using $\hat{u}_i$ and $\hat{v}_j$.

It can be shown [2] that this algorithm will converge to an optimum, if there is one, in a finite number of steps. The proof is not covered here.

As an example, consider a Hitchcock problem described by the array in Table 9.4(a). At each iteration of the algorithm, carry along two arrays of numbers, one containing unit costs and dual variables, and the other containing flows in the primal problem.

(b) shows the initial feasible dual solution. The circles in (c) correspond to the dual constraints that hold as equalities. Alternatively these are cells in which we may have flow $x_{ij} \geq 0$. However, any feasible flow can be assigned to the circled cells. Note that in noncircled cells x_{ij} must equal zero. The circled numbers are a just feasible primal flow. The column on the far right contains the quantities:

$$a_i - \sum_j x_{ij}, \text{ for all } i$$

This is the supply still remaining at each source. The bottom row contains the quantities:

$$b_j - \sum_i x_{ij}, \text{ for all } j$$

TABLE 9.4
Solution of a Hitchcock Problem

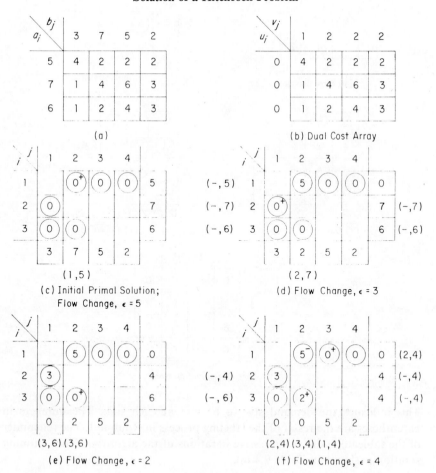

(a)

(b) Dual Cost Array

(1,5)

(c) Initial Primal Solution;
Flow Change, $\epsilon = 5$

(2,7)

(d) Flow Change, $\epsilon = 3$

(3,6)(3,6)

(e) Flow Change, $\epsilon = 2$

(2,4)(3,4)(1,4)

(f) Flow Change, $\epsilon = 4$

TABLE 9.4 (Continued)

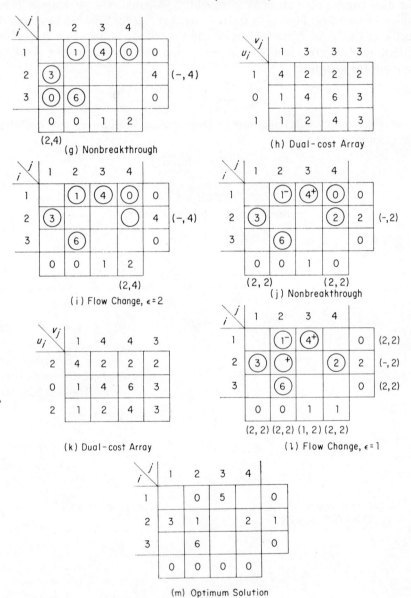

(g) Nonbreakthrough

(h) Dual-cost Array

(i) Flow Change, $\epsilon = 2$

(j) Nonbreakthrough

(k) Dual-cost Array

(l) Flow Change, $\epsilon = 1$

(m) Optimum Solution

This indicates the demand still to be met at each sink. The numbers in parentheses are the result of the labeling process in Routine 1. The remainder of the tableaux indicate successive iterations of the algorithm. The optimum solution is shown in Table 9.4(m).

The Assignment Problem

The assignment problem is a classical problem in operations research. There are many alternative forms of the problem. Usually the problem is equivalent to one assigning N machines to N jobs so that the cost of the assignment is minimized. Each machine can only be assigned to one job. Mathematically, the problem is as follows:

$$\max z = \sum_{i=1}^{N} \sum_{j=1}^{N} k_{ij} x_{ij} \tag{9.42}$$

$$\sum_{j=1}^{N} x_{ij} = 1 \tag{9.43}$$

$$\sum_{i=1}^{N} x_{ij} = 1 \tag{9.44}$$

where $x_{ij} = 0$ if the ith machine is not assigned to the jth job and $x_{ij} = 1$ if it is assigned to the jth job.

With some thought the reader may feel that this problem is a special case of the transportation problem. The following theorem supplies the missing link.

Theorem: *The optimum solution to the assignment problem stated above is the same as the optimum solution to the linear programming problem defined by equations (9.42), (9.43), (9.44), and the constraints $x_{ij} \geq 0$.*

Proof of the theorem is left to the reader as an exercise. Further discussion is found in Dantzig [16].

9.13   The Transshipment Problem

In this section we are concerned with an extension of the Hitchcock problem where shipments to intermediate cities are allowed. The discussion is based on a treatment by Dantzig [16]. We will assume that for every city

$$\text{Gross supply} = \text{amount shipped in and produced}$$
$$= \text{amount shipped out and consumed}$$

Mathematically,

$$\sum_{\substack{i \\ i \neq k}} x_{ik} + a_k^* = \sum_{\substack{j \\ j \neq k}} x_{kj} + b_k^* = x_{kk} \qquad k = 1, \ldots, N \tag{9.45}$$

where we make the following definitions:

$$x_{ik} = \text{amount shipped from } i \text{ to } k,\ i \neq k$$
$$a_k^* = \text{supply, or production, at city } k$$
$$b_k^* = \text{demand, or consumption, at city } k$$
$$x_{kk} = \text{gross supply at city } k$$

We may define net supply, a_k, and net demand as follows:

$$a_k = 0 \text{ if } b_k^* \geq a_k^*$$
$$\quad = a_k^* - b_k^* \text{ if } b_k^* < a_k^* \tag{9.46}$$

$$b_k = 0 \text{ if } a_k^* \geq b_k^*$$
$$\quad = b_k^* - a_k^* \text{ if } a_k^* < b_k^* \tag{9.47}$$

We wish to find the admissible $x_{ij} \geq 0$ such that the objective function is minimized. We will tackle the following optimization problem:

$$\min z = \sum_{i=1}^{N} \sum_{j=1}^{N} k_{ij} x_{ij} \tag{9.48}$$

$$\text{s.t.} \quad \sum_{i=1}^{N} x_{ik} - \sum_{j=1}^{N} x_{kj} = a_k - b_k \qquad k = 1, \ldots, N \tag{9.49}$$

where $x_{ik}, x_{kj} \geq 0$ are admissible.

We choose to develop a method similar to the simplex algorithm on the network to solve this problem. Our aim is to demonstrate certain fundamental equivalences between the analysis of networks and the simplex solution to the linear programming problem.

Theorem: *A network having N nodes is a tree if it has $(N - 1)$ arcs and no cycles.*

Proof of the theorem may be found in Dantzig [16]. This relation will help us prove the following theorem concerning basic variables and the network.

Theorem: *The subnetwork corresponding to a set of basic variables is a tree.*

PROOF. It is obvious that a set of $(N - 1)$ basic variables corresponds to $(N - 1)$ arcs in the network. If we can show there are no cycles in this network, the theorem is proved.

If there is a cycle we would have the following relationship among some number of flows in the cycle:

$$x_{pg} = x_{g1} + x_{g2} + \cdots + x_{rp} \tag{9.50}$$

Let $\mathbf{P}_{ij}$ be the ijth vector in the activity matrix corresponding to equations (9.46).[6] Then a basic solution to the problem has the form

$$\sum_{i} \sum_{j} x_{ij} \mathbf{P}_{ij} = \mathbf{b} \tag{9.51}$$

---

[6] Note also this is the ijth vector in the node–arc incidence matrix discussed in Section 9.8.

If we substitute the relations of equation (9.47) into this, we could derive an alternative basic solution to the problem. But this contradicts the unique property of a basic solution. Hence, there can be no cycles in the network and the theorem is proved.

The theorem indicates that if we can find a basic feasible solution to the transshipment problem, this solution will generate a tree on the equivalent network. The basic variables x_{ij} will be equivalent to flow in the arcs of this tree.

Theorem: *Any subnetwork of a network that is a tree corresponds to a set of basic variables.*

This theorem, which is proved by Dantzig [16], is the converse of the theorem above. We now have enough background to construct the algorithm. There will be two phases,[7] one attempting to find an initial basic feasible solution and the second resulting in an optimal solution.

Phase I (Initial Basic Feasible Solution)

STEP 1. Join each source to other nodes j using only admissible arcs directed away from the source. Join sinks to other nodes using only admissible arcs pointing to the sinks. Repeat the process for nodes that have been connected. Do not form cycles. When a chain from a source meets a sink, connect nodes in the chain to nodes not in the chain with admissible arcs in either direction. Connect remaining unconnected nodes with arcs in either direction. Assign flows to satisfy supply and demand constraints. It can be shown [16] this process yields a tree.

STEP 2. Some basic variables (flows) may be negative in order to satisfy supply and demand. In this case, change the direction of the arc to generate an inadmissible arc. In essence, we let $x_{ij} = -x_{ji}$. This step may generate inadmissible arcs.

STEP 3. If all arcs are admissible, then the tree corresponds to a basic feasible solution. If some arcs are inadmissible, define an alternative transshipment problem that minimizes

$$w = \sum_i \sum_j d_{ij} x_{ij}$$

where

$$d_{ij} = 0 \text{ if } (i, j) \text{ is admissible}$$
$$= 1 \text{ if } (i, j) \text{ is inadmissible}$$

---

[7] This is equivalent to the two-phase method of linear programming.

STEP 4. If min $w > 0$ there is no feasible solution. If min $w = 0$ and no inadmissible arcs remain, we have a basic feasible solution. If min $w = 0$ and inadmissible arcs remain, reverse the direction of the inadmissible arc (i, j), making it admissible and set $x_{ji} = 0$. In this we can still construct a basic feasible solution if there is one.

Phase I of the algorithm has constructed a proof of the following theorem:

Theorem: *If a connected network possesses a feasible solution, then there exists a tree corresponding to a basic feasible solution.*

Phase II: Finding an Optimal Solution

Let $\mathbf{k}_B$ be the vector of unit costs k_{ij} corresponding to the basic variables. $\mathbf{B}$ is the collection of basis vectors. Define

$$z_{ij} = \mathbf{k}_B \mathbf{B}^{-1} \mathbf{P}_{ij} \tag{9.52}$$

Note that $\mathbf{P}_{ij}$ has only two nonzero elements for any value of i and j. Therefore we define $z_{ij} = \pi_j - \pi_i$ where π_j and π_i are dual variables. After completing Phase I we have sufficient information to compute the values of $z_{ij} - k_{ij}$.

STEP 1. Start at a source node i ($x_{ij} = 0$) and make the corresponding $z_{ij} - k_{ij} = 0$ by setting $\pi_i = 0$ and determining π_j for all nodes connected to it. We call these π_j labels. Repeat until all nodes are labeled.

STEP 2. If $k_{ij} - (\pi_j - \pi_i)$ is nonnegative for all arcs, the optimal solution has been obtained. This conclusion is simply an extension of the primal optimality criterion derived in Chapter 3.

STEP 3. Choose the most negative $k_{ij} - (\pi_j - \pi_i)$. This test is used to determine which arc will be used in the next solution.

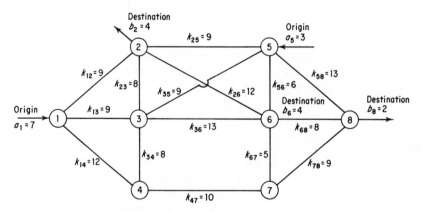

Figure 9.28. A transshipment problem.

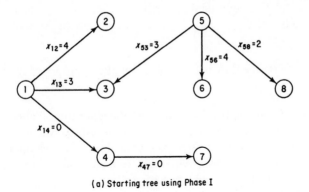

(a) Starting tree using Phase I

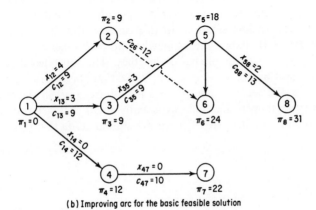

(b) Improving arc for the basic feasible solution

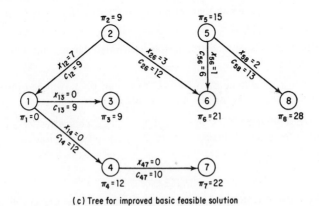

(c) Tree for improved basic feasible solution

Figure 9.29. Solution of a transshipment problem.

STEP 4. We wish to increase x_{ij} by an amount θ while maintaining feasibility. Note that this additional arc creates a cycle. Within the cycle θ must be chosen such that $\hat{x}_{mn} = x_{mn} - \theta = 0$ for some arc in the cycle. Therefore we choose $\theta = \min_{ij} x_{ij}$.

STEP 5. Increase the flow in x_{ij} by θ and make appropriate changes in the arcs of the cycle.

An example from Dantzig [16] illustrates the algorithm. Figure 9.28 shows the network with eight nodes corresponding to cities. Admissible arcs are shown undirected indicating there can be a flow in either direction. Unit shipping costs, k_{ij}, are shown. Although we have assumed in this example $k_{ij} = k_{ji}$, the algorithm is valid when $k_{ij} \neq k_{ji}$.

Figure 9.29(a) shows an initial starting tree found by using Phase I of the algorithm. The values of the flows, x_{ij}, we determined by equations (9.46). Note that x_{53} is not feasible. Reversing the arc and setting $x_{35} = 3$ will produce a basic feasible solution. In this case all arcs are admissible. We proceed to Phase II. Labels are assigned to all nodes using Step 1 recalling that the $k_{ij} - z_{ij} = 0$ for all basic variables. The most negative $k_{ij} - z_{ij}$ is $k_{26} - z_{26}$ and arc [2, 6] is inserted. Note that the insertion of this arc forms a cycle. We set $\theta = \min_{ij} x_{ij} = 3$ for all arcs (i, j) in the cycle. As is the case in the simplex method, we usually break ties arbitrarily. Figure 9.29(c) shows the resulting tree. The reader should verify that this solution is optimal.

Problems

1. Give a physical example of a geometric graph.

2. Prove that a necessary and sufficient condition for a graph $G = (V, E)$ to be connected is that its vertices cannot be partitioned into two nonempty subsets V_1 and V_2 in such a way that both end points of every edge are in the same subset.

3. Prove that every spanning tree has at least one edge in common with every cut set of a graph.

4. Prove that a nonsimple path from v_1 to v_2 can be partitioned into a simple path from v_1 to v_2 and one or more simple cycles.

5. Prove the following: If a simple graph $G = (V, E)$ has n vertices, a necessary condition for a set of vertices $S = (v_1, \ldots, v_k)$ to be a dominating set is that

$$k + \sum_{i=1}^{k} \delta(v_i) \geq n$$

6. Consider the traveling salesman problem defined by the graph in Figure 9.30. Define three hamiltonian circuits for the graph. Use dynamic programming to find the hamiltonian circuit of minimum length.

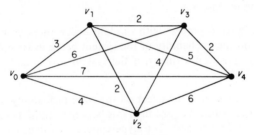

Figure 9.30.

7. Construct the duals of the graphs shown in Figure 9.31.

8. Consider a Markov chain with the transition matrix shown below:

$$\pi = \begin{bmatrix} 0.6 & 0.4 & 0 & 0 & 0 \\ 0 & 0 & 0.5 & 0.5 & 0 \\ 0.3 & 0.2 & 0.5 & 0 & 0 \\ 0.2 & 0 & 0 & 0.1 & 0.7 \\ 0.6 & 0 & 0 & 0.4 & 0 \end{bmatrix}$$

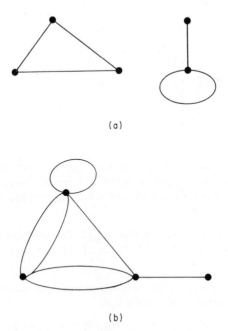

(a)

(b)

Figure 9.31.

If the system is initially in state 1, find the steady-state probability of the system being in state 4.

9. Consider a Poisson process with random occurrences at a rate λ. Use flow graphs to find the probability of the system being in state i after the system has been in operation a time t, if the system was initially in state j, where $j < i$.

10. Use flow graphs to find the effect on the state probability expression for the Poisson process when the time intervals between random occurrences follow: (1) a k-Erlang density and (2) a hyperexponential density.

11. Use flow graphs to draw some conclusion about the effect of k-Erlang time intervals between breakdowns on the steady-state probabilities of the one-machine breakdown problem.

12. Draw the flow graph for the one-machine breakdown problem where time intervals between breakdowns follow a 2-Erlang distribution and the service times follow a hyperexponential distribution. Find the steady-state probability of the machine operating at time t after it has been started. Assume it was running at $t = 0$.

13. (Elmaghraby [15].) Consider a problem where there are 6 jobs to be performed and 5 machines available to do the jobs. The machines are somewhat different in nature and some of them are not able to complete certain jobs. This is shown in the table below.

		JOBS				
	1	2	3	4	5	6
1			0	0	0	
2		0			0	
3	0			0		0
4			0		0	
5		0	0		0	0

(rows labeled MACHINES 1–5)

Some $a_{ij} = 0$ indicates that machine i cannot work on job j. Interpret machines as sources and jobs as sinks. It is desired to assign the maximum number of machines. Formulate and solve the problem as a maximal flow problem.

14. Consider the network shown in Figure 9.32. The numbers shown on each one are the capacities associated with that arc. Find the maximal flow from node 1 to node 9.

15. Formulate a dynamic programming algorithm for the solution of the traveling salesman problem given in Figure 9.30.

16. (Berge [4].) A certain product is shipped from ports P_1, P_2, P_3, and P_4 to ports D_1, D_2, and D_3. The stock available at P_i is a_i and the demand at D_j

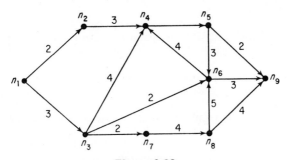

Figure 9.32.

is d_j. Let c_{ij} be the total amount that can be shipped over the route from P_i to D_j by one or more ships using this route. Capacities, available demand, and available stock are shown below.

	D_1	D_2	D_3	a_i
P_1	3	4	2	2
P_2		5	4	9
P_3	5		1	6
P_4		10		1
d_j	6	4	5	

Blanks indicate routes that are not permissible.

What quantities of shipping should be allocated to each route?

To reduce this problem to one of maximal flow connect P_i to D_j, when permissible, by an arc with capacity c_{ij}. Connect a source s_o to each note P_i by an arc of capacity a_i. Connect each D_j to a sink t_o by an arc of capacity d_j. Find maximum flow from source to sink.

17. Formulate Problem 16 as a linear programming problem.

18. (Berge [4].) A wolf, a goat, and a cabbage are on the bank of a river. A ferry man wants to take them across, but since his boat is small, he can take only one of them at a time. Neither the wolf and the goat, nor the goat and cabbage can be left unguarded. How is the ferry man going to get them across?

19. How may the discussion of directed networks in this chapter be applied to networks with undirected arcs? Show this with a numerical example.

20. State the dual of the maximum flow problem.

21. Use duality theory to give an alternative proof of the maximum flow minimum cut theorem.

22. State and prove a minimum flow maximum cut theorem.

23. Consider a maximum flow problem where each node has associated with a capacity k_i. How may this be handled? Demonstrate with a numerical example.

24. In the maximum flow problem, prove that the subnetwork corresponding to a set of basic variables is a tree.

25. Prove that in a finite graph the number of vertices of odd degree is even.

26. Interpret, on a network, the simplex algorithm applied to a transportation problem. Use an example to demonstrate the technique.

27. In the event of alternative optima for the Hitchcock problem, how can these optima be determined?

28. Under what conditions may the traveling salesman problem be formulated as an assignment problem? Give a numerical example.

29. Formulate Problem 25 of Chapter 3 as an assignment problem. Show why this is a special case of the Hitchcock problem. Use the algorithm developed in Section 9.12 to solve the problem.

30. The "marriage game" has been cited by Dantzig [16] as demonstration of the assignment problem. We will consider a version of it here.

   A pioneering colony of 10 bachelors is joined by 10 prospective brides. Each bride is given a list of 10 names on which she is to list her preferences in scale of 10. She may assign her first choice the number 10, her second choice number 9, etc. She may also cross out names unacceptable to her. We assumed that the sum of the assigned numbers constitutes a valid measure of the anticipated happiness of the colony in marital bliss. Show that the above problem can be formulated as a network problem and given the following table find an assignment that gives the greatest total "happiness" where the rating of the jth bachelor by the ith bride is the ending ij in the Table 9.5.

TABLE 9.5

	Bill	Tim	John	Mike	Joe	Fred	Ron	James	Tom	Clyde
Jane	9	6	3	x	2	8	7	4	1	5
Mary	3	7	8	2	1	x	5	4	x	6
Alice	4	2	1	6	x	8	3	9	7	5
Ruth	6	3	5	7	9	x	1	4	2	8
Wanda	7	5	6	9	1	8	3	x	2	4
Cindy	1	10	8	4	5	3	6	9	2	7
Maggie	6	8	10	9	4	3	5	1	7	2
Doris	7	8	4	3	2	6	1	9	5	x
Helen	3	9	4	2	5	6	7	x	8	1
Brenda	9	3	1	8	x	4	2	7	6	5

31. Find the maximum flow from 0 to 4 in the network shown below. The numbers associated with each arc are capacities.

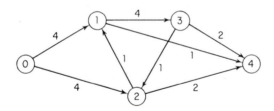

References Cited and Bibliography

[1] Busacker, R. G., and T. L. Saaty. *Finite Graphs and Networks*. New York: McGraw-Hill, 1965.

[2] Ford, L. R., Jr., and D. R. Fulkerson. *Flows in Networks*. Princeton, N.J.: Princeton University Press, 1962.

[3] Ore, Oystein. *Theory of Graphs*. American Mathematical Society Colloquim Publications, Vol. 38, 1962.

[4] Berge, Claude. *The Theory of Graphs*. New York: Wiley, 1962.

[5] Seshu, S., and M. B. Reed. *Linear Graphs and Electrical Networks*. Reading, Mass.: Addison-Wesley, 1961.

[6] Mason, Samuel J. "Feedback Theory—Some Properties of Signal Flow Graphs." *Proceedings of the I.R.E.*, Vol. 41 (September 1953).

[7] Gue, Ronald L. "Signal Flow Graphs and Analog Computation in the Analysis of Finite Queues." *Operations Research*, Vol. 14, No. 2 (March–April 1966).

[8] Huggins, W. H. "Flow Graph Representation of Systems." In *Operations Research and Systems Engineering* (C. D. Flagle, W. H. Huggins, and R. H. Roy, eds.). Baltimore: Johns Hopkins Press, 1960.

[9] Mason, Samuel J. "Feedback Theory—Further Properties of Signal Flow Graphs." *Proceedings of the I.R.E.*, Vol. 44 (July 1956).

[10] Lorens, Charles S. "Theory and Application of Flow Graphs." M.I.T. Technical Report No. 317, Cambridge, 1956.

[11] Sittler, R. W. "Systems Analysis of Discrete Markov Processes." *Transactions of the I.R.E.*, CT-3, 1956.

[12] Huggins, W. H. "Signal Flow Graphs and Random Signals." *Proceedings of the I.R.E.*, Vol. 45, 1957.

[13] Fulkerson, D. R. "Flow Networks and Combinatorial Operations Research." *The American Mathematical Monthly*, Vol. 73, No. 2 (February 1966).

[14] Pollock, M., and W. Wiebenson. "Solutions of the Shortest Route Problem —A Review." *Operations Research*, Vol. 8, No. 2 (1960).

[15] Elmaghaby, Salah. *The Design of Production Systems*. New York: Reinhold, 1966.

[16] Dantzig, George B. *Linear Programming and Extensions*. Princeton, N.J.: Princeton University Press, 1963.

Matrix Algebra

A.1 Definitions

The purpose of this appendix is to give the reader a brief introduction to some of the concepts of matrix algebra. We shall develop those tools that are required to read Chapters 2, 3, 4, and 8. The reader who desires to delve more deeply into matrix algebra is referred to Hadley [1], Perlis [2], Aitken [3], and Gantmacher [4].

Definitions

In this section we shall attempt to give operational definitions rather than mathematically precise ones.

> Set: *A set is a collection of objects or a group of things.*

Normally members of a set have certain properties that allow us to identify them as belonging to the set. As an example consider the set A of all professional baseball players. Any professional baseball player is a member of the set. We can apply a test to determine if a person is a member or element of the set.

> Subset: *A subset B of the set A is a set whose members are elements of A.*

If we define the set A to be the set whose elements (members) are professional baseball players, we can define a set B whose elements consist of all professional baseball players that play in the National League. Thus members of B are also members of A. This is written as

$$B \subset A$$

Point Set: *Point sets are sets whose elements are points.*

For example, we may define the set A as all points x for which $x < 1$. This set is then all values of x less than 1 and A may be written

$$A = \{x \mid x < 1\}$$

which is read as A is the set of points x that satisfy the inequality $x < 1$.

Vector: *An n-component vector* **x** *is an ordered N-tuple of numbers.*

A vector can be either a column vector

$$\mathbf{x} = \begin{pmatrix} x_1 \\ \vdots \\ x_N \end{pmatrix}$$

or a row vector

$$\mathbf{x} = (x_1, \ldots, x_N)$$

The numbers $x_1, \ldots, x_N$ are called components of the vector. The dimension of the vector is the number of components in a vector.

Matrix: *A matrix is an ordered, rectangular array of numbers.*

It may represent an ordered collection of row or column vectors. For example, the $M \times N$ matrix **A**, written $\mathbf{A}_{M \times N}$, whose components are a_{ij}, is displayed as follows:

$$\mathbf{A}_{M \times N} = \begin{pmatrix} a_{11} & a_{12} & \cdots & a_{1N} \\ \vdots & & & \vdots \\ a_{M1} & a_{M2} & \cdots & a_{MN} \end{pmatrix}$$

A matrix has no numerical value—it is just a convenient way of arranging those numbers. However, each square $N \times N$ matrix A has a number associated with it that is called the determinant, written

$$\det \mathbf{A} = |\mathbf{A}| = \begin{vmatrix} a_{11} & \cdots & a_{1N} \\ \vdots & & \vdots \\ a_{N1} & \cdots & a_{NN} \end{vmatrix}$$

The determinant of an $N \times N$ matrix A has order N. For a 2×2 matrix, the determinant is found as follows:

$$\det \mathbf{A}_{2 \times 2} = |\mathbf{A}_{2 \times 2}| = \begin{vmatrix} a_{11} & a_{12} \\ a_{21} & a_{22} \end{vmatrix} = a_{11}a_{22} - a_{21}a_{12}$$

For N greater than 2, we can define the determinant by the following recurrence relationship:

$$\det \mathbf{A}_{N \times N} = \begin{vmatrix} a_{11} & \cdots & a_{1N} \\ \vdots & & \vdots \\ a_{N1} & \cdots & a_{NN} \end{vmatrix}$$

$$= \sum_{j=1}^{N} a_{1j} A_{1j}$$

where the A_{1j} are the cofactors of a_{1j}. The cofactor of a_{1j} is defined as $(-1)^{1+j}$ times the determinant of the matrix formed by deleting from $\mathbf{A}$ the first row and the jth column. For example, let

$$\mathbf{A} = \begin{pmatrix} 3 & 5 & 7 \\ 2 & 4 & 6 \\ -1 & 3 & 2 \end{pmatrix}$$

Then

$$A_{11} = (-1)^{1+1} \begin{vmatrix} 4 & 6 \\ 3 & 2 \end{vmatrix} \qquad A_{12} = (-1)^{1+2} \begin{vmatrix} 2 & 6 \\ -1 & 2 \end{vmatrix}$$

$$A_{13} = (-1)^{1+3} \begin{vmatrix} 2 & 4 \\ -1 & 3 \end{vmatrix}$$

Hence

$$\mathbf{A} = 3 \begin{vmatrix} 4 & 6 \\ 3 & 2 \end{vmatrix} - 5 \begin{vmatrix} 2 & 6 \\ -1 & 2 \end{vmatrix} + 7 \begin{vmatrix} 2 & 4 \\ -1 & 3 \end{vmatrix}$$
$$= 3(-10) - 5(10) + 7(10) = -10$$

Addition of Matrices: *The sum of two matrices* $\mathbf{A}$ *and* $\mathbf{B}$ *is defined as*

$$\mathbf{C} = \mathbf{A} + \mathbf{B}$$

where the elements of $\mathbf{C}$, c_{ij}, *are the sum of the corresponding elements of* $\mathbf{A}$ *and* $\mathbf{B}$. *Hence*

$$c_{ij} = a_{ij} + b_{ij} \qquad i = 1, \ldots, M; j = 1, \ldots, N$$

Addition of two matrices is not defined if the number of rows or columns of the first is different from the number of rows or columns of the second. Notice that the addition operation for vectors and matrices is commutative and associative.

A.2   Multiplication by a Scalar

We may multiply any vector or matrix by a scalar. The result is obtained simply by multiplying every component of the vector or matrix by this scalar. Thus if

$$\mathbf{a} = \alpha\mathbf{b}$$

then $\mathbf{a}$ is a vector whose component a_i is given by

$$a_i = \alpha b_i$$

Similarly, if

$$\mathbf{A} = \alpha\mathbf{B}$$

where $\mathbf{A}$ and $\mathbf{B}$ are both $M \times N$ matrices,

$$a_{ij} = \alpha b_{ij} \qquad i = 1, \ldots, M; \, j = 1, \ldots, N$$

Scalar Product: *The scalar product of two column vectors, $\mathbf{a}$ and $\mathbf{b}$, is the scalar*

$$\mathbf{a}^T\mathbf{b} = \sum_{i=1}^{N} a_i b_i$$

Notice that we took the scalar product of two column vectors and in doing this we introduced the symbol $\mathbf{a}^T$. This symbol defines the transposition operation, which means simply making the column vector a row vector. Thus if

$$\mathbf{a} = \begin{pmatrix} a_1 \\ \vdots \\ a_N \end{pmatrix} \qquad \mathbf{a}^T = (a_1, \ldots, a_N)$$

then

$$\mathbf{a}^T\mathbf{b} = (a_1, \ldots, a_N)\begin{pmatrix} b_1 \\ \vdots \\ b_N \end{pmatrix} = \sum_{i=1}^{N} a_i b_i$$

Matrices also possess transposes. Given a $M \times N$ matrix $\mathbf{A}$, the transpose of $\mathbf{A}$, written $\mathbf{A}^T$, is the $N \times M$ matrix whose element $\hat{a}_{ji}$ is the element a_{ij} of $\mathbf{A}$. For example, if

$$\mathbf{A} = \begin{pmatrix} a_{11} & a_{12} & a_{13} \\ a_{21} & a_{22} & a_{23} \end{pmatrix} = \begin{pmatrix} 2 & 4 & 6 \\ 4 & 6 & 8 \end{pmatrix}$$

$$\mathbf{A}^T = \begin{pmatrix} a_{11} & a_{21} \\ a_{12} & a_{22} \\ a_{13} & a_{23} \end{pmatrix} = \begin{pmatrix} 2 & 4 \\ 4 & 6 \\ 6 & 8 \end{pmatrix}$$

Multiplication of two matrices, **A** and **B**, is defined only under certain conditions. If we write

$$\mathbf{C} = \mathbf{AB}$$

this means **C** equals **B**, premultiplied by **A**. The elements of **C**, c_{ij}, are found by the equation

$$c_{ij} = \sum_{k=1}^{N} a_{ik} b_{kj}$$

Notice that multiplication is defined only if the number of columns of **A** equals the number of rows of **B**. Hence if

$$\mathbf{A} = \begin{pmatrix} 3 & 4 & 5 \\ 1 & -1 & 7 \end{pmatrix} \qquad \mathbf{B} = \begin{pmatrix} 2 & 4 & 6 & 8 \\ 1 & 5 & 7 & -1 \\ -2 & 3 & 5 & 8 \end{pmatrix}$$

$$\mathbf{C} = \mathbf{AB} = \begin{pmatrix} 3 & 4 & 5 \\ 1 & -1 & 7 \end{pmatrix} \begin{pmatrix} 2 & 4 & 6 & 8 \\ 1 & 5 & 7 & -1 \\ -2 & 3 & 5 & 8 \end{pmatrix}$$

$$= \begin{pmatrix} 0 & 47 & 71 & 60 \\ -13 & 20 & 34 & 65 \end{pmatrix}$$

The product **BA** is not defined, because the number of columns of **B** is not the same as the number of rows of **A**.

Each square matrix **A** whose determinant is different from zero possesses an inverse, $\mathbf{A}^{-1}$. The inverse has the property that

$$\mathbf{AA}^{-1} = \mathbf{I}$$

where **I** is a matrix whose elements equal δ_{ik}, where

$$\delta_{ik} = \begin{cases} 1 & i = k \\ 0 & i \neq k \end{cases} \qquad \text{or} \qquad \mathbf{I}_{3 \times 3} = \begin{pmatrix} 1 & 0 & 0 \\ 0 & 1 & 0 \\ 0 & 0 & 1 \end{pmatrix}$$

I is called the identity matrix. It plays a role similar to the number 1 in the real number system. Thus

$$\mathbf{BI} = \mathbf{B}$$

A.3   Solution of Systems of Linear Equations

Suppose we are given the set of M linear equations in N variables x_i, $i = 1, \ldots, N$:

$$
\begin{aligned}
a_{11}x_1 &+ a_{12}x_2 + \cdots + a_{1N}x_N = b_1 \\
a_{21}x_1 &+ a_{22}x_2 + \cdots + a_{2N}x_N = b_2 \\
&\vdots \qquad\qquad\qquad\qquad \vdots \\
a_{M1}x_1 &+ a_{M2}x_2 + \cdots + a_{MN}x_N = b_M
\end{aligned}
$$

We may write these equations in matrix form,

$$\mathbf{Ax} = \mathbf{b}$$

where $\mathbf{A}$ is an $M \times N$ matrix, $\mathbf{x}$ is an N-component column vector, and $\mathbf{b}$ is an M-component column vector. We are interested in obtaining information about the existence and uniqueness of the solution.

Theorem: *The system of equations*

$$\mathbf{Ax} = \mathbf{b}$$

will have a solution if and only if[1]

$$r(\mathbf{A}\!:\!\mathbf{b}) = r(\mathbf{A})$$

where

$$(\mathbf{A}\!:\!\mathbf{b}) = \begin{pmatrix} a_{11} & \cdots & a_{1N} & b_1 \\ a_{21} & \cdots & a_{2N} & b_2 \\ \vdots & & \vdots & \vdots \\ a_{M1} & \cdots & a_{MN} & b_M \end{pmatrix}$$

Since every determinant that can be formed from $\mathbf{A}$ also appears in $(\mathbf{A}\!:\!\mathbf{b})$, we conclude that the rank of $(\mathbf{A}\!:\!\mathbf{b})$ cannot be less than the rank of $\mathbf{A}$. Two other possibilities exist. They are: (1) $r(\mathbf{A}\!:\!\mathbf{b}) > r(\mathbf{A})$, and (2) $r(\mathbf{A}\!:\!\mathbf{b}) = r(\mathbf{A})$. When (1) holds there is no solution, because the vector $\mathbf{b}$ cannot be expressed as a linear combination of the columns of $\mathbf{A}$. In this case the equations are said to be inconsistent.

We shall now consider condition 2. Suppose $r(\mathbf{A}\!:\!\mathbf{b}) = r(\mathbf{A}) = k$. If $k = N$, there is a unique vector $\mathbf{x}$ that satisfies the equations. If $k < N$, there are an infinite number of solutions to the equation

$$\mathbf{Ax} = \mathbf{b}$$

When $k < N$ we can solve for k of the x_i's, say $\mathbf{x}_k$, and express them in terms of the remaining $(N - k)x_i$, say $\mathbf{x}_{N-k}$. Choosing the submatrix of order k that has rank k, we may write the k equations as

$$a_{11}x_1 + \cdots + a_{1N}x_N = b_1$$
$$\vdots \qquad\qquad \vdots \qquad \vdots$$
$$a_{k1}x_1 + \cdots + a_{kN}x_N = b_k$$

Suppose

$$|\mathbf{A}_k| = \begin{vmatrix} a_{11} & \cdots & a_{1k} \\ \vdots & & \\ a_{k1} & \cdots & a_{kk} \end{vmatrix} \neq 0$$

---

[1] The rank of a matrix $\mathbf{A}$, written $r(\mathbf{A})$, is defined as the order associated with the largest nonvanishing determinant in $\mathbf{A}$.

Then we can write

$$\mathbf{A}_k\mathbf{x}_k + \mathbf{B}_{N-k}\mathbf{x}_{N-k} = \mathbf{b}_k$$

where

$$\mathbf{B}_{N-k} = \begin{pmatrix} a_{1,k+1} & \cdots & a_{1N} \\ \vdots & & \vdots \\ a_{k,k+1} & \cdots & a_{kN} \end{pmatrix} \qquad \mathbf{b}_k = \begin{pmatrix} b_1 \\ \vdots \\ b_k \end{pmatrix}$$

$$\mathbf{x}_k = \begin{pmatrix} x_1 \\ \vdots \\ x_k \end{pmatrix} \qquad \mathbf{x}_{N-k} = \begin{pmatrix} x_{k+1} \\ \vdots \\ x_N \end{pmatrix}$$

Since $\det \mathbf{A}_k \neq 0$, $\mathbf{A}_k^{-1}$ exists and thus we may write

$$\mathbf{x}_k = \mathbf{A}_k^{-1}\mathbf{b}_k - \mathbf{A}_k^{-1}\mathbf{B}_{N-k}\mathbf{x}_{N-k}$$

We see that any arbitrary values for $\mathbf{x}_{N-k}$ may be assigned to generate values of $\mathbf{x}_k$.

Example: Given

$$\mathbf{Ax} = \mathbf{b}$$

where

$$\mathbf{A} = \begin{pmatrix} 3 & 5 & 7 \\ 8 & 4 & 2 \\ 4 & 2 & 1 \end{pmatrix} \qquad \mathbf{b} = \begin{pmatrix} 5 \\ 6 \\ 3 \end{pmatrix}$$

$$\det \mathbf{A} = 3\begin{vmatrix} 4 & 2 \\ 2 & 1 \end{vmatrix} - 5\begin{vmatrix} 8 & 2 \\ 4 & 1 \end{vmatrix} + 7\begin{vmatrix} 8 & 4 \\ 4 & 2 \end{vmatrix} = 3(0) - 5(0) + 7(0) = 0$$

However, choosing

$$\mathbf{A}_k = \begin{pmatrix} 3 & 5 \\ 8 & 4 \end{pmatrix}$$

whose determinant is not zero, we conclude that $r(\mathbf{A}_k) = 2$. We now must determine $r(\mathbf{A} : \mathbf{b})$:

$$(\mathbf{A} : \mathbf{b}) = \begin{pmatrix} 3 & 5 & 7 & 5 \\ 8 & 4 & 2 & 6 \\ 4 & 2 & 1 & 3 \end{pmatrix}$$

We must check all possible 3×3 submatrices of $(\mathbf{A} : \mathbf{b})$. They are

$$\begin{pmatrix} 3 & 5 & 5 \\ 8 & 4 & 6 \\ 4 & 2 & 3 \end{pmatrix} \qquad \begin{pmatrix} 3 & 7 & 5 \\ 8 & 2 & 6 \\ 4 & 1 & 3 \end{pmatrix} \qquad \begin{pmatrix} 5 & 5 & 7 \\ 6 & 4 & 2 \\ 3 & 2 & 1 \end{pmatrix}$$

The rank of each of these is 2 and thus $r(\mathbf{A} : \mathbf{b}) = 2$. Hence we have an infinite number of solutions. These solutions may be found as follows. Define

$$\mathbf{A}_k = \begin{pmatrix} 3 & 5 \\ 8 & 4 \end{pmatrix} \quad \mathbf{b}_k = \begin{pmatrix} 5 \\ 6 \end{pmatrix} \quad \mathbf{x}_k = \begin{pmatrix} x_1 \\ x_2 \end{pmatrix}$$

Then

$$\mathbf{B}_{N-k} = \begin{pmatrix} 7 \\ 2 \end{pmatrix} \quad \mathbf{x}_{N-k} = x_3$$

Since

$$\mathbf{A}_k^{-1} = -\frac{1}{28} \begin{pmatrix} 4 & -5 \\ -8 & 3 \end{pmatrix}$$

$$\mathbf{x}_k = -\frac{1}{28} \begin{pmatrix} 4 & -5 \\ -8 & 3 \end{pmatrix} \begin{pmatrix} 5 \\ 6 \end{pmatrix} + \frac{1}{28} \begin{pmatrix} 4 & -5 \\ -8 & 3 \end{pmatrix} \begin{pmatrix} 7 \\ 2 \end{pmatrix} x_3$$

$$= \frac{1}{28} \begin{pmatrix} 10 \\ 22 \end{pmatrix} + \frac{1}{28} \begin{pmatrix} 18 \\ -50 \end{pmatrix} x_3$$

A.4 Quadratic Forms

This section will be devoted to a brief development of quadratic forms. A quadratic form may be written as

$$f(\mathbf{x}) = \mathbf{x}^T \mathbf{A} \mathbf{x}$$

$\mathbf{A}$ is called the matrix of the quadratic form and is a square matrix. Notice that this matrix can always be written as a symmetric matrix ($\mathbf{A} = \mathbf{A}^T$), because the coefficient of $x_i x_j$ is ($a_{ij} + a_{ji}$). If $\mathbf{A}$ is not symmetric, we can construct a new matrix $\mathbf{B}$ with the property that

$$\mathbf{x}^T \mathbf{B} \mathbf{x} = \mathbf{x}^T \mathbf{A} \mathbf{x}$$
$$b_{ij} = b_{ji} = \tfrac{1}{2}(a_{ij} + a_{ji})$$

$\mathbf{B}$ is symmetric by construction.

We are interested in properties of quadratic forms because sufficiency conditions for extreme points may be expressed in terms of a quadratic form. The following definitions will prove useful in our investigation of critical points.

Positive Definite Quadratic Form: *A quadratic form $f(\mathbf{x}) = \mathbf{x}^T \mathbf{A} \mathbf{x}$ is positive definite if $f(\mathbf{x}) > 0$ for all $\mathbf{x}$ with the exception of $\mathbf{x} = \mathbf{0}$.*

Negative Definite Quadratic Form: *A quadratic form $h(\mathbf{x}) = \mathbf{x}^T \mathbf{B} \mathbf{x}$ is negative definite if $f(\mathbf{x}) = -h(\mathbf{x})$ is positive definite.*

Positive Semidefinite Quadratic Form: *A quadratic form $f(\mathbf{x}) = \mathbf{x}^T \mathbf{A} \mathbf{x}$ is positive semidefinite if $f(\mathbf{x}) \geq 0$ for all $\mathbf{x}$ and there is at least one nonnull $\mathbf{x}$ for which $f(\mathbf{x}) = 0$.*

Negative Semidefinite Quadratic Form: *A quadratic form* $h(\mathbf{x}) = \mathbf{x}^T\mathbf{B}\mathbf{x}$ *is negative semidefinite if* $f(\mathbf{x}) = -h(\mathbf{x})$ *is positive semidefinite.*

Indefinite Quadratic Form: *A quadratic form* $f(\mathbf{x}) = \mathbf{x}^T\mathbf{A}\mathbf{x}$ *is indefinite if* $f(\mathbf{x}) > 0$ *for some* $\mathbf{x}$ *and* $f(\mathbf{x}) < 0$ *for some other* $\mathbf{x}$.

Examples: Consider the quadratic forms

(1) $$f(\mathbf{x}) = (x_1, x_2)\begin{pmatrix} 2 & 0 \\ 0 & 4 \end{pmatrix}\begin{pmatrix} x_1 \\ x_2 \end{pmatrix} = 2x_1^2 + 4x_2^2$$

which is positive definite;

(2) $$f(\mathbf{x}) = (x_1, x_2)\begin{pmatrix} 8 & -4 \\ -4 & 2 \end{pmatrix}\begin{pmatrix} x_1 \\ x_2 \end{pmatrix} = 8x_1^2 - 8x_1x_2 + 2x_2^2 = 2(2x_1 - x_2)^2$$

which is zero for all $\mathbf{x}$ where $2x_1 = x_2$ and positive for all other $\mathbf{x}$ and thus $f(\mathbf{x})$ is positive semidefinite; and

(3) $$f(\mathbf{x}) = (x_1, x_2, x_3)\begin{pmatrix} 3 & 0 & 0 \\ 0 & -1 & 0 \\ 0 & 0 & 2 \end{pmatrix}\begin{pmatrix} x_1 \\ x_2 \\ x_3 \end{pmatrix} = 3x_1^2 - x_2^2 + 2x_3^2$$

which is positive for

$$\mathbf{x} = \begin{pmatrix} y \\ 0 \\ z \end{pmatrix}$$

where y and z are any arbitrary real numbers and negative for

$$\mathbf{x} = \begin{pmatrix} 0 \\ \omega \\ 0 \end{pmatrix}$$

where ω is any real number. Thus $f(\mathbf{x})$ is indefinite.

There are several tests one may perform on the matrix of the quadratic form to determine the character of the quadratic form under consideration. We shall discuss two of these tests. The first test involves constructing the N determinants:

$$|a_{11}|, \quad \begin{vmatrix} a_{11} & a_{12} \\ a_{21} & a_{22} \end{vmatrix}, \quad \begin{vmatrix} a_{11} & a_{12} & a_{13} \\ a_{21} & a_{22} & a_{23} \\ a_{31} & a_{32} & a_{33} \end{vmatrix}, \ldots, |A|$$

$\mathbf{x}^T\mathbf{A}\mathbf{x}$ will be positive definite if and only if each of these N determinants is positive.

The second test for definiteness involves determining the signs of the roots of the polynomial-characteristic-equation

$$g(\lambda) = |\mathbf{A} - \lambda\mathbf{I}| = 0 = \begin{vmatrix} a_{11} - \lambda & a_{12} & a_{13} & \cdots & a_{1N} \\ a_{21} & a_{22} - \lambda & a_{23} & \cdots & a_{2N} \\ \vdots & \vdots & \vdots & & \vdots \\ a_{N1} & a_{N2} & a_{N3} & \cdots & a_{NN} - \lambda \end{vmatrix}$$

The roots of this equation, $\lambda_1, \ldots, \lambda_N$, are called eigenvalues.

The determinant will, in general, be an Nth-order polynomial in λ. All the N roots of $g(\lambda) = 0$ are real, because $\mathbf{A}$ is symmetric. If all the λ_i, $i = 1, \ldots, N$, are positive, $\mathbf{x}^T\mathbf{A}\mathbf{x}$ is positive definite. If some λ_i are positive with the remaining ones being zero, then $\mathbf{x}^T\mathbf{A}\mathbf{x}$ is positive semidefinite. Finally, if some λ_i are positive while others are negative, $\mathbf{x}^T\mathbf{A}\mathbf{x}$ is indefinite. We need not solve $g(\lambda) = 0$ for its roots, because Descartes' rule of signs gives us the desired information. According to the rule of signs the number of positive roots of $g(\lambda)$ will equal the number of sign changes from term to term of the polynomial while the number of negative roots equals the order of the polynomial minus the number of positive roots.

Example: Consider the quadratic form

$$f(\mathbf{x}) = (x_1, x_2, x_3) \begin{pmatrix} 3 & 0 & 0 \\ 0 & -2 & 0 \\ 0 & 0 & 1 \end{pmatrix} \begin{pmatrix} x_1 \\ x_2 \\ x_3 \end{pmatrix} = \mathbf{x}^T\mathbf{A}\mathbf{x}$$

to obtain the characteristic equation form

$$g(\lambda) = 0 = |\mathbf{A} - \lambda\mathbf{I}| = \left| \begin{pmatrix} 3 & 0 & 0 \\ 0 & -2 & 0 \\ 0 & 0 & 1 \end{pmatrix} - \begin{pmatrix} \lambda & 0 & 0 \\ 0 & \lambda & 0 \\ 0 & 0 & \lambda \end{pmatrix} \right|$$

$$= \begin{vmatrix} 3 - \lambda & 0 & 0 \\ 0 & -2 - \lambda & 0 \\ 0 & 0 & 1 - \lambda \end{vmatrix}$$

$$= (3 - \lambda)(-2 - \lambda)(1 - \lambda)$$

Expanding this we obtain

$$g(\lambda) = -\lambda^3 + 2\lambda^2 + 5\lambda - 6$$

There are two sign changes: (1) from -1 (the coefficient to λ^3) to 2 (the coefficient of λ^2), and (2) from 5 (the coefficient of λ) to -6. Thus according to the rule of signs, we have two positive roots. The number of negative roots is found by subtracting 2—the number of positive roots—from the order of the polynomial—in this case 3. Hence there is one negative root and, as two roots of $g(\lambda)$ are positive whereas the other is negative, the quadratic form is indefinite.

References Cited and Bibliography

[1] Hadley, G. L. *Linear Algebra*. Reading, Mass.: Addison-Wesley, 1964.

[2] Perlis, S. *Theory of Matrices*. Reading, Mass.: Addison-Wesley, 1952.

[3] Aitken, A. C. *Determinants and Matrices*. Edinburgh: Oliver and Boyd, 1948.

[4] Gantmacher, F. R. *Applications of the Theory of Matrices*. New York: Wiley, 1959.

z **Transforms**

B.1   Definitions

This appendix is concerned with the *z*-transform method for the solution of *linear difference equations*. Difference equations are the discrete analog to differential equations and there is a striking similarity in the solution procedures. A difference equation is an equation defined on a discrete set of points of the independent variable. One might view this as similar to a differential equation in time, where we observe the values of the dependent variable at discrete intervals of time. Difference equations arise naturally in modeling physical systems. Examples of difference equations were presented in Chapters 5, 6, and 7.

We shall now present definitions useful in characterizing difference equations. The reader will recognize their similarity to analogous definitions from differential equations.

Consider the difference equation

$$Q(k) = f_0(k)y_{k+N} + f_1(k)y_{k+N-1} + \cdots + f_N(k)y_k$$

Linearity: *$Q(k)$ is a linear difference equation if $f_0(k), f_1(k), \ldots,$*
$f_N(k)$ are functions of k only.

As an example, the first equation shown below is linear while the second is nonlinear:

$$k^2 y_{k+1} - y_k + e^k y_{k-1} = k^3$$
$$y_k y_{k+1} - y_k = k$$

Properties of Coefficients: *If $f_0(k), \ldots, f_N(k)$ are constants, $Q(k)$ is called a linear difference equation with constant coefficients.*

Homogeneity: *If $Q(k) = 0$, the equation becomes a homogeneous difference equation.*

Order: *The order of a linear difference equation is the difference between the largest and smallest subscript appearing in the equation.*

Example:

$$y_{k+2} - (k + 1)y_{k+1} + y_k - 2y_{k-1} = 0$$

is a third-order homogeneous difference equation with nonconstant coefficients.

As was the case with linear differential equations, we can define a transform for difference equations. This transform, called the z transform, has the property that it converts the difference equation in y_k to an algebraic equation in z and $y(z)$ which is easier to solve than the corresponding difference equation. Once the algebraic equation is solved, the equation relating $y(z)$ to z may be inverted to obtain the solution to the difference equation. The literature on z *transforms* offers conflicting definitions of the transform. There is no real difference between the two approaches. We shall define the z transform of y_k as

$$Y(z) = \sum_{n=0}^{\infty} y_n z^n \equiv Z(y_k)$$

The other definition is written as

$$Y(z) = \sum_{n=0}^{\infty} y_n z^{-n}$$

Our definition, which is consistent with Howard's [1], is related to the probability generating function. When y_n defines a set of probabilities,

$$y_n \geq 0 \qquad n = 1, 2, \ldots$$
$$\sum y_n = 1$$

$Y(z)$ becomes the probability generating function. Those interested in investigating the alternative definition are encouraged to see Aseltine [2] or a similar text.

B.2   Solution of Difference Equations

There are several methods of solving linear difference equations (as there are for differential equations). One method involves recognizing, from the structure of the equation, the form of the solution. This procedure is most useful when we are dealing with linear, homogeneous difference equations with constant coefficients. For example, consider

$$\phi(k) = y_{N+k} + A_1 y_{N+k-1} + \cdots + A_N y_k = 0$$

Assume the solution has the form

$$y_k = B^k$$

Substituting this into the equation we find

$$B^{N+k} + A_1 B^{N+k-1} + \cdots + A_N B^k = 0$$

Factoring out B^k yields

$$B^k[B^N + A_1 B^{N-1} + \cdots + A_N B^0] = 0$$

The term in brackets is an Nth-order polynomial. Since we are interested only in nontrivial solutions, we shall disregard the solution corresponding to $B = 0$. Assuming the roots are real and distinct, we obtain N roots $B_1, \ldots, B_N$. The solution will be some linear combination of these terms,

$$\hat{y}_k = \sum_{i=1}^{N} \alpha_i B_i^k$$

The α_i are found from the specified boundary conditions. The fact that the solution is a linear combination of the individual solutions given above is established in the following theorem:

Theorem: *Given a linear, homogeneous difference equation that yields N roots, $B_1, \ldots, B_N$. Each root yields a solution y_k^i. Any linear combination of the solutions y_k^i is also a solution.*

PROOF. Let

$$\hat{y}_k = \sum_{i=1}^{N} \alpha_i y_k^i$$

Then

$$\phi(\hat{y}_k) = \hat{y}^{N+k} + A_1 \hat{y}^{N+k-1} + \cdots + A_N \hat{y}^k$$

$$= \sum_{i=1}^{N} \alpha_i y_{N+k}^i + A_1 \sum_{i=1}^{N} \alpha_i y_{N+k-1}^i + \cdots + A_N \sum_{i=1}^{N} \alpha_i y_k^i$$

$$= \sum_{i=1}^{N} \alpha_i (y_{N+k}^i + A_1 y_{N+k-1}^i + \cdots + A_N y_k^i)$$

Since each term in parentheses is, by construction, a solution to the difference equation, it must vanish. Hence the equation becomes

$$\phi(\hat{y}_k) = \sum_{i=1}^{N} \alpha_i(0) = 0$$

and thus $\hat{y}_k$ is also a solution. This procedure is very effective in solving linear, homogeneous difference equations with constant coefficients. However, its usefulness in nonconstant coefficients and/or nonhomogeneous problems is limited. Since most O.R. problems involving difference equations fall into the latter category, we prefer to use the z-transform approach.

We defined the z transform of y_k earlier as

$$Y(z) = \sum_{n=0}^{\infty} y_n z^n = Z(y_k)$$

To solve difference equations by z transforms we must determine how to find the transform of y_{k+1}, y_{k+2}, and so on. Let us illustrate how this might be accomplished for y_{k+1} and y_{k+2}. The generalization should be obvious. For y_{k+1} the transform is

$$Z(y_{k+1}) = \sum_{n=0}^{\infty} y_{n+1} z^n$$

$$= z^{-1} \left[\sum_{n=0}^{\infty} y_{n+1} z^{n+1} \right]$$

$$= z^{-1} \left[\sum_{m=1}^{\infty} y_m z^m \right]$$

which is in the desired form except that the sum begins at 1 instead of 0. If we add and subtract $z^{-1} y_0$ to the right side of the last equation we have

$$Z(y_{k+1}) = z^{-1} \left(\sum_{m=1}^{\infty} y_m z^m \right) + y_0 z^{-1} - y_0 z^{-1}$$

$$= z^{-1} \left(\sum_{m=1}^{\infty} y_m z^m + y_0 - y_0 \right)$$

$$= z^{-1} \left(\sum_{m=0}^{\infty} y_m z^m - y_0 \right)$$

$$= z^{-1} [Y(z) - y_0]$$

Hence the z transform of y_{k+1} is just

$$z^{-1} [Y(z) - y_0]$$

where $Y(z)$ is the z transform of y_k.

We can determine the transform of y_{k+2} in a similar manner:

$$Z(y_{k+2}) = \sum_{n=0}^{\infty} y_{n+2} z^n$$

$$= z^{-2} \sum_{n=0}^{\infty} y_{n+2} z^{n+2}$$

$$= z^{-2} \sum_{m=2}^{\infty} y_m z^m$$

Adding and subtracting $y_0 z^{-2} + y_1 z^{-1}$ we obtain

$$Z(y_{k+2}) = z^{-2} \left(\sum_{m=2}^{\infty} y_m z^m \right) + y_0 z^{-2} + y_1 z^{-1} - y_0 z^{-2} - y_1 z^{-1}$$

$$= z^{-2} \left(\sum_{m=2}^{\infty} y_m z^m + y_0 + y_1 z - y_0 - y_1 z \right)$$

$$= z^{-2} \left(\sum_{m=0}^{\infty} y_m z^m - y_0 - y_1 z \right)$$

$$= z^{-2} Y(z) - z^{-2} y_0 - z^{-1} y_1$$

In general the z transform of y_{k+p} is given by

$$Z(y_{k+p}) = z^{-p}[Y(z) - y_0 - z y_1 - z^2 y_2 - \cdots - z^p y_p]$$

We must have p boundary conditions specified to completely specify the solution to a pth-order difference equation. As is seen above, the solution is obtained in terms of the first p terms of the difference equation. However, if boundary conditions are specified at other points, we can still obtain a solution.

Suppose we wish to find the z transform of the following second-order, homogeneous difference equation:

$$y_{k+2} - 3y_{k+1} + 2y_k = 0$$

with $y_0 = 0$, $y_1 = 1$. We know the z transform of y_{k+2}, y_{k+1}, and y_k.

It is easy to show that the z transform of a sum is the sum of z transforms,

$$\sum_{n=0}^{\infty} (y_{n+2} - 3y_{n+1} + 2y_n) z^n = \sum_{n=0}^{\infty} y_{n+2} z^n - \sum_{n=0}^{\infty} 3y_{n+1} z^n + \sum_{n=0}^{\infty} 2y_n z^n$$

From the above equation it is obvious that

$$\sum_{n=0}^{\infty} \alpha y_n z^n = \alpha Y(z)$$

where α is a scalar. Using these results we have

$$z^{-2}[Y(z) - y_0 - y_1 z] - 3z^{-1}[Y(z) - y_0] + 2Y(z) = 0$$

Using the boundary conditions given and simplifying we obtain

$$z^{-2}[Y(z) - 0 - 1z] - 3z^{-1}[Y(z) - 0] + 2Y(z) = 0$$

or

$$Y(z)[z^{-2} - 3z^{-1} + 2] - z^{-1} = 0$$

Multiplying by z^2 we obtain

$$Y(z)[1 - 3z + 2z^2] - z = 0$$

Solving for $Y(z)$ yields

$$Y(z) = \frac{z}{1 - 3z + 2z^2} = \frac{z}{(1 - 2z)(1 - z)}$$

Using partial fraction expansion this becomes

$$Y(z) = \frac{A}{(1 - 2z)} + \frac{B}{(1 - z)}$$

The simplification by partial fractions is identical to the procedure followed in Laplace transforms. To determine A we multiply $Y(z)$ by $1 - 2z$ and let $z = \frac{1}{2}$. Hence A:

$$(1 - 2z)Y(z) = A + \frac{(1 - 2z)B}{1 - z}$$

Evaluated for $z = \frac{1}{2}$ we find

$$(1 - 2z)Y(z)\Big|_{z = 1/2} = \frac{z}{1 - z}\Big|_{z=2} = A = \frac{\frac{1}{2}}{1 - \frac{1}{2}} = 1$$

B is determined by multiplying $Y(z)$ by $1 - z$ and evaluating this result for $z = 1$. Thus

$$(1 - z)Y(z)\Big|_{z=1} = \frac{z}{1 - 2z}\Big|_{z=1} = \frac{1}{1 - 2} = -1$$

Thus

$$Y(z) = \frac{1}{1 - 2z} - \frac{1}{1 - z}$$

All that remains now is to obtain the inverse transform of these terms to find the solution. Normally, inverse transforms may be found in tables such as the one contained at the end of this appendix. We shall derive a few of these to illustrate how they are obtained. Consider the function $y_k = 1$.

$$Y(z) = \sum_{n=0}^{\infty} z^n = \frac{1}{1 - z} \qquad \text{for } |z| < 1$$

As the next example consider

$$y_k = a^k$$

where a is a real scalar. Then

$$Y(z) = \sum_{n=0}^{\infty} y_n z^n = \sum_{n=0}^{\infty} a^n z^n = \sum_{n=0}^{\infty} (az)^n = \frac{1}{1 - az}$$

The z transform is unique and the inverse transform is also unique. Thus the inverse transform of $1/(1 - az)$ is written

$$y_k = Z^{-1}\left(\frac{1}{1 - az}\right) = a^k$$

We now have the tools to invert the z transform that was obtained from the difference equation shown above. Recall that we had

$$Y(z) = \frac{1}{1 - 2z} - \frac{1}{1 - z}$$

which was obtained from the z transform of

$$y_{k+2} - 3y_{k+1} + 2y_k = 0$$

The inverse transform of the first term is

$$Z^{-1}\left(\frac{1}{1 - 2z}\right) = 2^k$$

while

$$Z^{-1}\left(\frac{1}{1 - z}\right) = 1$$

Thus

$$y_k = 2^k - 1$$

This is the solution, which can be verified by substituting it into the equation.

Next we derive the z transform of $y_k = k$:

$$Y(z) = \sum_{n=0}^{\infty} y_n z^n = \sum_{n=0}^{\infty} nz^n$$

We have seen nothing of this form. Let us attempt to obtain something similar. Recall that when $y_k = 1$,

$$Y(z) = \sum_{n=0}^{\infty} z^n = \frac{1}{1 - z}$$

Differentiating this equation we obtain

$$\frac{dY(z)}{dz} = \sum_{n=0}^{\infty} nz^{n-1} = \frac{1}{(1 - z)^2}$$

This is almost the desired form. Suppose we multiply the equation by z. This yields

$$\frac{z\,dY(z)}{dz} = z\sum_{n=0}^{\infty} nz^{n-1} = \sum_{n=0}^{\infty} nz^n$$

which is the desired result. But

$$\frac{z\,dY(z)}{dz} = \frac{z}{(1-z)^2}$$

Hence

$$Z(n) = \frac{z}{(1-z)^2}$$

As the last example consider the z transform of ny_n:

$$Z(ny_n) = \sum_{n=0}^{\infty} ny_n z^n = z\frac{d}{dz}\sum_{n=0}^{\infty} y_n z^n = z\frac{dY(z)}{dz}$$

With these tools now available, let us solve the following difference equation:

$$(n+1)y_{n+1} - y_n = 0$$

Taking the z transform of both sides we obtain

$$\sum_{n=0}^{\infty} (n+1)y_{n+1}z^n - \sum_{n=0}^{\infty} y_n z^n = 0$$

The first term becomes

$$\sum_{k=1}^{\infty} ky_k z^{k-1}$$

which is identical to

$$\sum_{k=0}^{\infty} ky_k z^{k-1}$$

since the first term is zero. We have shown above that

$$\sum_{k=0}^{\infty} ky_k z^{k-1} = \frac{dY(z)}{dz}$$

Hence upon transforming the difference equation to an equation in z and $Y(z)$ we are faced with a differential equation,

$$\frac{dY(z)}{dz} - Y(z) = 0$$

Taking the Laplace transform we obtain

$$s Y(s) - y(0) - Y(s) = 0$$
$$(s - 1) Y(s) = y(0)$$

or

$$Y(s) = \frac{y_0}{s - 1}$$

Inverting this yields

$$Y(z) = y_0 e^z$$

Recall that

$$e^z = \sum_{n=0}^{\infty} \frac{z^n}{n!}$$

Therefore,

$$y_k = \frac{y_0}{k!}$$

Initial Value Theorem:

$$y_0 = \lim_{z \to 0} Y(z)$$

PROOF

$$Y(z) = \sum_{n=0}^{\infty} y_n z^n = y_0 + y_1 z + y_2 z^2 + \cdots$$

Hence

$$\lim_{z \to 0} Y(z) = \lim_{z \to 0} (y_0 + y_1 z + y_2 z^2 + \cdots)$$
$$= y_0$$

Final Value Theorem:

$$\lim_{n \to \infty} y_n = \lim_{z \to 1} (1 - z) Y(z)$$

PROOF

$$(1 - z) Y(z) = Y(z) - z Y(z)$$
$$= y_0 + y_1 z + y_2 z^2 + y_3 z^3 + \cdots$$
$$- y_0 z - y_1 z^2 - y_2 z^3 - y_3 z^4 - \cdots$$

Hence

$$\lim (1 - z) Y(z)$$
$$= \lim_{z \to 1} [y_0 + (y_1 - y_0) z + (y_2 - y_1) z^2 + \cdots + (y_n - y_{n-1}) z^n + \cdots]$$
$$= y_\infty$$

Examples: Consider

$$Y(z) = \frac{a + bz}{(z - 1)(z - 2)}$$

$$y_0 = \lim_{z \to 0} Y(z) = \frac{a + b(0)}{(0 - 1)(0 - 2)} = \frac{a}{2}$$

$$y_\infty = \lim_{z \to 1} (1 - z) Y(z) = \frac{a + b(1)}{2 - z} = (a + b)$$

As a final topic of this section we shall consider problems with two independent variables. These are analogous to partial differential equations. The Laplace transform is defined for several independent variables. We can define the z transform also. Consider the difference equation

$$y_{m+1,n+1} - \alpha y_{m+1,n} - \beta y_{m,n} = 0$$

where

$$y_{m,n} = 0 \qquad m > n$$
$$y_{0,k} = \alpha^k$$

Define

$$Y_n(z) = \sum_{m=0}^{\infty} y_{m,n} z^m$$

Then

$$Y(z, v) = \sum_{n=0}^{\infty} Y_n(z) v^n = \sum_{n=0}^{\infty} \sum_{m=0}^{\infty} y_{m,n} z^m v^n$$

Let us determine the transform of $y_{m+1,n+1}$.

$$Z(y_{m+1,n+1}) = \sum_{n=0}^{\infty} \sum_{m=0}^{\infty} y_{m+1,n+1} z^m v^n$$

$$= \sum_{k=1}^{\infty} \sum_{j=1}^{\infty} y_{j,k} z^{j-1} v^{k-1}$$

$$= (zv)^{-1} \sum_{k=1}^{\infty} \sum_{j=1}^{\infty} y_{j,k} z^j v^k$$

$$= (zv)^{-1} \left(\sum_{k=0}^{\infty} \sum_{j=0}^{\infty} y_{j,k} z^j v^k - \sum_{k=0}^{\infty} y_{0,k} v^k - \sum_{j=1}^{\infty} y_{j,0} z^j \right)$$

In this case $y_{j,0} = 0, j > 0$. Thus

$$Z(y_{m+1,n+1}) = (zv)^{-1} \left[Y(z, v) - \frac{1}{1 - \alpha v} \right]$$

Similarly,

$$Z(y_{m+1,n}) = z^{-1} \left[Y(z, v) - \frac{1}{1 - \alpha v} \right]$$

The transform of the equation becomes

$$(zv)^{-1}\left[Y(z, v) - \frac{1}{1 - \alpha v}\right] - \alpha z^{-1}\left[Y(z, v) - \frac{1}{1 - \alpha v}\right] - \beta Y(z, v) = 0$$

Simplifying yields

$$Y(z, v) = \frac{1}{1 - \alpha v - \beta vz} = \frac{1}{1 - (\alpha + \beta z)v}$$

Thus

$$Y_n(z) = (\alpha + \beta z)^n$$

Recall that

$$(x + y)^n = \sum_{m=0}^{\infty} \binom{n}{m} x^{n-m} y^m \qquad \text{where} \quad \binom{n}{m} = 0, \quad m > n$$

Hence

$$y_{m,n} = \binom{n}{m} \alpha^{n-m} \beta^m$$

B.3   Differential-Difference Equations

Differential-difference equations arise naturally in the study of queueing systems. For example, the time-dependent probabilities describing the single-channel queue with Poisson arrivals and negative exponential services may be described by the following differential equation:

$$\frac{dp(n; t)}{dt} = -(\lambda + v)p(n; t) + vp(n + 1; t) + \lambda p(n - 1; t) \qquad n > 1$$

$$\frac{dp(0; t)}{dt} = -\lambda p(0; t) + vp(1; t)$$

Another example is the Poisson process, which is defined by

$$\frac{dp(n + 1; t)}{dt} = -\lambda p(n + 1; t) + \lambda p(n; t) \qquad n \geq 0$$

$$\frac{dp(0; t)}{dt} = -\lambda p(0; t)$$

We solve for $p(0; t)$ by Laplace transforms as shown:

$$sP(0; s) - p(0; 0) + \lambda P(0; s) = 0$$

Solving for $P(0; s)$ we obtain

$$p(0; s) = \frac{p(0; 0)}{s + \lambda}$$

Inverting this transform to find $p(0; t)$ yields

$$p(0; t) = p(0; 0)e^{-\lambda t}$$

Defining the initial conditions to be

$$p(0; 0) = 1$$
$$p(n; 0) = 0 \qquad n \geq 1$$

Using these conditions $p(0; t)$ becomes

$$p(0; t) = e^{-\lambda t}$$

Returning to the general equation and taking the z transform we find that

$$z^{-1}\frac{d}{dt}[P(z; t) - p(0; t)] = -z^{-1}[\lambda P(z; t) - \lambda p(0; t)] + \lambda P(z; t)$$

Multiplying by z and recalling that

$$p(0; t) = e^{-\lambda t}$$

so that

$$\frac{d}{dt}p(0; t) = -\lambda e^{-\lambda t}$$

we have

$$\frac{d}{dt}P(z; t) = -\lambda P(z; t) + \lambda z P(z; t)$$

which simplifies to

$$\frac{d}{dt}P(z; t) = -\lambda P(z; t) + \lambda z P(z; t) = \lambda(z - 1)P(z; t)$$

Solving this differential equation by Laplace transforms yields

$$sP(z; s) - P(z; 0) - \lambda(z - 1)P(z; s) = 0$$

But

$$P(z, 0) = \sum_{n=0}^{\infty} p(n; 0)z^n = 1$$

because

$$p(n; 0) = 0 \qquad n > 0$$

Hence

$$[s - \lambda(z - 1)]P(z; s) = 1$$

or

$$P(z; s) = \frac{1}{(s - \lambda)(z - 1)}$$

Inverting the Laplace transform we obtain

$$P(z; t) = e^{\lambda(z-1)t} = e^{\lambda zt} e^{-\lambda t}$$

We can now invert the z transform to obtain

$$p(0; t) = \frac{(\lambda t)^n}{n!} e^{-\lambda t}$$

which is the desired solution.

B.4 Table of z Transforms

Definition	y_n	$\sum y_n z^n$
1.	$au_n + bv_n + \cdots$	$aU(z) + bV(z) + \cdots$
2.	u_{n+k}	$z^{-k}U(z) - \sum_{r=0}^{k-1} u_r z^{r-k}$
3.	$y_n = \begin{cases} 0 & (n < k) \\ u_{n-k} & (n \geq k) \end{cases}$	$z^k U(z)$
4.	$c^{an}u_n$	$U(c^a z)$
5.	$\sum_{r=0}^{r=n} u_r v_{n-r}$	$U(z)V(z)$
6.	$\Delta u_n = u_{n+1} - u_n$	$z^{-1}[(1 - z)U(z) - u_0]$
7.	$y_n = \begin{cases} 1 & (n = k) \\ 0 & (n \neq k) \end{cases}$	z^k
8.	c	$c/(1 - z)$
9.	n	$z/(1 - z)^2$
10.	n^2	$z(1 + z)/(1 - z)^3$
11.	n^3	$z(z^2 + 4z + 1)/(1 - z)^4$
12.	n^k	$z\, dU(z)/dz$ with $u_n = n^{k-1}$
13.	c^n	$1/(1 - cz)$
14.	nc^n	$cz/(1 - cz)^2$
15.	$n^2 c^n$	$cz(1 + cz)/(1 - cz)^3$
16.	$n^3 c^n$	$cz(c^2 z^2 + 4cz + 1)/(1 - cz)^4$
17.	$c^n n^k$	$z\, dU(cz)/dz$ with $u_n = n^{k-1}$
18.	$\binom{n + k}{k} c^n$	$1/(1 - cz)^{k+1}$
19.	$\binom{b}{n} c^n a^{b-n}$	$(a + cz)^b$
20.	$c^n/n \ (n = 1, 2, 3, \ldots)$	$-\ln(1 - cz)$
21.	$c^n/n \ (n = 1, 3, 5, \ldots)$	$\frac{1}{2}\ln\left(\frac{1 + cz}{1 - cz}\right) = \tanh^{-1} cz$
22.	$c^n/n \ (n = 2, 4, 6, \ldots)$	$-\frac{1}{2}\ln(1 - c^2 z^2)$
23.	$c^n/n!$	e^{cz}
24.	$c^n/n! \ (n = 1, 3, 5, \ldots)$	$\sinh cz$
25.	$c^n/n! \ (n = 0, 2, 4, \ldots)$	$\cosh cz$

Definition	y_n	$\sum y_n z^n$
26.	$(\ln c)^n/n!$	c^z
27.	$\sin (nc)$	$\dfrac{z \sin c}{z^2 + 1 - 2z \cos c}$
28.	$\cos (nc)$	$\dfrac{1 - z \cos c}{z^2 + 1 - 2z \cos c}$
29.	$b^{-an} \sin (nc)$	$\dfrac{z \sin c}{b^a + b^{-a}z^2 - 2z \cos c}$
30.	$b^{-an} \cos (nc)$	$\dfrac{b^a - z \cos c}{b^{-a}z^2 + b^a - 2z \cos c}$
31.	$[y_{ij}(n)]$ (a matrix)	$[Y_{ij}(z)]$

Source: Mitten, Nemhauser, and Beightler [3].

References Cited and Bibliography

[1] Howard, R. A. *Dynamic Programming and Markov Processes*. New York: Wiley, 1960.

[2] Aseltine, J. A. *Transform Method in Linear System Analysis*. New York: McGraw-Hill, 1958.

[3] Mitten, L. G., G. L. Nemhauser, and C. Beightler, *ORSA*, Vol. 9, No. 3 (1961), 574–78.

Definition	a_n	Z
26	$(\ln r)^n / n!$	
27	$\sin(n\alpha)$	$\dfrac{z \sin \alpha}{z^2 - 2z \cos \alpha + 1}$
28	$\cos(n\alpha)$	$\dfrac{1 - z^{-1} \cos \alpha}{1 - 2z^{-1} \cos \alpha + z^{-2}}$
29	$r^n \sin(n\alpha)$	$\dfrac{zr \sin \alpha}{z^2 - 2zr \cos \alpha + r^2}$
30	$r^n \cos(n\alpha)$	$\dfrac{z^2 - zr \cos \alpha}{z^2 - 2zr \cos \alpha + r^2}$
31	$a(c t) n$ (in general)	$Z_c[F_c(z)]$

Source: Miller, Nauheimer, and Brandolf [3].

References Cited and Bibliography

[1] Howard, R. A., Dynamic Programming and Markov Processes, New York, Wiley, 1960.

[2] Aseltine, J. A., Transform Method in Linear System Analysis, New York, McGraw-Hill, 1958.

[3] Miller, J. G., C. L. Nauheimer, and C. Reichel, JASA, Vol. 9, No. 3 (1961), 77ff.

Index